Praise God From Whom All Blessings Flow

Thomas Ken, 1709

Genevan Psalter, 1551

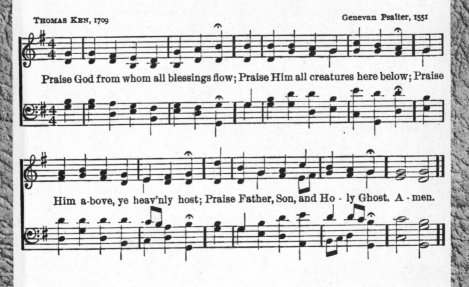

Praise God from whom all blessings flow; Praise Him all creatures here below; Praise

Him a-bove, ye heav'nly host; Praise Father, Son, and Ho - ly Ghost. A - men.

Glory Be to the Father

H. W. Greatorex

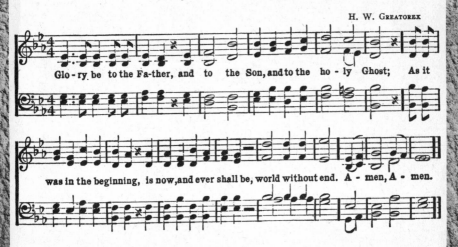

Glo - ry be to the Fa-ther, and to the Son, and to the ho - ly Ghost; As it

was in the beginning, is now, and ever shall be, world without end. A - men, A - men.

Inspiring Hymns

A choice selection of
Hymns and Gospel Songs
for the singing Church

COMPILED BY

ALFRED B. SMITH

Singspiration® *Inc.*
WORLD DISTRIBUTORS
ZONDERVAN PUBLISHING HOUSE
GRAND RAPIDS, MICHIGAN
Printed in the United States of America
1965

Just a word . . .

Many years of diligent and thorough research have gone into the production of this fine hymnal INSPIRING HYMNS. On its pages will be found only "the best" of the great Hymns and Gospel songs of the Church. These have been chosen not only for the truths proclaimed, but great effort also has been made to secure the best and most singable musical setting for each one. Because of this, we are sure you will find the "singability" of INSPIRING HYMNS far exceeds that of other hymn books available today.

A rich and instructive responsive-reading section is also an important part of this volume. The Scripture portions have been taken from the American Standard Version, thus making for easier congregational participation.

We wish to thank the many who have counseled and assisted so wisely in making this book the great instrument that it is.

Every effort has been made to trace the authorship and copyright ownership of all songs, and we thank the copyright owners for permission to use their material. If there are omissions, proper acknowledgement will be made in subsequent editions, after notification.

THE PUBLISHERS

Inspiring Hymns

1

May Jesus Christ Be Praised

From the German   Sir Joseph Barnby

1. When morn - ing gilds the skies, My heart a - wak - ing cries:
2. When sleep her balm de - nies, My si - lent spir - it sighs:
3. Does sad - ness fill my mind, A sol - ace here I find:
4. In heav'n's e - ter - nal bliss The love - liest strain is this:
5. Be this, while life is mine, My can - ti - cle di - vine,

May Je - sus Christ be praised; A - like at work and prayer . .
May Je - sus Christ be praised; When e - vil thoughts mo - lest, ...
May Je - sus Christ be praised; Or fades my earth - ly bliss, . .
May Je - sus Christ be praised; The pow'rs of dark - ness fear, ...
May Je - sus Christ be praised; Be this th' e - ter - nal song, . .

To Je - sus I re - pair: . . May Je - sus Christ be praised.
With this I shield my breast: . May Je - sus Christ be praised.
My com - fort still is this: . . May Je - sus Christ be praised.
When this sweet chant they hear: . May Je - sus Christ be praised.
Thro' all the a - ges on: . . . May Je - sus Christ be praised.

2 O Could I Speak

SAMUEL MEDLEY

DR. LOWELL MASON

1. O could I speak the match-less worth, O could I sound the
2. I'd sing the pre-cious blood He spilt, My ran-som from the
3. I'd sing the char-ac-ters He bears, And all the forms of
4. Well, the de-light-ful day will come When my dear Lord will

glo-ries forth, Which in my Sav-iour shine, I'd soar and touch the
dread-ful guilt Of sin, and wrath di-vine; I'd sing His glo-rious
love He wears, Ex-alt-ed on His throne; In loft-iest songs of
bring me home, And I shall see His face; Then with my Sav-iour,

heaven-ly strings, And vie with Ga-briel while he sings In
right-eous-ness, In which all-per-fect, heaven-ly dress My
sweet-est praise, I would to ev-er-last-ing days Make
Broth-er, Friend, A blest e-ter-ni-ty I'll spend, Tri-

notes al-most di-vine, In notes al-most di-vine.
soul shall ev-er shine, My soul shall ev-er shine.
all His glo-ries known, Make all His glo-ries known.
um-phant in His grace, Tri-um-phant in His grace.

3   The Spacious Firmament

JOSEPH ADDISON   FRANZ J. HAYDN

1. The spa-cious fir-ma-ment on high, With all the blue, e-
2. Soon as the eve-ning shades pre-vail, The moon takes up the
3. What though, in sol-emn si-lence, all Move round the dark ter-

the-real sky, And spangled heavens, a shin-ing frame, Their great O-
won-drous tale; And night-ly, to the lis-tening earth, Re-peats the
res-trial ball? What though no re-al voice nor sound A-mid their

rig-i-nal pro-claim: Th'un-wea-ried sun, from day to day,
sto-ry of her birth; While all the stars that round her burn,
ra-diant orbs be found? In rea-son's ear they all re-joice,

Does his Cre-a-tor's power dis-play; And pub-lish-es to
And all the plan-ets in their turn, Con-firm the ti-dings
And ut-ter forth a glo-rious voice, For-ev-er sing-ing

ev-ery land The work of an al-might-y hand.
as they roll, And spread the truth from pole to pole.
as they shine,"The hand that made us is di-vine." A-MEN.

4 Oh, It Is Wonderful!

C. H. G.

CHAS. H. GABRIEL

1. I stand all a-mazed at the love Je-sus of-fers me, Con-fused at the
2. I mar-vel that He would descend from His throne divine, To res-cue a
3. I think of His hands pierced and bleeding to pay the debt! Such mer-cy, such

grace that so ful-ly He proffers me; I trem-ble to know that for me He was
soul so re-bel-lious and proud as mine; That He should extend His great love un-to
love and de-vo-tion can I for-get? No, no! I will praise and a-dore at the

cru-ci-fied—That for me, a sin-ner, He suf-fered, He bled, and died.
such as I; Suf-fi-cient to own, to re-deem, and to jus-ti-fy.
mer-cy-seat, Un-til at the glo-ri-fied throne I kneel at His feet.

rit.

CHORUS *rit.*

Oh, it is won-der-ful that He should care for me, E-nough to
won-der-ful!

a tempo

die for me! Oh, it is won-der-ful, won-der-ful to me!
won-der-ful!

5

Blessed Be the Name

W. H. CLARK

Arr. by WM. J. KIRKPATRICK

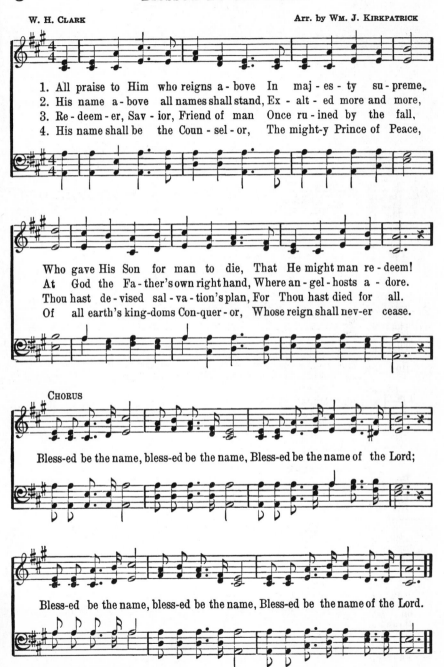

1. All praise to Him who reigns a - bove In maj - es - ty su - preme,
2. His name a - bove all names shall stand, Ex - alt - ed more and more,
3. Re - deem - er, Sav - ior, Friend of man Once ru - ined by the fall,
4. His name shall be the Coun - sel - or, The might-y Prince of Peace,

Who gave His Son for man to die, That He might man re - deem!
At God the Fa - ther's own right hand, Where an - gel - hosts a - dore.
Thou hast de - vised sal - va - tion's plan, For Thou hast died for all.
Of all earth's king-doms Con-quer - or, Whose reign shall nev-er cease.

CHORUS

Bless-ed be the name, bless-ed be the name, Bless-ed be the name of the Lord;

Bless-ed be the name, bless-ed be the name, Bless-ed be the name of the Lord.

Arise, My Soul, Arise

CHARLES WESLEY

Har. by D. B. TOWNER

1. A - rise, my soul, a - rise; Shake off thy guilt - y fears;
2. He ev - er lives a - bove, For me to in - ter-cede;
3. Five bleed - ing wounds He bears, Re - ceived on Cal - va - ry;
4. The Fa - ther hears Him pray, His dear a - noint - ed One;
5. My God is rec - on - ciled, His par - d'ning voice I hear;

The bleed - ing Sac - ri - fice In my be - half ap - pears.
His all - re - deem - ing love, His pre - cious blood to plead;
They pour ef - fec - tual prayers, They strong - ly plead for me.
He can - not turn a - way The pres - ence of His Son:
He owns me for His child, I can no lon - ger fear:

Be - fore the throne my Sure - ty stands; My name is writ - ten
His blood a - toned for all our race, And sprin-kles now the
"For - give him, O for - give!" they cry, "Nor let that ran - somed
His Spir - it an - swers to the blood, And tells me I am
With con - fi - dence I now draw nigh, And "Fa - ther, Ab - ba,

on His hands, My name is writ - ten on His hands.
throne of grace, And sprin - kles now the throne of grace.
sin - ner die, Nor let that ran - somed sin - ner die."
born of God, And tells me I am born of God.
Fa - ther!" cry, And "Fa - ther, Ab - ba, Fa - ther!" cry.

Still, Still with Thee

HARRIET B. STOWE   Arr. from FELIX MENDELSSOHN-BARTHOLDY

1. Still, still with Thee, when pur-ple morn-ing break-eth,
2. A-lone with Thee, a-mid the mys-tic shad-ows,
3. Still, still with Thee! As to each new-born morn-ing
4. When sinks the soul, sub-dued by toil, to slum-ber,
5. So shall it be at last in that bright morn-ing,

When the bird wak-eth, and the shad-ows flee;
The sol-emn hush of na-ture new-ly born;
A fresh and sol-emn splen-dor still is giv'n,
Its clos-ing eyes look up to Thee in prayer;
When the soul wak-eth, and the shad-ows flee;

Fair-er than morn-ing, love-li-er than day-light,
A-lone with Thee in breath-less ad-o-ra-tion,
So does this bless-ed con-scious-ness, a-wak-ing,
Sweet the re-pose be-neath Thy wings o'er-shad-ing,
O in that hour, fair-er than day-light dawn-ing,

Dawns the sweet con-scious-ness, I am with Thee.
In the calm dew and fresh-ness of the morn.
Breathe each day near-ness un-to Thee and heav'n.
But sweet-er still, to wake and find Thee there.
Shall rise the glo-rious thought, I am with Thee.

That Beautiful Name

JEAN PERRY, alt.   MABEL JOHNSTON CAMP

1. I know of a Name, A beau-ti-ful Name, That an-gels bro't
2. I know of a Name, A beau-ti-ful Name, That un-to a
3. The One of that Name, My Sav-ior be-came, My Sav-ior of
4. I love that blest Name, That won-der-ful Name, Made high-er than

down to earth; They whis-pered it low, One night long a-go,
Babe was given; The stars glit-tered bright Thro'-out that glad night,
Cal-va-ry; My sins nailed Him there, My bur-dens He bare,
all in heav'n; 'Twas whis-pered, I know, In my heart long a-go—

CHORUS

To a maid-en of low-ly birth.
And an-gels praised God in heav'n. That beau-ti-ful Name, That
He suf-fered all this for me.
To Je-sus my life I've giv'n.

rit.

beau-ti-ful Name, From sin has pow'r to free us! That beau-ti-ful

cres.   *ad lib.*

Name, That won-der-ful Name, That match-less Name is Je-sus!

The Name of Jesus

Rev. W. C. Martin

E. S. Lorenz

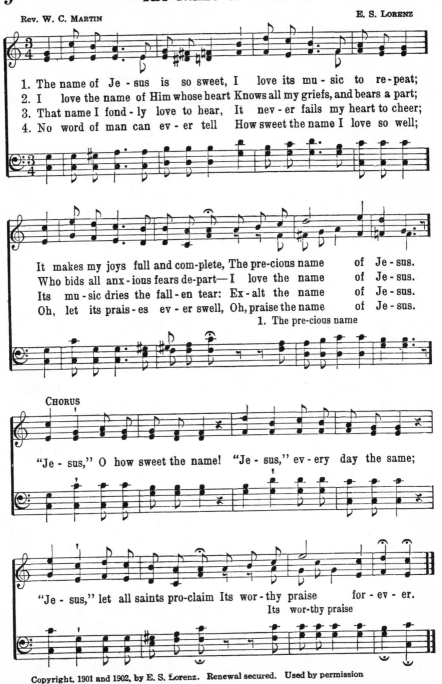

1. The name of Je - sus is so sweet, I love its mu - sic to re-peat;
2. I love the name of Him whose heart Knows all my griefs, and bears a part;
3. That name I fond - ly love to hear, It nev - er fails my heart to cheer;
4. No word of man can ev - er tell How sweet the name I love so well;

It makes my joys full and com-plete, The pre-cious name of Je - sus.
Who bids all anx - ious fears de-part— I love the name of Je - sus.
Its mu - sic dries the fall - en tear: Ex - alt the name of Je - sus.
Oh, let its prais - es ev - er swell, Oh, praise the name of Je - sus.

1. The pre-cious name

CHORUS

"Je - sus," O how sweet the name! "Je - sus," ev - ery day the same;

"Je - sus," let all saints pro-claim Its wor - thy praise for - ev - er.

Its wor-thy praise

Angel Voices, Ever Singing

Francis Pott

Arthur S. Sullivan

1. An - gel voi - ces, ev - er sing - ing Round Thy throne of
2. Thou, who art be - yond the far - thest Men - tal eye can
3. Hear, great God, to - day we of - fer Of Thine own to
4. Hon - or, glo - ry, might, and mer - it, Thine shall ev - er

light; An - gel harps, for - ev - er ring - ing,
scan, Can it be that Thou re - gard - est
Thee; And for Thine ac - cept - ance prof - fer,
be, Fa - ther, Son, and Ho - ly Spir - it,

Rest not day nor night. Thou - sands on - ly live to
Songs of sin - ful man? Can we feel that Thou art
All un - wor - thi - ly, Hearts and minds, and hands and
Bless - ed Trin - i - ty! Of the best that Thou hast

bless Thee, And con - fess Thee, Lord of might.
near us, And wilt hear us? Yea, we can.
voi - ces, In our choic - est Mel - o - dy.
giv - en Earth and heav - en Ren - der Thee.

11 Wonderful

A. H. ACKLEY

A. H. ACKLEY

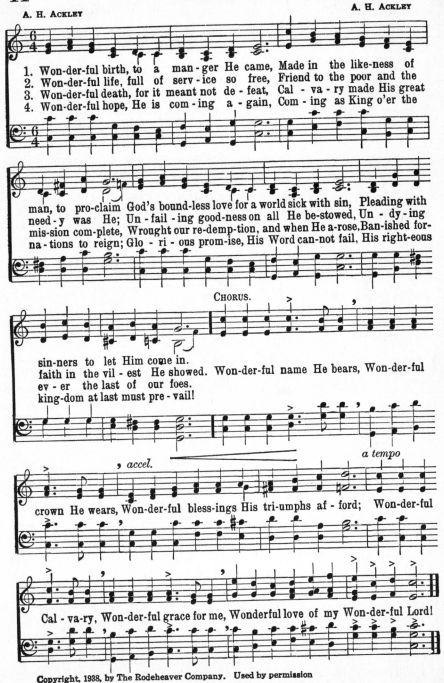

1. Won-der-ful birth, to a man-ger He came, Made in the like-ness of
2. Won-der-ful life, full of serv-ice so free, Friend to the poor and the
3. Won-der-ful death, for it meant not de-feat, Cal-va-ry made His great
4. Won-der-ful hope, He is com-ing a-gain, Com-ing as King o'er the

man, to pro-claim God's bound-less love for a world sick with sin, Pleading with
need-y was He; Un-fail-ing good-ness on all He be-stowed, Un-dy-ing
mis-sion com-plete, Wrought our re-demp-tion, and when He a-rose, Ban-ished for-
na-tions to reign; Glo-ri-ous prom-ise, His Word can-not fail, His right-eous

CHORUS.

sin-ners to let Him come in.
faith in the vil-est He showed. Won-der-ful name He bears, Won-der-ful
ev-er the last of our foes.
king-dom at last must pre-vail!

accel.

a tempo

crown He wears, Won-der-ful bless-ings His tri-umphs af-ford; Won-der-ful

Cal-va-ry, Won-der-ful grace for me, Wonderful love of my Won-der-ful Lord!

12 Wonderful, Wonderful Jesus

Annie B. Russell

Ernest O. Sellers

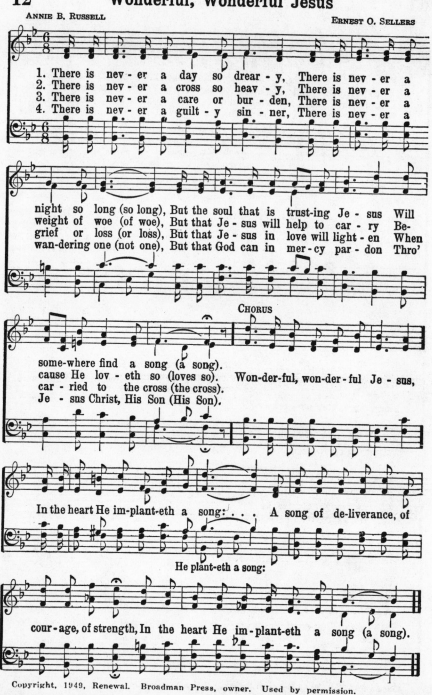

1. There is nev-er a day so drear-y, There is nev-er a
2. There is nev-er a cross so heav-y, There is nev-er a
3. There is nev-er a care or bur-den, There is nev-er a
4. There is nev-er a guilt-y sin-ner, There is nev-er a

night so long (so long), But the soul that is trust-ing Je - sus Will
weight of woe (of woe), But that Je - sus will help to car-ry Be-
grief or loss (or loss), But that Je - sus in love will light-en When
wan-dering one (not one), But that God can in mer-cy par-don Thro'

some-where find a song (a song).
cause He lov-eth so (loves so).
car-ried to the cross (the cross).
Je - sus Christ, His Son (His Son).

Chorus

Won-der-ful, won-der-ful Je - sus,

In the heart He im-plant-eth a song: . . . A song of de-liverance, of

He plant-eth a song:

cour-age, of strength, In the heart He im-plant-eth a song (a song).

13 O Day of Rest and Gladness

C. WORDSWORTH

Arr. by L. MASON

1. O day of rest and glad - ness, O day of joy and light,
2. On thee, at the cre - a - tion, The light first had its birth;
3. To - day on wea - ry na - tions The heaven - ly man - na falls;
4. New grac - es ev - er gain - ing From this our day of rest,

O balm of care and sad - ness, Most beau - ti - ful, most bright;
On thee, for our sal - va - tion, Christ rose from depths of earth;
To ho - ly con - vo - ca - tions The sil - ver trump - et calls,
We reach the rest re - main - ing To spir - its of the blest.

On thee, the high and low - ly, Bend - ing be - fore the throne,
On thee, our Lord, vic - to - rious, The Spir - it sent from heaven;
Where Gos - pel light is glow - ing With pure and ra - diant beams,
To Ho - ly Ghost be prais - es, To Fa - ther, and to Son;

Sing "Ho - ly, Ho - ly, Ho - ly," To the great Three in One.
And thus on thee, most glo - rious, A tri - ple light was given.
And liv - ing wa - ter flow - ing With soul - re - fresh - ing streams.
The Church her voice up - rais - es To Thee, blest Three in One.

14 Safely Through Another Week

JOHN NEWTON

LOWELL MASON

1. Safe - ly through an - oth - er week God has brought us on our way;
2. While we pray for par-doning grace, Thro' the dear Re-deem-er's name,
3. Here we come Thy name to praise; Let us feel Thy pres-ence near:
4. May Thy Gos - pel's joy - ful sound Con - quer sin - ners, com-fort saints;

Let us now a bless-ing seek, Wait-ing in His courts to - day:
Show Thy rec - on - cil - ed face, Take a - way our sin and shame;
May Thy glo - ry meet our eyes, While we in Thy house ap - pear:
May the fruits of grace a - bound, Bring re - lief for all com-plaints:

Day of all the week the best, Em - blem of e - ter - nal rest:
From our world - ly cares set free, May we rest this day in Thee:
Here af - ford us, Lord, a taste Of our ev - er - last - ing feast:
Thus may all our Sab-baths prove, Till we join the Church a - bove:

Day of all the week the best, Em - blem of e - ter - nal rest.
From our world - ly cares set free, May we rest this day in Thee.
Here af - ford us, Lord, a taste Of our ev - er - last - ing feast.
Thus may all our Sab-baths prove, Till we join the Church a - bove.

Come, Ye Thankful People

HENRY ALFORD

GEORGE J. ELVEY

1. Come, ye thank-ful peo-ple, come, Raise the song of har-vest-home:
2. All the world is God's own field, Fruit un-to His praise to yield;
3. For the Lord our God shall come, And shall take His har-vest home;
4. E-ven so, Lord, quick-ly come To Thy fi-nal har-vest-home;

All is safe-ly gath-ered in, Ere the win-ter storms be-gin;
Wheat and tares to-geth-er sown, Un-to joy or sor-row grown;
From His field shall in that day All of-fens-es purge a-way;
Gath-er Thou Thy peo-ple in, Free from sor-row, free from sin;

God, our Ma-ker, doth pro-vide For our wants to be sup-plied:
First the blade, and then the ear, Then the full corn shall ap-pear:
Give His an-gels charge at last In the fire the tares to cast;
There, for-ev-er pu-ri-fied, In Thy pres-ence to a-bide:

Come to God's own tem-ple, come, Raise the song of har-vest-home.
Lord of har-vest, grant that we Wholesome grain and pure may be.
But the fruit-ful ears to store In His gar-ner ev-er-more.
Come, with all Thine an-gels, come, Raise the glo-rious har-vest-home.

16

For the Beauty of the Earth

FOLLIOTT S. PIERPONT

CONRAD KOCHER

1. For the beau-ty of the earth, For the glo-ry of the skies,
2. For the won-der of each hour Of the day and of the night,
3. For the joy of hu-man love, Broth-er, sis-ter, par-ent, child,
4. For Thy Church that ev-er-more Lift-eth ho-ly hands a-bove,

For the love which from our birth O-ver and a-round us lies;
Hill and vale, and tree and flower, Sun and moon, and stars of light;
Friends on earth, and friends a-bove, For all gen-tle thoughts and mild;
Of-fering up on ev-ery shore Her pure sac-ri-fice of love;

Christ our God, to Thee we raise This our hymn of grate-ful praise.
Christ our God, to Thee we raise This our hymn of grate-ful praise.
Christ our God, to Thee we raise This our hymn of grate-ful praise.
Christ our God, to Thee we raise This our hymn of grate-ful praise.

17

Art Thou Weary?

JOHN M. NEALE

HENRY W. BAKER

1. Art thou wea-ry, art thou lan-guid, Art thou sore dis-trest?
2. Hath He marks to lead me to Him, If He be my Guide?
3. If I still hold close-ly to Him, What hath He at last?
4. If I ask Him to re-ceive me, Will He say me nay?

Art Thou Weary?

"Come to Me," saith One, "and, com - ing, Be at rest."
"In His feet and hands are wound-prints, And His side."
"Sor - row van - quished, la - bor end - ed, Jor - dan passed."
"Not till earth and not till heav - en Pass a - way."

18 Hail to the Brightness

THOMAS HASTINGS

LOWELL MASON

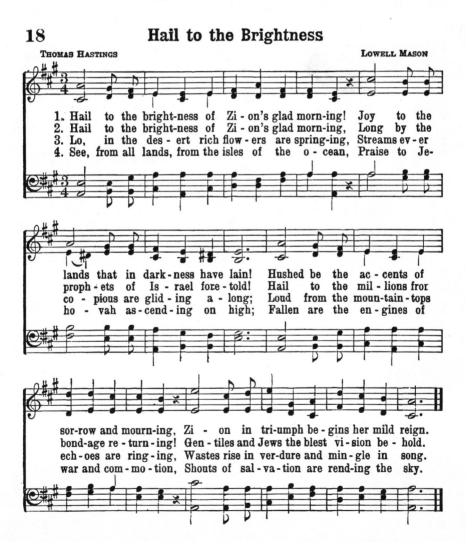

1. Hail to the bright-ness of Zi - on's glad morn-ing! Joy to the
2. Hail to the bright-ness of Zi - on's glad morn-ing, Long by the
3. Lo, in the des - ert rich flow - ers are spring-ing, Streams ev - er
4. See, from all lands, from the isles of the o - cean, Praise to Je -

lands that in dark - ness have lain! Hushed be the ac - cents of
proph - ets of Is - rael fore - told! Hail to the mil - lions from
co - pious are glid - ing a - long; Loud from the moun-tain - tops
ho - vah as - cend - ing on high; Fallen are the en - gines of

sor-row and mourn-ing, Zi - on in tri-umph be - gins her mild reign.
bond-age re - turn-ing! Gen - tiles and Jews the blest vi - sion be - hold.
ech - oes are ring-ing, Wastes rise in ver-dure and min - gle in song.
war and com - mo - tion, Shouts of sal - va - tion are rend-ing the sky.

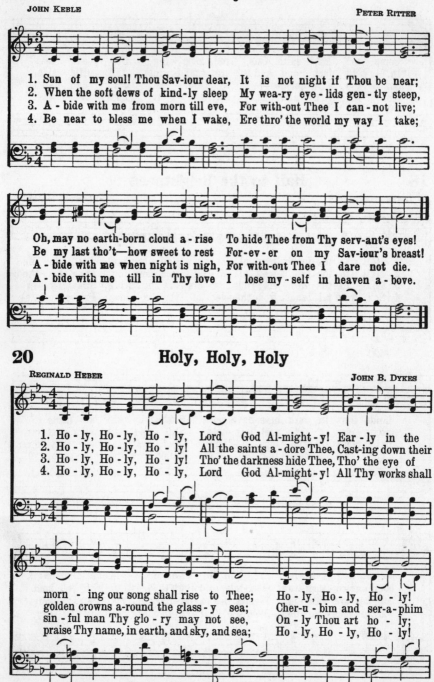

19

Sun of My Soul

JOHN KEBLE

PETER RITTER

1. Sun of my soul! Thou Sav-iour dear, It is not night if Thou be near;
2. When the soft dews of kind-ly sleep My wea-ry eye-lids gen-tly steep,
3. A-bide with me from morn till eve, For with-out Thee I can-not live;
4. Be near to bless me when I wake, Ere thro' the world my way I take;

Oh, may no earth-born cloud a-rise To hide Thee from Thy serv-ant's eyes!
Be my last tho't—how sweet to rest For-ev-er on my Sav-iour's breast!
A-bide with me when night is nigh, For with-out Thee I dare not die.
A-bide with me till in Thy love I lose my-self in heaven a-bove.

20

Holy, Holy, Holy

REGINALD HEBER

JOHN B. DYKES

1. Ho-ly, Ho-ly, Ho-ly, Lord God Al-might-y! Ear-ly in the
2. Ho-ly, Ho-ly, Ho-ly! All the saints a-dore Thee, Cast-ing down their
3. Ho-ly, Ho-ly, Ho-ly! Tho' the darkness hide Thee, Tho' the eye of
4. Ho-ly, Ho-ly, Ho-ly, Lord God Al-might-y! All Thy works shall

morn-ing our song shall rise to Thee; Ho-ly, Ho-ly, Ho-ly!
golden crowns a-round the glass-y sea; Cher-u-bim and ser-a-phim
sin-ful man Thy glo-ry may not see, On-ly Thou art ho-ly;
praise Thy name, in earth, and sky, and sea; Ho-ly, Ho-ly, Ho-ly!

Holy, Holy, Holy

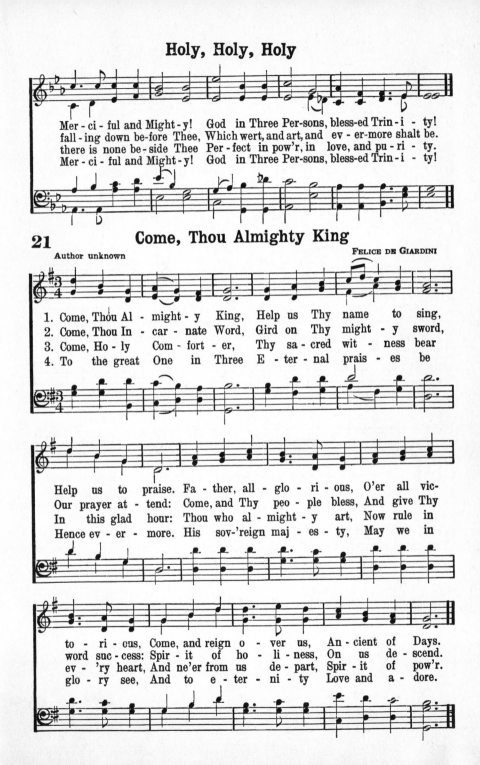

Mer - ci - ful and Might - y! God in Three Per-sons, bless-ed Trin-i - ty!
fall - ing down be-fore Thee, Which wert, and art, and ev - er-more shalt be.
there is none be-side Thee Per - fect in pow'r, in love, and pu - ri - ty.
Mer - ci - ful and Might - y! God in Three Per-sons, bless-ed Trin-i - ty!

21 Come, Thou Almighty King

Author unknown

FELICE DE GIARDINI

1. Come, Thou Al - might - y King, Help us Thy name to sing,
2. Come, Thou In - car - nate Word, Gird on Thy might - y sword,
3. Come, Ho - ly Com - fort - er, Thy sa - cred wit - ness bear
4. To the great One in Three E - ter - nal prais - es be

Help us to praise. Fa - ther, all - glo - ri - ous, O'er all vic-
Our prayer at - tend: Come, and Thy peo - ple bless, And give Thy
In this glad hour: Thou who al - might - y art, Now rule in
Hence ev - er - more. His sov-'reign maj - es - ty, May we in

to - ri - ous, Come, and reign o - ver us, An - cient of Days.
word suc - cess: Spir - it of ho - li - ness, On us de - scend.
ev - 'ry heart, And ne'er from us de - part, Spir - it of pow'r.
glo - ry see, And to e - ter - ni - ty Love and a - dore.

All the Way My Saviour Leads Me

FANNY J. CROSBY

ROBERT LOWRY

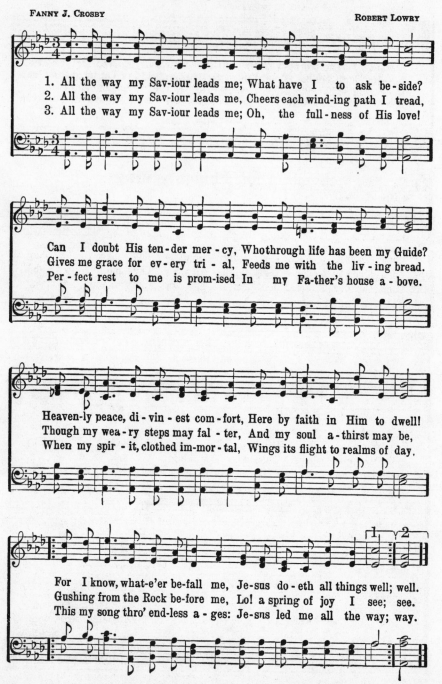

1. All the way my Sav-iour leads me; What have I to ask be-side?
2. All the way my Sav-iour leads me, Cheers each wind-ing path I tread,
3. All the way my Sav-iour leads me; Oh, the full-ness of His love!

Can I doubt His ten-der mer-cy, Who through life has been my Guide?
Gives me grace for ev-ery tri-al, Feeds me with the liv-ing bread.
Per-fect rest to me is prom-ised In my Fa-ther's house a-bove.

Heaven-ly peace, di-vin-est com-fort, Here by faith in Him to dwell!
Though my wea-ry steps may fal-ter, And my soul a-thirst may be,
When my spir-it, clothed im-mor-tal, Wings its flight to realms of day.

For I know, what-e'er be-fall me, Je-sus do-eth all things well; well.
Gushing from the Rock be-fore me, Lo! a spring of joy I see; see.
This my song thro' end-less a-ges: Je-sus led me all the way; way.

23 Anywhere With Jesus

Jessie H. Brown and Mrs. C. M. Alexander   D. B. Towner

1. An - y-where with Je - sus I can safe-ly go; An - y-where He
2. An - y-where with Je - sus I am not a - lone; Oth - er friends may
3. An - y-where with Je - sus o - ver land and sea, Tell - ing souls in
4. An - y-where with Je - sus I can go to sleep, When the dark-'ning

leads me in this world be - low; An - y-where with-out Him dear-est
fail me, He is still my own; Tho' His hand may lead me o - ver
dark-ness of sal - va - tion free; Read - y as He sum-mons me to
shad-ows round a - bout me creep; Know-ing I shall wak - en nev - er

joys would fade; An - y-where with Je - sus I am not a - fraid.
drear - y ways, An - y-where with Je - sus is a house of praise.
go or stay, An - y-where with Je - sus when He points the way.
more to roam, An - y-where with Je - sus will be home, sweet home.

CHORUS

An - y-where! an - y-where! Fear I can - not know;

An - y-where with Je - sus I can safe - ly go.

24 I Will Praise Him

M. J. H.

Mrs. M. J. HARRIS

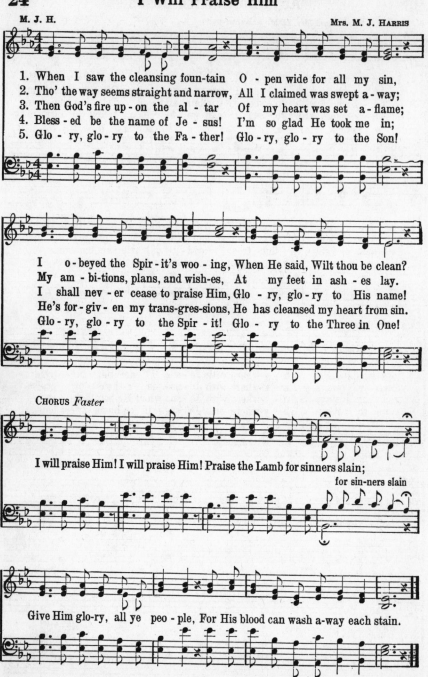

1. When I saw the cleansing foun-tain O - pen wide for all my sin,
2. Tho' the way seems straight and narrow, All I claimed was swept a - way;
3. Then God's fire up - on the al - tar Of my heart was set a - flame;
4. Bless - ed be the name of Je - sus! I'm so glad He took me in;
5. Glo - ry, glo - ry to the Fa - ther! Glo - ry, glo - ry to the Son!

I o-beyed the Spir-it's woo-ing, When He said, Wilt thou be clean?
My am - bi-tions, plans, and wish-es, At my feet in ash - es lay.
I shall nev - er cease to praise Him, Glo - ry, glo - ry to His name!
He's for-giv - en my trans-gres-sions, He has cleansed my heart from sin.
Glo - ry, glo - ry to the Spir - it! Glo - ry to the Three in One!

CHORUS *Faster*

I will praise Him! I will praise Him! Praise the Lamb for sinners slain;

for sin-ners slain

Give Him glo-ry, all ye peo - ple, For His blood can wash a-way each stain.

25 He'll Walk with Me All the Way

L. J. WILLIAMS

CHAS. H. GABRIEL

1. I know that my Sav-iour will nev-er for-sake, I know that my
2. He'll lead me in paths that are pleas-ant and green, And show me new
3. My eyes will new beau-ty and glo-ry per-ceive, As dai-ly His

faith in Him nev-er will shake; My jour-ney a path-way of
glo-ries, so long since un-seen; His hand will I hold all se-
bless-ing life's tan-gles un-weave; I'll hold to His hand and no

glad-ness He'll make, He'll walk with me all the way.
cure and se-rene, He'll walk with me all the way.
more let Him leave; He'll walk with me all the way.

CHORUS

He'll walk with me all the way,.... He'll walk with me all the way,....
He'll walk with me all the way, He'll walk with me all the way,

He'll help me o'er sin the vic-t'ry to win, And walk with me all the way.

In the Cross of Christ

Sir John Bowring

Ithamar Conkey

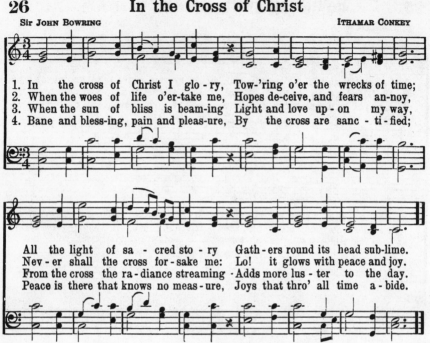

1. In the cross of Christ I glo-ry, Tow-'ring o'er the wrecks of time;
2. When the woes of life o'er-take me, Hopes de-ceive, and fears an-noy,
3. When the sun of bliss is beam-ing Light and love up-on my way,
4. Bane and bless-ing, pain and pleas-ure, By the cross are sanc-ti-fied;

All the light of sa-cred sto-ry Gath-ers round its head sub-lime.
Nev-er shall the cross for-sake me: Lo! it glows with peace and joy.
From the cross the ra-diance streaming Adds more lus-ter to the day.
Peace is there that knows no meas-ure, Joys that thro' all time a-bide.

27 ## Guide Me, O Thou Great Jehovah

William Williams.

Thomas Hastings

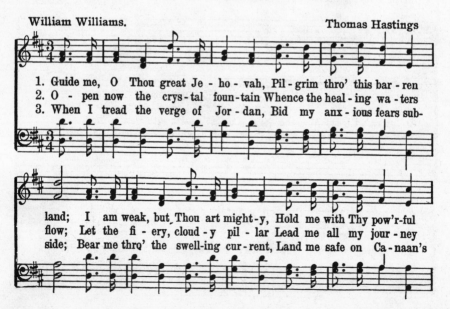

1. Guide me, O Thou great Je-ho-vah, Pil-grim thro' this bar-ren
2. O-pen now the crys-tal foun-tain Whence the heal-ing wa-ters
3. When I tread the verge of Jor-dan, Bid my anx-ious fears sub-

land; I am weak, but Thou art might-y, Hold me with Thy pow'r-ful
flow; Let the fi-er-y, cloud-y pil-lar Lead me all my jour-ney
side; Bear me thro' the swell-ing cur-rent, Land me safe on Ca-naan's

Guide Me, O Thou Great Jehovah

hand: Bread of Heav - en, Feed me till I want no more;
thro': Strong De - liv - 'rer, Be Thou still my Strength and Shield;
side: Songs of prais - es I will ev - er give to Thee;

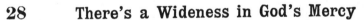

Bread of Heav - en, Feed me till I want no more.
Strong De - liv - 'rer, Be Thou still my Strength and Shield.
Songs of prais - es I will ev - er give to Thee. A - MEN.

28 There's a Wideness in God's Mercy

FREDERICK W. FABER

LIZZIE S. TOURJÉE

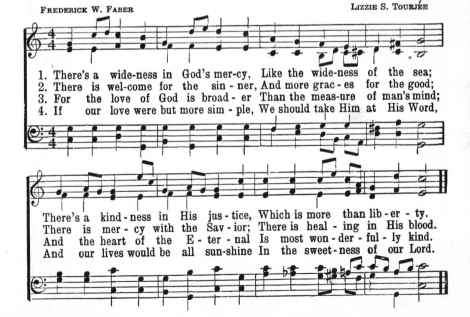

1. There's a wide-ness in God's mer-cy, Like the wide-ness of the sea;
2. There is wel-come for the sin - ner, And more grac - es for the good;
3. For the love of God is broad - er Than the meas-ure of man's mind;
4. If our love were but more sim - ple, We should take Him at His Word,

There's a kind - ness in His jus - tice, Which is more than lib - er - ty.
There is mer - cy with the Sav - ior; There is heal - ing in His blood.
And the heart of the E - ter - nal Is most won - der - ful - ly kind.
And our lives would be all sun-shine In the sweet-ness of our Lord.

29 If Jesus Goes With Me

C. A. M.

C. Austin Miles

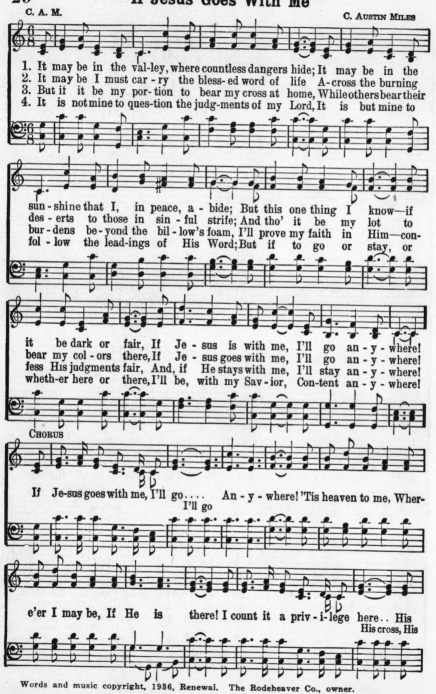

1. It may be in the val-ley, where countless dangers hide; It may be in the
2. It may be I must car-ry the bless-ed word of life A-cross the burning
3. But if it be my por-tion to bear my cross at home, While others bear their
4. It is not mine to ques-tion the judg-ments of my Lord, It is but mine to

sun-shine that I, in peace, a-bide; But this one thing I know—if
des-erts to those in sin-ful strife; And tho' it be my lot to
bur-dens be-yond the bil-low's foam, I'll prove my faith in Him—con-
fol-low the lead-ings of His Word; But if to go or stay, or

it be dark or fair, If Je-sus is with me, I'll go an-y-where!
bear my col-ors there, If Je-sus goes with me, I'll go an-y-where!
fess His judgments fair, And, if He stays with me, I'll stay an-y-where!
wheth-er here or there, I'll be, with my Sav-ior, Con-tent an-y-where!

CHORUS

If Je-sus goes with me, I'll go.... An-y-where! 'Tis heaven to me, Wher-
I'll go

e'er I may be, If He is there! I count it a priv-i-lege here.. His
His cross, His

Words and music copyright, 1936, Renewal. The Rodeheaver Co., owner.

If Jesus Goes With Me

cross to bear;.. If Je-sus goes with me, I'll go... An - y - where!
cross, His cross to bear;

30 Sweet Hour of Prayer

W. W. WALFORD

WM. B. BRADBURY

1. Sweet hour of prayer, sweet hour of prayer, That calls me from a world of care,
2. Sweet hour of prayer, sweet hour of prayer, Thy wings shall my pe - ti - tion bear,
3. Sweet hour of prayer, sweet hour of prayer, May I thy con - so - la - tion share,

And bids me at my Fa-ther's throne Make all my wants and wish-es known,
To Him whose truth and faith-ful-ness En-gage the wait - ing soul to bless;
Till, from Mount Pisgah's loft - y height, I view my home, and take my flight:

In sea - sons of dis-tress and grief, My soul has oft - en found re - lief,
And since He bids me seek His face, Be-lieve His word and trust His grace,
This robe of flesh I'll drop, and rise To seize the ev - er - last - ing prize;

And oft es-caped the tempter's snare, By thy re - turn, sweet hour of prayer.
I'll cast on Him my ev - 'ry care, And wait for thee, sweet hour of prayer.
And shout, while passing thro' the air, Farewell, fare-well, sweet hour of prayer!

I'll Go Where You Want Me to Go

RY BROWN

CARRIE E. ROUNSEFELL

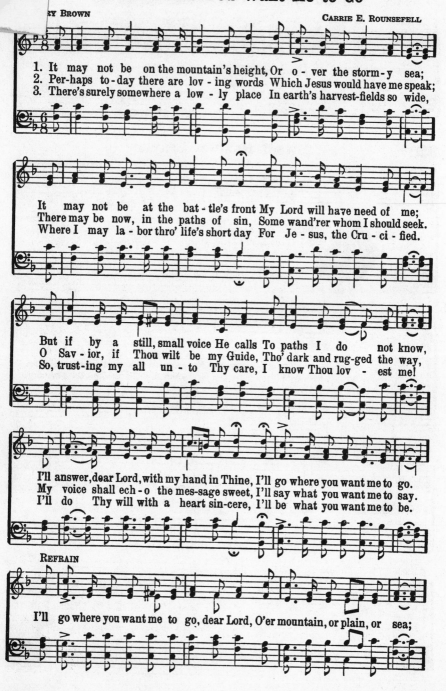

1. It may not be on the mountain's height, Or o - ver the storm-y sea;
2. Per-haps to-day there are lov-ing words Which Jesus would have me speak;
3. There's surely somewhere a low-ly place In earth's harvest-fields so wide,

It may not be at the bat-tle's front My Lord will have need of me;
There may be now, in the paths of sin, Some wand'rer whom I should seek.
Where I may la-bor thro' life's short day For Je-sus, the Cru-ci-fied.

But if by a still, small voice He calls To paths I do not know,
O Sav-ior, if Thou wilt be my Guide, Tho' dark and rug-ged the way,
So, trust-ing my all un-to Thy care, I know Thou lov-est me!

I'll answer, dear Lord, with my hand in Thine, I'll go where you want me to go.
My voice shall ech-o the mes-sage sweet, I'll say what you want me to say.
I'll do Thy will with a heart sin-cere, I'll be what you want me to be.

REFRAIN

I'll go where you want me to go, dear Lord, O'er mountain, or plain, or sea;

I'll Go Where You Want Me to Go

I'll say what you want me to say, dear Lord, I'll be what you want me to be.

32 Bring Them In

ALEXCENAH THOMAS

W. A. OGDEN

1. Hark! 'tis the Shepherd's voice I hear, Out in the des-ert dark and drear,
2. Who'll go and help this Shepherd kind, Help Him the wand'ring ones to find?
3. Out in the des-ert hear their cry, Out on the mountains wild and high;

Call-ing the sheep who've gone a-stray Far from the Shepherd's fold a-way.
Who'll bring the lost ones to the fold, Where they'll be sheltered from the cold?
Hark! 'tis the Mas-ter speaks to thee, "Go find my sheep wher-e'er they be."

CHORUS

Bring them in, bring them in, Bring them in from the fields of sin;

Bring them in, bring them in, Bring the wand'ring ones to Je-sus.

33 Jesus, the Very Thought of Thee

BERNARD of CLAIRVAUX
Tr. by EDWARD CASWALL

JOHN B. DYKES

1. Je - sus! the ver - y thought of Thee   With sweet-ness fills my breast:
2. No voice can sing, no heart can frame,   Nor can the mem-'ry find
3. O hope of ev - 'ry con - trite heart,   O   joy of   all the meek,
4. But what to those who find? Ah! this   Nor tongue nor pen can show,

But sweet-er far Thy face to   see,   And in Thy pres-ence rest.
A sweet-er sound than Je-sus' name,   The Sav-ior of man-kind.
To those who ask, how kind Thou art!   How good to those who seek!
The love of Je - sus, what it   is   None but His loved ones know. A-MEN.

34 Lead, Kindly Light

JOHN H. NEWMAN

JOHN B. DYKES

1. Lead, kind-ly Light, a-mid th' en-cir-cling gloom,   Lead Thou me on!
2. I   was not ev - er thus, nor prayed that Thou   Shouldst lead me on;
3. So long Thy pow'r hath blest me, sure it still   Will lead me on

The night is dark, and I   am far from home;   Lead Thou me on!
I loved to choose and see my path; but now   Lead Thou me on!
O'er moor and fen, o'er crag and torrent, till   The night is gone,

Lead, Kindly Light

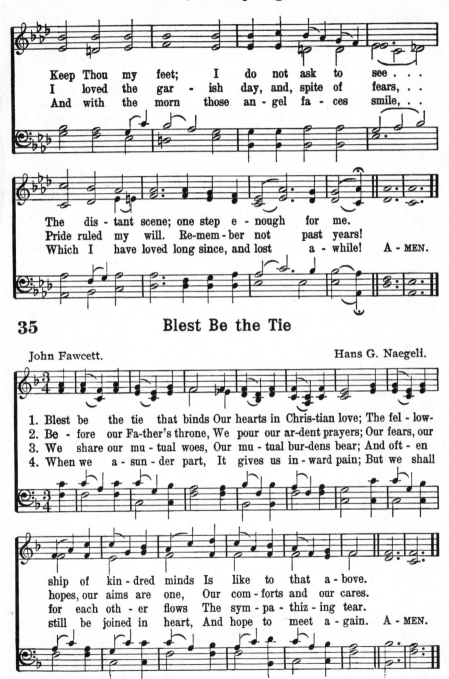

Keep Thou my feet; I do not ask to see . . . .
I loved the gar - ish day, and, spite of fears, . .
And with the morn those an - gel fa - ces smile, . .

The dis - tant scene; one step e - nough for me.
Pride ruled my will. Re-mem - ber not past years!
Which I have loved long since, and lost a - while! A - MEN.

35   Blest Be the Tie

John Fawcett.

Hans G. Naegeli.

1. Blest be the tie that binds Our hearts in Chris-tian love; The fel - low-
2. Be - fore our Fa-ther's throne, We pour our ar-dent prayers; Our fears, our
3. We share our mu - tual woes, Our mu - tual bur-dens bear; And oft - en
4. When we a - sun - der part, It gives us in - ward pain; But we shall

ship of kin - dred minds Is like to that a - bove.
hopes, our aims are one, Our com - forts and our cares.
for each oth - er flows The sym - pa - thiz - ing tear.
still be joined in heart, And hope to meet a - gain. A - MEN.

Precious Promise

NATHANIEL NILES

P. P. BLISS

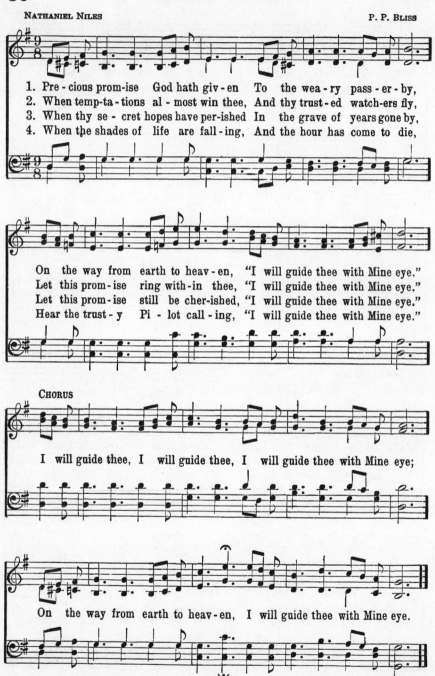

1. Pre - cious prom-ise God hath giv-en To the wea-ry pass-er-by,
2. When temp-ta-tions al - most win thee, And thy trust-ed watch-ers fly,
3. When thy se - cret hopes have per-ished In the grave of years gone by,
4. When the shades of life are fall-ing, And the hour has come to die,

On the way from earth to heav-en, "I will guide thee with Mine eye."
Let this prom-ise ring with-in thee, "I will guide thee with Mine eye."
Let this prom-ise still be cher-ished, "I will guide thee with Mine eye."
Hear the trust-y Pi - lot call-ing, "I will guide thee with Mine eye."

CHORUS

I will guide thee, I will guide thee, I will guide thee with Mine eye;

On the way from earth to heav-en, I will guide thee with Mine eye.

37 Leaving It All With Jesus

James M. Gray

O. F. Pugh

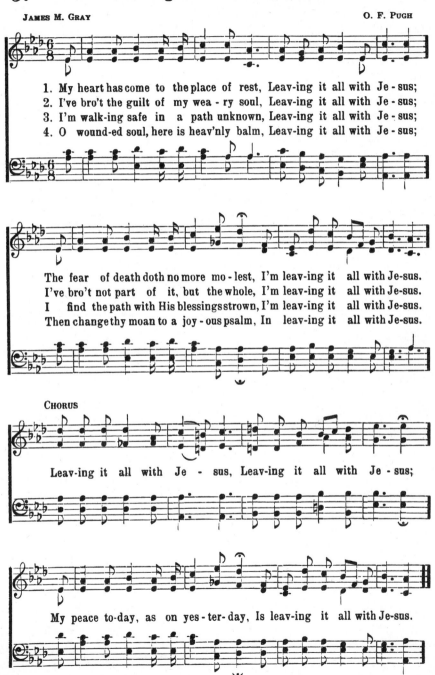

1. My heart has come to the place of rest, Leav-ing it all with Je - sus;
2. I've bro't the guilt of my wea - ry soul, Leav-ing it all with Je - sus;
3. I'm walk-ing safe in a path unknown, Leav-ing it all with Je - sus;
4. O wound-ed soul, here is heav'nly balm, Leav-ing it all with Je - sus;

The fear of death doth no more mo - lest, I'm leav-ing it all with Je-sus.
I've bro't not part of it, but the whole, I'm leav-ing it all with Je-sus.
I find the path with His blessings strown, I'm leav-ing it all with Je-sus.
Then change thy moan to a joy - ous psalm, In leav-ing it all with Je-sus.

Chorus

Leav-ing it all with Je - sus, Leav-ing it all with Je - sus;

My peace to-day, as on yes - ter- day, Is leav-ing it all with Je-sus.

38 Savior, Like a Shepherd Lead Us

Anonymous

WILLIAM B. BRADBURY

1. Sav - ior, like a shep-herd lead us, Much we need Thy ten-der care;
2. We are Thine; do Thou be - friend us, Be the Guardian of our way;
3. Thou hast promised to re - ceive us, Poor and sin-ful though we be;
4. Ear - ly let us seek Thy fa - vor; Ear - ly let us do Thy will;

In Thy pleas-ant pas-tures feed us, For our use Thy folds pre-pare:
Keep Thy flock, from sin de - fend us, Seek us when we go a - stray:
Thou hast mer - cy to re - lieve us, Grace to cleanse, and pow'r to free:
Bless-ed Lord and on - ly Sav - ior, With Thy love our bos-oms fill:

Bless-ed Je - sus, Bless-ed Je - sus, Thou hast bought us, Thine we are;
Bless-ed Je - sus, Bless-ed Je - sus, Hear Thy chil-dren when they pray;
Bless-ed Je - sus, Bless-ed Je - sus, Ear - ly let us turn to Thee;
Bless-ed Je - sus, Bless-ed Je - sus, Thou hast loved us, love us still;

Bless-ed Je - sus, Bless-ed Je - sus, Thou hast bought us, Thine we are.
Bless-ed Je - sus, Bless-ed Je - sus, Hear Thy chil-dren when they pray.
Bless-ed Je - sus, Bless-ed Je - sus, Ear - ly let us turn to Thee.
Bless-ed Je - sus, Bless-ed Je - sus, Thou hast loved us, love us still.

Where He Leads I'll Follow

W. A. O.

W. A. OGDEN

1. Sweet are the prom-is-es, Kind is the word, Dear-er far than
2. Sweet is the ten-der love Je-sus hath shown, Sweet-er far than
3. List to His lov-ing words, "Come un-to Me;" Wea-ry, heav-y-

an-y mes-sage man ev-er heard; Pure was the mind of Christ,
an-y love that mor-tals have known; Kind to the err-ing one,
la-den, there is sweet rest for thee; Trust in His prom-is-es,

Sin-less I see; He the great ex-am-ple is, and pat-tern for me.
Faith-ful is He; He the great ex-am-ple is, and pat-tern for me.
Faith-ful and sure; Lean up-on the Sav-ior, and thy soul is se-cure.

CHORUS

Where . . . . He leads I'll fol - - - - low,
Where He leads I'll fol-low,   Where He leads I'll fol-low,

Fol - - - low all the way.
Fol-low all the way, yes,   fol-low all the way.

Fol-low Je-sus ev-'ry day.

40   Wherever He Leads I'll Go

B. B. McK.   B. B. McKinney

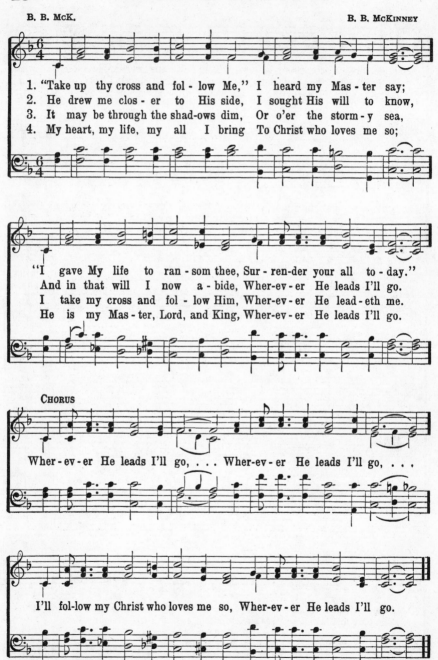

1. "Take up thy cross and fol - low Me," I heard my Mas - ter say;
2. He drew me clos - er to His side, I sought His will to know,
3. It may be through the shad-ows dim, Or o'er the storm - y sea,
4. My heart, my life, my all I bring To Christ who loves me so;

"I gave My life to ran - som thee, Sur - ren-der your all to - day."
And in that will I now a - bide, Wher-ev - er He leads I'll go.
I take my cross and fol - low Him, Wher-ev - er He lead - eth me.
He is my Mas - ter, Lord, and King, Wher-ev - er He leads I'll go.

CHORUS

Wher - ev - er He leads I'll go, . . . Wher-ev - er He leads I'll go, . . .

I'll fol-low my Christ who loves me so, Wher-ev - er He leads I'll go.

Copyright, 1937, by The Sunday School Board of the Southern Baptist Convention

41   God Rest You Merry, Gentlemen

Traditional   Traditional

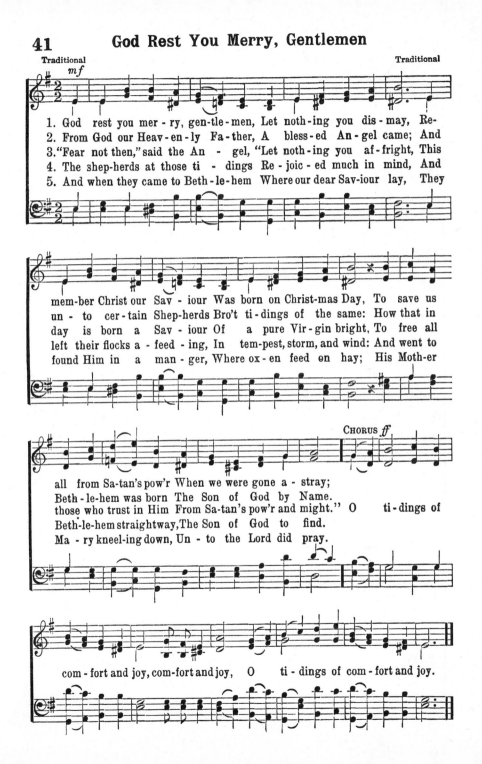

1. God rest you mer - ry, gen-tle-men, Let noth-ing you dis - may, Re-
2. From God our Heav-en-ly Fa-ther, A bless-ed An-gel came; And
3. "Fear not then," said the An - gel, "Let noth-ing you af-fright, This
4. The shep-herds at those ti - dings Re - joic-ed much in mind, And
5. And when they came to Beth-le-hem Where our dear Sav-iour lay, They

mem-ber Christ our Sav - iour Was born on Christ-mas Day, To save us
un - to cer-tain Shep-herds Bro't ti-dings of the same: How that in
day is born a Sav - iour Of a pure Vir-gin bright, To free all
left their flocks a - feed - ing, In tem-pest, storm, and wind: And went to
found Him in a man - ger, Where ox-en feed on hay; His Moth-er

CHORUS *ff*

all from Sa-tan's pow'r When we were gone a - stray;
Beth - le-hem was born The Son of God by Name.
those who trust in Him From Sa-tan's pow'r and might." O   ti-dings of
Beth-le-hem straightway, The Son of God to find.
Ma - ry kneel-ing down, Un - to the Lord did pray.

com - fort and joy, com-fort and joy, O ti - dings of com - fort and joy.

42   O Little Town of Bethlehem

PHILLIPS BROOKS

LEWIS H. REDNER

1. O lit-tle town of Beth-le-hem, How still we see thee lie! A-bove thy deep and
2. For Christ is born of Ma - ry; And gathered all a-bove, While mortals sleep, the
3. How si-lent-ly, how si-lent-ly The wondrous gift is giv'n! So God im-parts to
4. O ho - ly Child of Beth-le-hem, Descend to us, we pray; Cast out our sin and

dreamless sleep The si - lent stars go by; Yet in thy dark streets shineth The
an - gels keep Their watch of wond'ring love. O morn-ing stars, to-geth - er Pro-
hu - man hearts The bless-ings of His heav'n. No ear may hear His com-ing; But
en - ter in,—Be born in us to - day. We hear the Christmas an-gels The

ev - er-last-ing Light; The hopes and fears of all the years Are met in thee to-night.
claim the ho-ly birth, And praises sing to God the King, And peace to men on earth.
in this world of sin, Where meek souls will receive Him still, The dear Christ enters in.
great glad tidings tell,—O come to us, a-bide with us, Our Lord Em-man-u-el!

43   Angels, From the Realms of Glory

JAMES MONTGOMERY

HENRY SMART

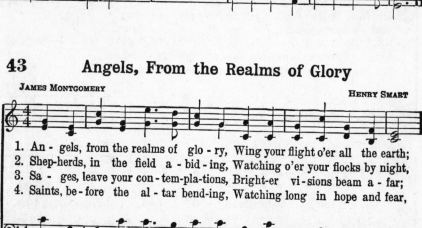

1. An - gels, from the realms of glo - ry, Wing your flight o'er all the earth;
2. Shep-herds, in the field a - bid - ing, Watching o'er your flocks by night,
3. Sa - ges, leave your con - tem-pla-tions, Bright-er vi - sions beam a - far;
4. Saints, be - fore the al - tar bend-ing, Watching long in hope and fear,

Angels, From the Realms of Glory

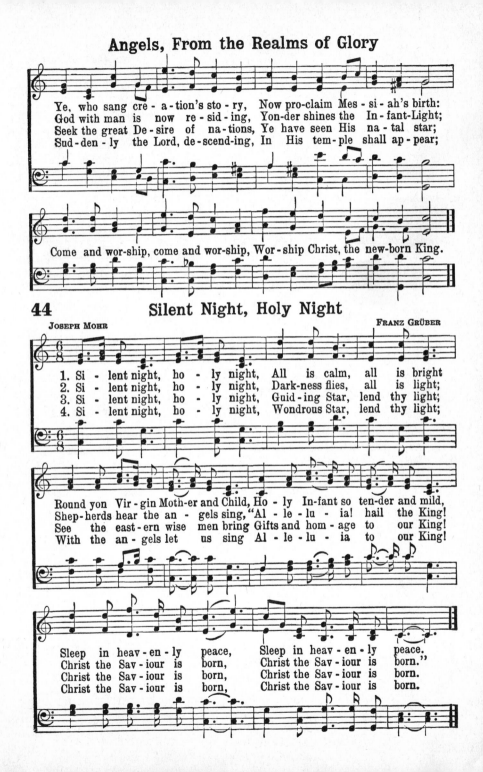

Ye, who sang cre - a - tion's sto - ry, Now pro-claim Mes - si - ah's birth:
God with man is now re - sid - ing, Yon-der shines the In - fant-Light;
Seek the great De - sire of na - tions, Ye have seen His na - tal star;
Sud - den - ly the Lord, de - scend-ing, In His tem - ple shall ap - pear;

Come and wor-ship, come and wor-ship, Wor - ship Christ, the new-born King.

44   Silent Night, Holy Night

JOSEPH MOHR   FRANZ GRÜBER

1. Si - lent night, ho - ly night, All is calm, all is bright
2. Si - lent night, ho - ly night, Dark-ness flies, all is light;
3. Si - lent night, ho - ly night, Guid-ing Star, lend thy light;
4. Si - lent night, ho - ly night, Wondrous Star, lend thy light;

Round yon Vir - gin Moth-er and Child, Ho - ly In-fant so ten-der and mild,
Shep-herds hear the an - gels sing, "Al - le - lu - ia! hail the King!
See the east-ern wise men bring Gifts and hom - age to our King!
With the an - gels let us sing Al - le - lu - ia to our King!

Sleep in heav - en - ly peace, Sleep in heav - en - ly peace.
Christ the Sav - iour is born, Christ the Sav - iour is born."
Christ the Sav - iour is born, Christ the Sav - iour is born.
Christ the Sav - iour is born, Christ the Sav - iour is born.

45 Joy to the World

ISAAC WATTS

GEORGE F. HANDEL

1. Joy to the world! the Lord is come; Let earth re-
2. Joy to the earth! the Sav-ior reigns; Let men their
3. No more let sins and sor-rows grow, Nor thorns in-
4. He rules the world with truth and grace, And makes the

ceive her King; Let ev-'ry heart pre-pare Him room,
songs em-ploy; While fields and floods, rocks, hills and plains
fest the ground; He comes to make His bless-ings flow
na-tions prove The glo-ries of His right-eous-ness,

And Heav'n and na-ture sing, And Heav'n and na-ture
Re-peat the sound-ing joy, Re-peat the sound-ing
Far as the curse is found, Far as the curse is
And won-ders of His love, And won-ders of His
1. And Heav'n and na-ture sing,.......... And

sing, And Heav'n, and Heav'n and na-ture sing.
joy, Re-peat, re-peat the sound-ing joy.
found, Far as, far as the curse is found.
love, And won-ders, and won-ders of His love.
Heav'n and na-ture sing,

Thou Didst Leave Thy Throne

EMILY E. S. ELLIOTT   TIMOTHY R. MATTHEWS

1. Thou didst leave Thy throne And Thy king - ly crown When Thou
2. Heav-en's arch - es rang When the an - gels sang, Pro- - -
3. The fox - es found rest, And the birds their nest In the
4. Thou cam - est, O Lord, With the liv - ing word That should
5. When the heav - ens shall ring, And the an - gels sing, At Thy

cam - est to earth for me; But in Beth - le-hem's home
claim - ing Thy roy - al de-gree; But of low - ly birth
shade of the for - est tree; But Thy couch was the sod,
set Thy peo - ple free; But with mock - ing scorn,
com - ing to vic - to - ry, Let Thy voice call me home,

Was there found no room For Thy ho - ly na - tiv - i - ty:
Didst Thou come to earth, And in great-est hu - mil - i - ty:
O Thou Son of God, In the des - erts of Gal - i - lee:
And with crown of thorn, They bore Thee to Cal - va - ry:
Say - ing, "Yet there is room, There is room at My side for thee:"

REFRAIN

1-4. O come to my heart, Lord Je - sus, There is room in my heart for Thee.
5. My heart shall rejoice, Lord Je - sus, When Thou comest and call-est for me.

47   Hark, the Herald Angels Sing

CHARLES WESLEY

FELIX MENDELSSOHN

1. Hark! the her - ald an - gels sing, "Glo - ry to the new-born King;
2. Christ, by high - est heaven a - dored; Christ, the ev - er - last - ing Lord:
3. Hail the heaven-born Prince of Peace! Hail the Sun of right-eous-ness!
4. Come, De - sire of na - tions, come! Fix in us Thy hum - ble home:

Peace on earth, and mer - cy mild; God and sin - ners rec - on - ciled."
Late in time be-hold Him come, Off - spring of a vir-gin's womb.
Light and life to all He brings, Risen with heal - ing in His wings:
Rise, the wom - an's conquering seed, Bruise in us the ser-pent's head;

Joy - ful, all ye na - tions, rise, Join the tri - umph of the skies;
Veiled in flesh the God - head see, Hail th' in-car-nate De - i - ty!
Mild He lays His glo - ry by, Born that man no more may die;
Ad - am's like-ness now ef - face, Stamp Thine im-age in its place:

With th' an-gel - ic hosts pro - claim, "Christ is born in Beth - le - hem."
Pleased as man with men t'ap-pear, Je - sus our Im-man-uel here.
Born to raise the sons of earth; Born to give them sec - ond birth.
Sec - ond Ad - am from a - bove, Re - in - state us in Thy love.

Hark! the Herald Angels Sing

Hark! the her-ald an-gels sing, "Glo-ry to the new-born King."

48   O Come, All Ye Faithful

Tr. by FREDERICK OAKELEY

WADE'S Cantus Diversi

1. O come, all ye faith-ful, joy-ful and tri-um-phant, O
2. Sing, choirs of an-gels, sing in ex-ul-ta-tion, O
3. Yea, Lord, we greet Thee, born this hap-py morn-ing,

come ye, O come ye to Beth-le-hem; Come and be-hold Him
sing, all ye bright hosts of heaven a-bove; Glo-ry to God, all
Je-sus, to Thee be all glo-ry given; Word of the Fa-ther,

REFRAIN

born the King of an-gels;
glo-ry in the high-est; O come, let us a-dore Him, O
now in flesh ap-pear-ing;

come, let us a-dore Him, O come, let us a-dore Him, Christ, the Lord.

49 It Came Upon the Midnight Clear

EDMUND H. SEARS

RICHARD S. WILLIS

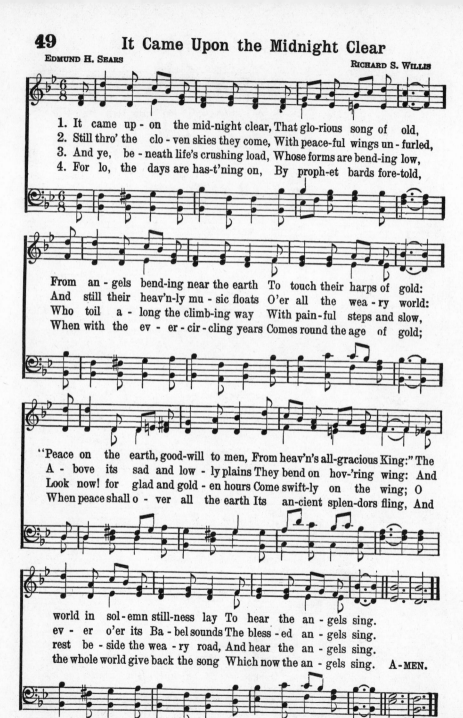

1. It came up-on the mid-night clear, That glo-rious song of old,
2. Still thro' the clo-ven skies they come, With peace-ful wings un-furled,
3. And ye, be-neath life's crushing load, Whose forms are bend-ing low,
4. For lo, the days are has-t'ning on, By proph-et bards fore-told,

From an-gels bend-ing near the earth To touch their harps of gold:
And still their heav'n-ly mu-sic floats O'er all the wea-ry world:
Who toil a-long the climb-ing way With pain-ful steps and slow,
When with the ev-er-cir-cling years Comes round the age of gold;

"Peace on the earth, good-will to men, From heav'n's all-gracious King:" The
A-bove its sad and low-ly plains They bend on hov-'ring wing: And
Look now! for glad and gold-en hours Come swift-ly on the wing; O
When peace shall o-ver all the earth Its an-cient splen-dors fling, And

world in sol-emn still-ness lay To hear the an-gels sing.
ev-er o'er its Ba-bel sounds The bless-ed an-gels sing.
rest be-side the wea-ry road, And hear the an-gels sing.
the whole world give back the song Which now the an-gels sing. A-MEN.

50   The First Noel the Angel Did Say

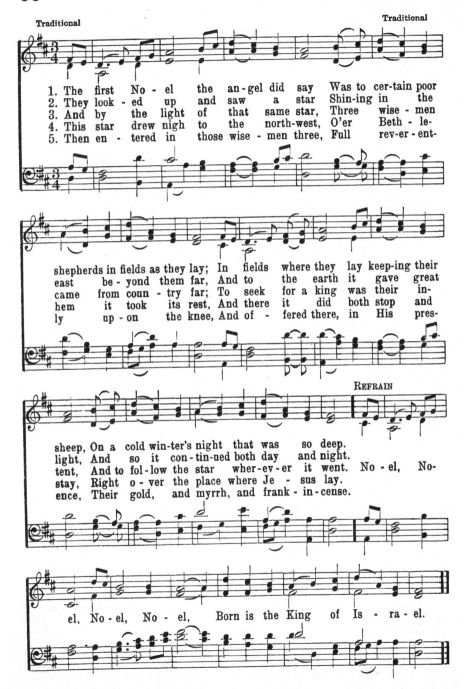

Traditional

Traditional

1. The first No - el the an-gel did say Was to cer-tain poor
2. They look - ed up and saw a star Shin-ing in the
3. And by the light of that same star, Three wise - men
4. This star drew nigh to the north-west, O'er Beth - le-
5. Then en - tered in those wise - men three, Full rev-er - ent-

shepherds in fields as they lay; In fields where they lay keep-ing their
east be - yond them far, And to the earth it gave great
came from coun - try far; To seek for a king was their in-
hem it took its rest, And there it did both stop and
ly up - on the knee, And of - fered there, in His pres-

REFRAIN

sheep, On a cold win-ter's night that was so deep.
light, And so it con - tin-ued both day and night.
tent, And to fol-low the star wher-ev - er it went. No - el, No-
stay, Right o - ver the place where Je - sus lay.
ence, Their gold, and myrrh, and frank - in - cense.

el, No - el, No - el, Born is the King of Is - ra - el.

51   While Shepherds Watched Their Flocks

NAHUM TATE

GEORGE F. HÄNDEL

1. While shep-herds watched their flocks by night, All seat-ed
2. "Fear not!" said he; for might-y dread Had seized their
3. "To you, in Da-vid's town, this day Is born, of
4. "All glo-ry be to God on high, And to the

on the ground, The an-gel of the Lord came down,
trou-bled mind, "Glad ti-dings of great joy I bring,
Da-vid's line, The Sav-iour, who is Christ the Lord;
earth be peace: Good-will hence-forth from heav'n to men,

And glo-ry shone a-round, And glo-ry shone a-round.
To you and all man-kind, To you and all man-kind.
And this shall be the sign: And this shall be the sign:
Be-gin and nev-er cease, Be-gin and nev-er cease!"

52   I Heard the Bells on Christmas Day

HENRY W. LONGFELLOW

J. BAPTISTE CALKIN

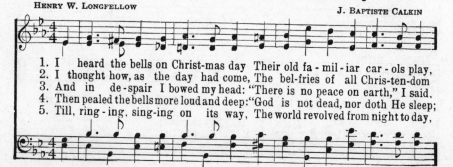

1. I heard the bells on Christ-mas day Their old fa-mil-iar car-ols play,
2. I thought how, as the day had come, The bel-fries of all Chris-ten-dom
3. And in de-spair I bowed my head: "There is no peace on earth," I said,
4. Then pealed the bells more loud and deep: "God is not dead, nor doth He sleep;
5. Till, ring-ing, sing-ing on its way, The world revolved from night to day,

I Heard the Bells on Christmas Day

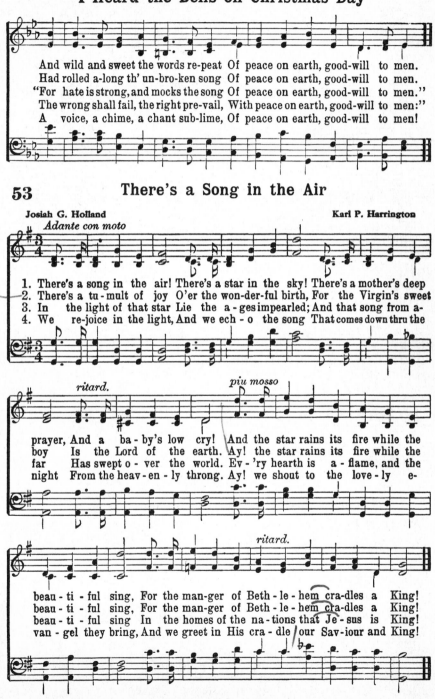

And wild and sweet the words re-peat Of peace on earth, good-will to men.
Had rolled a-long th' un-bro-ken song Of peace on earth, good-will to men.
"For hate is strong, and mocks the song Of peace on earth, good-will to men."
The wrong shall fail, the right pre-vail, With peace on earth, good-will to men:"
A voice, a chime, a chant sub-lime, Of peace on earth, good-will to men!

53   There's a Song in the Air

Josiah G. Holland   Karl P. Harrington

Adante con moto

1. There's a song in the air! There's a star in the sky! There's a mother's deep
2. There's a tu-mult of joy O'er the won-der-ful birth, For the Virgin's sweet
3. In the light of that star Lie the a-ges impearled; And that song from a-
4. We re-joice in the light, And we ech-o the song That comes down thru the

ritard.   *piu mosso*

prayer, And a ba-by's low cry! And the star rains its fire while the
boy   Is the Lord of the earth. Ay! the star rains its fire while the
far   Has swept o-ver the world. Ev-'ry hearth is a-flame, and the
night From the heav-en-ly throng. Ay! we shout to the love-ly e-

ritard.

beau-ti-ful sing, For the man-ger of Beth-le-hem cra-dles a King!
beau-ti-ful sing, For the man-ger of Beth-le-hem cra-dles a King!
beau-ti-ful sing In the homes of the na-tions that Je-sus is King!
van-gel they bring, And we greet in His cra-dle our Sav-iour and King!

'Neath the Old Olive Trees

B. B. McKinney

B. B. McKinney

DUET Slowly

1. 'Neath the stars of the night Walked the Saviour of light, In the gar-den of
2. All the sin of the world On the Sav-iour was hurled, As He knelt in the
3. May my song ev-er be Of the love prof-fered me, By my Lord all a-

dew-la-dened breeze; Where no light could be found, Je-sus knelt on the ground,
gar-den a-lone; Hear His soul-burdened plea, Let this cup pass from Me,
lone on His knees: Praise His won-der-ful name, He who bore all my blame,

CHORUS

There He prayed 'neath the old ol-ive trees.
"E - ven so, not My will, Thine be done." 'Neath the old ol-ive trees, 'Neath the
As He knelt 'neath the old ol-ive trees.

old ol-ive trees, Went the Sav-iour a-lone on His knees: "Not My will, Thine be

done," Cried the Fa-ther's own Son, As He knelt 'neath the old ol-ive trees.

55   At the Cross

ISAAC WATTS

R. E. HUDSON

1. A - las, and did my Sav - ior bleed? And did my Sov-'reign die?
2. Was it for crimes that I have done, He groaned up - on the tree?
3. Well might the sun in dark-ness hide, And shut his glo - ries in,
4. But drops of grief can ne'er re - pay The debt of love I owe:

Would He de - vote that sa - cred head For such a worm as I?
A - maz - ing pit - y! grace unknown! And love be - yond de - gree!
When Christ, the might-y Mak - er, died For man the crea-ture's sin.
Here, Lord, I give my - self a - way, 'Tis all that I can do!

CHORUS

At the cross, at the cross where I first saw the light, And the

bur-den of my heart rolled a-way, (rolled a-way,) It was there by faith

I re-ceived my sight, And now I am hap - py all the day!

At the Foot of the Cross

ROBERT HARKNESS   ROBERT HARKNESS

1. I met Je-sus at the foot of the cross When I was bound by sin;
2. I found par-don at the foot of the cross, For-give-ness full and free;
3. I met Je-sus when I need-ed Him most, De-spair pos-sessed my soul;

Je-sus met me, cleansed my heart of its dross, He gave sweet peace with-in. . . .
Now I love Him on - ly, all else is loss, His grace a-vailed for me. . .
I was un - der con-dem - na-tion and lost, When Je-sus made me whole. .

CHORUS

I met Je-sus at the foot of the cross, I met Je-sus at the
foot of the cross; All my sins were washed a-way; Sin's dark night turned
in - to day When I met Je - sus at the foot of the cross.

Beneath the Cross of Jesus

Elizabeth C. Clephane

Frederick C. Maker

1. Be-neath the cross of Je - sus I fain would take my stand,
2. Up-on that cross of Je - sus Mine eye at times can see
3. I take, O cross, thy shad-ow For my a - bid - ing place;

The shad-ow of a might-y rock With-in a wea-ry land;
The ver-y dy-ing form of One Who suf-fered there for me;
I ask no oth-er sun-shine than The sun-shine of His face;

A home with-in the wil-der-ness, A rest up-on the way,
And from my smit-ten heart with tears Two won-ders I con-fess,—
Con-tent to let the world go by, To know no gain nor loss,

From the burn-ing of the noon-tide heat, And the bur-den of the day.
The won-ders of His glo-rious love And my un-wor-thi-ness.
My sin-ful self my on-ly shame, My glo-ry all the cross.

58 Glorious Calvary

ALFRED B. SMITH
Free trans. from Swedish

Arr. by HERMAN VOSS

1. Once by the sin of the world I was bound, But Je-sus res-cued me;
2. Now I am free from the pow-er of sin, Since Je-sus set me free;
3. Come, then, to Cal-v'ry, O sin bur-dened soul, Let Je-sus set you free;

Lift-ed me up, put my feet on high ground, Glo-ri-ous Cal-va-ry.
Joy-bells are ring-ing, there's gladness with-in, Glo-ri-ous Cal-va-ry.
You, too, will join with the ran-somed made whole, Glo-ri-ous Cal-va-ry.

CHORUS

Glo-ri-ous Cal-va-ry, Glo-ri-ous Cal-va-ry, My debt there was

rit.

paid and my soul was set free, Glo-ri-ous Cal-va-ry.

59 I Saw the Cross of Jesus

F WHITFIELD   From Greek Melody

1. I saw the cross of Je - sus, When bur-dened with my sin:
2. I love the cross of Je - sus, It tells me what I am—
3. I clasp the cross of Je - sus In ev - ery try - ing hour,
4. Sweet is the cross of Je - sus! There let my wea - ry heart

I sought the cross of Je - sus, To give me peace with - in;
A vile and guilt - y crea - ture, Saved on - ly through the Lamb;
My sure and cer - tain ref - uge, My nev - er - fail - ing tower;
Still rest in peace un - shak - en, Till with Him, ne'er to part;

I brought my soul to Je - sus, He cleansed it in His blood;
No right-eous - ness, nor mer - it, No beau - ty can I plead;
In ev - ery fear and con - flict, I more than con - queror am;
And then in strains of glo - ry I'll sing His won - drous power,

And in the cross of Je - sus I found my peace with God.
Yet in the cross I glo - ry, My ti - tle there I read.
Liv - ing I'm safe, or dy - ing, Thro' Christ, the ris - en Lamb.
Where sin can nev - er en - ter, And death is known no more.

60
Cleanse Me

EDWIN ORR

Maori Melody by JOHN MCNEILL

1. Search me, O God,........ and know my heart to-day;......
2. I praise Thee, Lord,........ for cleans-ing me from sin: ......
3. Lord, take my life, ... and make it whol-ly Thine:......
4. O Ho-ly Ghost,........ re-viv-al comes from Thee:.....

Try me, O Sav-ior, know my thoughts, I pray:....
Ful-fill Thy Word, and make me pure with-in;....
Fill my poor heart with Thy great love di-vine;....
Send a re-viv-al— start the work in me:......

See if there be........ some wick-ed way in me:.....
Fill me with fire,..... where once I burned with shame:...
Take all my will,...... my pas-sion, self and pride;....
Thy Word de-clares...... Thou wilt sup-ply our need:....

Cleanse me from ev-'ry sin, and set me free.......
Grant my de-sire to mag-ni-fy Thy name......
I now sur-ren-der: Lord, in me a-bide.......
For bless-ing now, O Lord, I hum-bly plead......

61
I'll Be So Glad

Anon.

I'll be so glad when day is done, I'll be so glad when vic-t'ry's won;

I'll Be So Glad

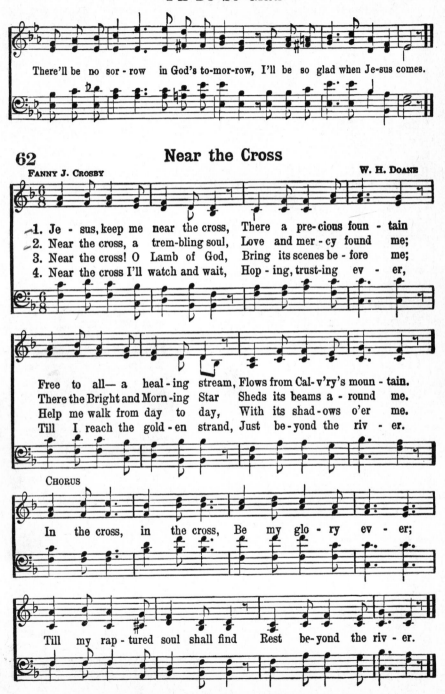

There'll be no sor-row in God's to-mor-row, I'll be so glad when Je-sus comes.

62. Near the Cross

FANNY J. CROSBY

W. H. DOANE

1. Je - sus, keep me near the cross, There a pre-cious foun - tain
2. Near the cross, a trem-bling soul, Love and mer - cy found me;
3. Near the cross! O Lamb of God, Bring its scenes be - fore me;
4. Near the cross I'll watch and wait, Hop - ing, trust-ing ev - er,

Free to all— a heal-ing stream, Flows from Cal-v'ry's moun - tain.
There the Bright and Morn-ing Star Sheds its beams a - round me.
Help me walk from day to day, With its shad-ows o'er me.
Till I reach the gold-en strand, Just be-yond the riv - er.

CHORUS

In the cross, in the cross, Be my glo - ry ev - er;

Till my rap-tured soul shall find Rest be-yond the riv - er.

63   # A Charge to Keep

CHARLES WESLEY   LOWELL MASON

1. A charge to keep I have, A God to glo - ri - fy;
2. To serve the pres - ent age, My call - ing to ful - fill,—
3. Arm me with jeal - ous care, As in Thy sight to live;

Who gave His Son my soul to save, And fit it for the sky;
O may it all my powers en - gage To do my Mas - ter's will!
And O, Thy serv - ant, Lord, pre - pare A strict ac - count to give!

64   # Jesus, Saviour, Pilot Me

EDWARD HOPPER   J. E. GOULD

1. Je - sus, Sav - iour, pi - lot me O - ver life's tem - pes - tuous sea:
2. As a moth - er stills her child, Thou canst hush the o - cean wild;
3. When at last I near the shore, And the fear - ful break - ers roar

Un-known waves be - fore me roll, Hid - ing rocks and treacherous shoal;
Bois-terous waves o - bey Thy will When Thou sayest to them "Be still!"
'Twixt me and the peace-ful rest, Then, while lean-ing on Thy breast,

Chart and com - pass come from Thee, Je - sus, Sav - iour, pi - lot me.
Won-drous Sov-ereign of the sea, Je - sus, Sav - iour, pi - lot me.
May I hear Thee say to me, "Fear not, I will pi - lot thee."

65 The Old Rugged Cross

Rev. G. B.

Rev. Geo. Bennard

1. On a hill far a-way stood an old rug-ged cross, The em-blem of suf-f'ring and shame; And I love that old cross where the dear-est and best For a world of lost sin-ners was slain.

2. Oh, that old rug-ged cross so de-spised by the world, Has a wondrous at-trac-tion for me; For the dear Lamb of God left His glo-ry a-bove, To bear it to dark Cal-va-ry.

3. In the old rug-ged cross, stained with blood so di-vine, A won-drous beau-ty I see; For 'twas on that old cross Je-sus suf-fered and died, To par-don and sanc-ti-fy me.

4. To the old rug-ged cross I will ev-er be true, Its shame and re-proach gladly bear; Then He'll call me some day to my home far a-way, Where His glo-ry for-ev-er I'll share.

Chorus

So I'll cher-ish the old rug-ged cross, the old rugged cross, Till my tro-phies at last I lay down; I will cling to the old rug-ged cross, the old rug-ged cross, And ex-change it some day for a crown.

The Cross Is Not Greater

B. B.

BALLINGTON BOOTH

1. The cross that He gave may be heav-y, But it ne'er outweighs His grace;
2. The thorns in my path are not sharp-er Than composed His crown for me;
3. The light of His love shin-eth brighter As it falls on paths of woe,
4. His will I have joy in ful-fill-ing, As I'm walk-ing in His sight;

The storm that I feared may surround me, But it ne'er ex-cludes His face.
The cup that I drink not more bit-ter Than He drank in Geth-sem-a-ne.
The toil of my work groweth light-er As I stoop to raise the low.
My all to the blood I am bring-ing, It a-lone can keep me right.

CHORUS

The cross is not great-er than His grace, The storm can-not hide His bless-ed face; I am sat-is-fied to know That with Je-sus here be-low, I can con-quer ev-'ry foe.

The Broken Heart

T. D.

T. DENNIS

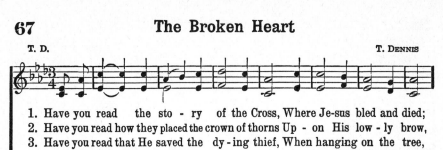

1. Have you read   the sto - ry   of the Cross, Where Je-sus bled and died;
2. Have you read how they placed the crown of thorns Up - on His low - ly brow,
3. Have you read that He saved the dy - ing thief, When hanging on the tree,
4. Have you read that He looked to heav'n and said, 'Tis fin-ished—'twas for thee?

Where your debt was paid by the pre-cious blood That gushed from His wounded side?
When He prayed, For-give them, oh! for-give; They know not what they do?
Who   looked with plead - ing eyes and said, Dear Lord, re - mem - ber me?
Have you ev - er   said, I thank Thee, Lord, For giv-ing Thy life   for   me?

CHORUS

He died of a   bro - ken heart for you, He died of a   bro - ken heart;

Oh, won-drous love! for you, for   me— He died of a   bro - ken heart.

68   The Way of the Cross Leads Home

Jessie Brown Pounds

Chas. H. Gabriel

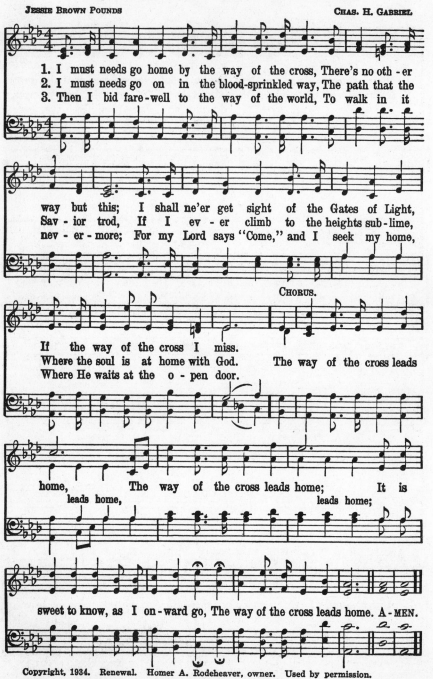

1. I must needs go home by the way of the cross, There's no oth - er
2. I must needs go on in the blood-sprinkled way, The path that the
3. Then I bid fare - well to the way of the world, To walk in it

way but this; I shall ne'er get sight of the Gates of Light,
Sav - ior trod, If I ev - er climb to the heights sub - lime,
nev - er - more; For my Lord says "Come," and I seek my home,

CHORUS.

If the way of the cross I miss.
Where the soul is at home with God.   The way of the cross leads
Where He waits at the o - pen door.

home,   The way of the cross leads home;   It is
leads home,   leads home;

sweet to know, as I on - ward go, The way of the cross leads home. A - MEN.

69 Wonderful Story of Love

J. M. D.   J. M. Driver

1. Won-der-ful sto-ry of love; Tell it to me a-gain; Won-der-ful
2. Won-der-ful sto-ry of love; Tho' you are far a-way; Won-der-ful
3. Won-der-ful sto-ry of love; Je-sus pro-vides a rest; Won-der-ful

sto-ry of love; Wake the im-mor-tal strain! Angels with rapture announce it,
sto-ry of love; Still He doth call to-day; Calling from Calvary's mountain,
sto-ry of love; For all the pure and blest, Rest in those mansions above us,

Shepherds with wonder re-ceive it; Sin-ner, O won't you be-lieve it?
Down from the crys-tal bright foun-tain, E'en from the dawn of cre-a-tion,
With those who've gone on be-fore us, Sing-ing the rap-tur-ous cho-rus,

Chorus

Won-der-ful sto-ry of love. Won - der - - ful! Won - der-
Won-der-ful sto-ry of love; Won-der-ful sto-ry of

ful! Won - der - - ful! Won-der-ful sto-ry of love!
love; Won-der-ful sto-ry of love;

70 It's Just Like His Great Love

EDNA R. WORRELL

DeKOVEN

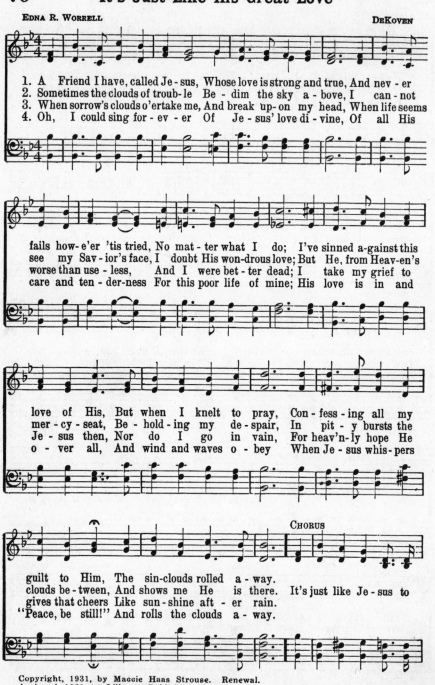

1. A Friend I have, called Je-sus, Whose love is strong and true, And nev-er
2. Sometimes the clouds of troub-le Be-dim the sky a-bove, I can-not
3. When sorrow's clouds o'ertake me, And break up-on my head, When life seems
4. Oh, I could sing for-ev-er Of Je-sus' love di-vine, Of all His

fails how-e'er 'tis tried, No mat-ter what I do; I've sinned a-gainst this
see my Sav-ior's face, I doubt His won-drous love; But He, from Heav-en's
worse than use-less, And I were bet-ter dead; I take my grief to
care and ten-der-ness For this poor life of mine; His love is in and

love of His, But when I knelt to pray, Con-fess-ing all my
mer-cy-seat, Be-hold-ing my de-spair, In pit-y bursts the
Je-sus then, Nor do I go in vain, For heav'n-ly hope He
o-ver all, And wind and waves o-bey When Je-sus whis-pers

CHORUS

guilt to Him, The sin-clouds rolled a-way.
clouds be-tween, And shows me He is there.   It's just like Je-sus to
gives that cheers Like sun-shine aft-er rain.
"Peace, be still!" And rolls the clouds a-way.

It's Just Like His Great Love

roll the clouds a-way, It's just like Je-sus to keep me day by day,

It's just like Je-sus all a-long the way, It's just like His great love.

71   He Leadeth Me

JOSEPH H. GILMORE

WILLIAM B. BRADBURY

1. He lead-eth, me O bless-ed tho't! O words with heav'nly comfort fraught!
2. Sometimes 'mid scenes of deepest gloom, Sometimes where Eden's bowers bloom,
3. Lord, I would clasp Thy hand in mine, Nor ev-er mur-mur nor re-pine,
4. And when my task on earth is done, When, by Thy grace, the vic-t'ry's won,

What-e'er I do, wher-e'er I be, Still 'tis God's hand that lead-eth me.
By wa-ters still, o'er trou-bled sea,—Still 'tis His hand that lead-eth me!
Con-tent, what-ev-er lot I see, Since 'tis my God that lead-eth me!
E'en death's cold wave I will not flee, Since God thro' Jor-dan lead-eth me.

REFRAIN

{ He lead-eth me, He lead-eth me! By His own hand He leadeth me!
{ His faithful foll'wer I would be, For by His hand He (*Omit*.....) leadeth me.

For God So Loved the World

E. E. HEWITT   J. LINCOLN HALL

1. A sto-ry sweet and won-drous, Like heav'n-ly mu-sic swells;
2. When, grieving, bro-ken-heart-ed, Be-cause of sin and shame,
3. This love, be-yond all meas-ure Of earth or sea or sky,
4. Come, broth-er, come to Je-sus; His word was meant for you;

In chim-ings clear to all who will hear, Ring out the gos-pel bells.
We find a joy earth can-not de-stroy, Be-liev-ing on His name.
Could on-ly show its full o-ver-flow, When Je-sus came to die.
His grace re-ceive, His prom-ise be-lieve, And sing His praise a-new.

CHORUS

For God so loved the world . . . that He gave His on-ly be-
For God . . . . so loved the world

got-ten Son, That who-so-ev-er be-liev-eth in Him, Who-so-

ev-er be-liev-eth in Him Should not per-ish, should not

For God So Loved the World

per-ish, But have ev - er - last - ing life. . . . .

ev - er - last - ing life.

73   Look to the Lamb of God

H. G. JACKSON   JAMES M. BLACK

1. If   you from sin are long-ing to be free, Look to the Lamb of God;
2. When Satan tempts, and doubts and fears assail, Look to the Lamb of God;
3. Are   you   a-wea - ry, does the way seem long? Look to the Lamb of God;
4. Fear not when shadows on your path-way fall, Look to the Lamb of God;

He, to re-deem you, died on Cal - va - ry, Look to the Lamb of God.
You in His strength shall o-ver all pre-vail, Look to the Lamb of God.
His love will cheer and fill your heart with song, Look to the Lamb of God.
In joy or sor - row Christ is all in all, Look to the Lamb of God.

CHORUS

Look to the Lamb of God,   Look to the Lamb of God,

the Lamb of God,   the Lamb of God

For He a - lone is a - ble to save you, Look to the Lamb of God.

74 I Know His Love is Mine

AVIS B. CHRISTIANSEN   ALBERT ALLEN KETCHUM

1. Oh! the Love that gave my Lord to die on Cal - va - ry! Match-less
2. Oh! the Love that sought me when I wan-dered far a - way! Bid - ding
3. Oh! the Love that o - pened wide the gates of God on high! For His

Love un - told, pur - er far than gold; Love that of - fered all up - on the
me come in from the paths of sin; Plead-ing with me gen - tly ev - 'ry
ransomed own, 'round the Heav'nly throne; Love Di - vine, I'll un - der-stand it

CHORUS.

Cross to set me free, This is the Love of Christ for me.
hour, ev - 'ry day, Such was the Love of Christ for me. Pre-cious Love, oh,
ful - ly bye and bye, Oh! Wondrous Love of Christ for me.

won-drous Love Di-vine—Can it be this match-less Love is mine? Yes! its pow-er

thrills me, and its glo - ry fills me, Praise His name, I know His love is mine.

75 For God So Loved the World

FRANCES TOWNSEND

ALFRED B. SMITH

For God so loved the world, He gave His on-ly Son, To die on Cal-v'ry's tree, From sin to set me free; Some day He's com-ing back, What glo-ry that will be Won-der-ful His love to me.——

76 I Know a Fount

O. C.

O. COOKE
Arr. by H. D. L.

Not too fast

I know a fount where sins are washed a-way (a-way), I know a place where night is turned to day (to day); Burdens are lift-ed, blind eyes made to see; There's a won-der work-ing pow'r in the blood of Cal-va-ry.

77 I Love Him

English Hymn Book

S. C. FOSTER

1. Gone from my heart the world and all its charm; Gone are my sins and
2. Once I was lost up - on the plains of sin; Once was a slave to
3. Once I was bound, but now I am set free; Once I was blind, but

all that would a - larm; Gone ev - er - more, and by His grace I know The
doubts and fears with-in; Once was a - fraid to trust a lov - ing God, But
now the light I see; Once I was dead, but now in Christ I live, To

D. S.—*Be-cause He first loved me, And*

FINE   CHORUS   D. S.

pre-cious blood of Je-sus cleans-es white as snow.
now my guilt is washed a-way in Je - sus' blood. I love Him, I love Him,
tell the world the peace that He a - lone can give.

pur-chased my sal - va - tion on Cal-vary's tree.

78 Fairest Lord Jesus

Anonymous

Arr. by R. S. WILLIS

1. Fair - est Lord Je - sus, Rul - er of all na - ture,
2. Fair are the mead - ows, Fair - er still the wood - lands,
3. Fair is the sun - shine, Fair - er still the moon - light,

Fairest Lord Jesus

O Thou of God and man the Son, Thee will I cher - ish,
Robed in the bloom-ing garb of spring; Je - sus is fair - er,
And all the twin-kling, star - ry host; Je - sus shines bright-er,

Thee will I hon - or, Thou my soul's glo-ry, joy, and crown.
Je - sus is pur - er, Who makes the woe-ful heart to sing.
Je - sus shines pur - er, Than all the an-gels heaven can boast.

79   O Master, Let Me Walk with Thee

Washington Gladden   Robert Schumann

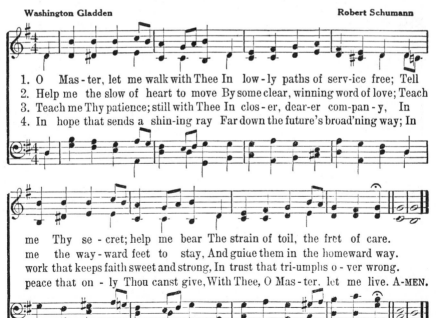

1. O Mas - ter, let me walk with Thee In low-ly paths of serv-ice free; Tell
2. Help me the slow of heart to move By some clear, winning word of love; Teach
3. Teach me Thy patience; still with Thee In clos - er, dear-er com-pan-y, In
4. In hope that sends a shin-ing ray Far down the future's broad'ning way; In

me Thy se - cret; help me bear The strain of toil, the fret of care.
me the way-ward feet to stay, And guide them in the homeward way.
work that keeps faith sweet and strong, In trust that tri-umphs o - ver wrong.
peace that on - ly Thou canst give, With Thee, O Mas-ter, let me live. A-MEN.

80 Like a Mighty Sea

A. I. ZELLEY

H. L. GILMOUR

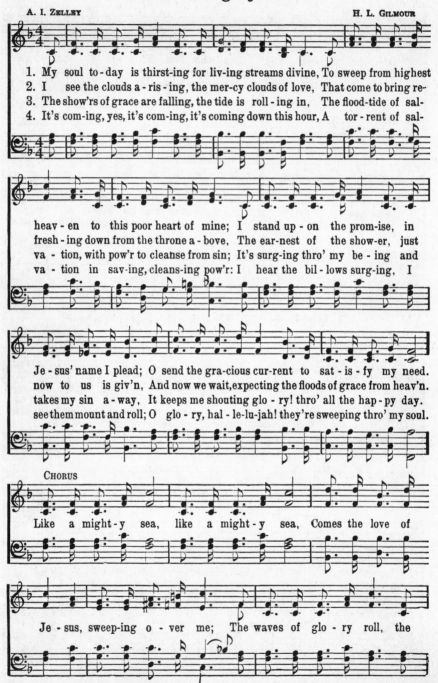

1. My soul to-day is thirst-ing for liv-ing streams divine, To sweep from highest
2. I see the clouds a-ris-ing, the mer-cy clouds of love, That come to bring re-
3. The show'rs of grace are falling, the tide is roll-ing in, The flood-tide of sal-
4. It's com-ing, yes, it's com-ing, it's coming down this hour, A tor-rent of sal-

heav-en to this poor heart of mine; I stand up-on the prom-ise, in
fresh-ing down from the throne a-bove, The ear-nest of the show-er, just
va-tion, with pow'r to cleanse from sin; It's surg-ing thro' my be-ing and
va-tion in sav-ing, cleans-ing pow'r: I hear the bil-lows surg-ing, I

Je-sus' name I plead; O send the gra-cious cur-rent to sat-is-fy my need.
now to us is giv'n, And now we wait, expecting the floods of grace from heav'n.
takes my sin a-way, It keeps me shouting glo-ry! thro' all the hap-py day.
see them mount and roll; O glo-ry, hal-le-lu-jah! they're sweeping thro' my soul.

CHORUS

Like a might-y sea, like a might-y sea, Comes the love of

Je-sus, sweep-ing o-ver me; The waves of glo-ry roll, the

Like a Mighty Sea

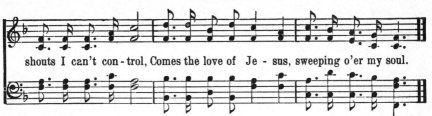

shouts I can't con - trol, Comes the love of Je - sus, sweeping o'er my soul.

81 Fully Surrendered

A. C. SNEAD

GEO. C. STEBBINS

1. Ful - ly sur-rend-ered, Lord, I would be, Ful - ly sur-rend-ered,
2. Ful - ly sur-rend-ered— life, time, and all, All Thou hast giv'n me
3. Ful - ly sur-rend-ered— sil - ver and gold, His, Who hath giv'n me
4. Ful - ly sur-rend-ered, Lord, I am Thine; Ful - ly sur-rend - ered,

dear Lord, to Thee; All on the al - tar laid, Sur - ren - der
held at Thy call. Speak but the word to me, Glad - ly I'll
rich - es un - told. All, all be - long to Thee, For Thou didst
Sav - iour di - vine; Live Thou Thy life in me, All ful - ness

ful - ly made, Thou hast my ran - som paid, I yield to Thee.
fol - low Thee, Now and e - ter - nal - ly O - bey my Lord.
pur - chase me, Thine ev - er - more to be, Je - sus my Lord.
dwells in Thee, Not I, but Christ in me, Christ all in all.

82 Love Led Him to Calvary

Geo. O. Webster

Chas. H. Gabriel

1. Love led the Sav-ior, in days long a - go, Down to earth's dark-ness, its
2. Love, for a man-ger, a-ban-doned a throne, Seek - ing the sin-ful, the
3. See - ing the soul in its in - fi-nite worth, Stoop-ing, in love, to the
4. Long-ing, in pit - y, the lost ones to save, Brav-ing the Gar-den, the

sin and its woe; Seek - ing the lost ones, His mer - cy to show,
sad and the lone; Yearn-ing to win them and make them His own,
low - li - est birth, Seek - ing the lost in the by - ways of earth,
Cross and the Grave, Seek - ing this on - ly, the sin - ful to save,

CHORUS *faster*

Love led Him to Cal - va - ry. Love led Him to Cal - va - ry,

Love led Him to Cal - va - ry; Seek - ing the lost, at the

ut - ter - most cost, Love led Him to Cal - va - ry.

83 Love Divine

CHARLES WESLEY

JOHN ZUNDEL

1. Love di-vine, all loves ex-cel-ling, Joy of heav'n, to earth come down;
2. Breathe, O breathe Thy lov-ing Spir-it In - to ev - 'ry troub-led breast!
3. Come, al-might-y to de-liv-er, Let us all Thy life re - ceive;
4. Fin - ish then Thy new cre-a-tion; Pure and spot-less let us be;

Fix in us Thy hum - ble dwell-ing; All Thy faith-ful mer - cies crown.
Let us all in Thee in - her - it, Let us find that sec - ond rest.
Sud-den-ly re - turn, and nev - er, Nev-er-more Thy tem-ples leave:
Let us see Thy great sal-va - tion, Per-fect-ly re-stored in Thee:

Je - sus, Thou art all com-pas-sion, Pure, un-bound-ed love Thou art;
Take a - way our bent to sin-ning, Al - pha and O - me - ga be;
Thee we would be al - ways blessing, Serve Thee as Thy hosts a - bove,
Changed from glo-ry in - to glo-ry, Till in heav'n we take our place,

Vis - it us with Thy sal-va - tion; En - ter ev - 'ry trem-bling heart.
End of faith, as its be - gin-ning, Set our hearts at lib - er - ty.
Pray, and praise Thee with-out ceas-ing, Glo - ry in Thy per-fect love.
Till we cast our crowns be-fore Thee, Lost in won-der, love, and praise.

84 Love Lifted Me

JAMES ROWE

HOWARD E. SMITH

1. I was sink-ing deep in sin, Far from the peaceful shore, Ver-y deep-ly
2. All my heart to Him I give, Ev-er to Him I'll cling, In His bless-ed
3. Souls in dan-ger, look a-bove, Je-sus com-plete-ly saves; He will lift you

stained with-in, Sink-ing to rise no more; But the Mas-ter of the sea
pres-ence live, Ev-er His prais-es sing. Love so might-y and so true
by His love Out of the an-gry waves. He's the Mas-ter of the sea,

Heard my de-spair-ing cry, From the wa-ters lift-ed me, Now safe am I.
Mer-its my soul's best songs; Faith-ful, lov-ing serv-ice, too, To Him be-longs.
Bil-lows His will o-bey; He your Sav-iour wants to be—Be saved to-day.

CHORUS

Love lift-ed me! .... Love lift-ed me! .... When noth-ing
e-ven me! e-ven me!

1

2

else could help, Love lift-ed me. Love lift-ed me.

85 My Savior's Love

C. H. G.

CHAS. H GABRIEL

1. I stand a-mazed in the pres-ence Of Je - sus the Naz - a - rene,
2. For me it was in the gar - den He prayed: "Not My will, but Thine;"
3. In pit - y an - gels be - held Him, And came from the world of light
4. He took my sins and my sor - rows, He made them His ver - y own;
5. When with the ransomed in glo - ry His face I at last shall see,

And won - der how He could love me, A sin-ner, condemned, un-clean.
He had no tears for His own griefs, But sweat-drops of blood for mine.
To com - fort Him in the sor - rows He bore for my soul that night.
He bore the bur - den to Cal - v'ry, And suf-fered, and died a - lone.
'Twill be my joy thro' the a - ges To sing of His love for me.

CHORUS.

How mar-vel-ous! how won-der-ful! And my song shall ev - er be:
Oh, how mar-vel-ous! oh, how won-der-ful!

How mar-vel-ous! how won-der-ful Is my Sav-ior's love for me! A-MEN.
Oh, how mar-vel-ous! oh, how won-der-ful

86 O Love That Wilt Not Let Me Go

GEORGE MATHESON

ALBERT L. PEACE

1. O Love that wilt not let me go, I rest my wea-ry
2. O Light that fol-lowest all my way, I yield my flick-ering
3. O Joy that seek-est me through pain, I can-not close my
4. O Cross that lift-est up my head, I dare not ask to

soul in Thee; I give Thee back the life I owe. That
torch to Thee; My heart re-stores its bor-rowed ray, That
heart to Thee; I trace the rain-bow through the rain, And
fly from Thee; I lay in dust life's glo-ry dead, And

in Thine o-cean depths its flow May rich-er, full-er be.
in Thy sunshine's blaze its day May bright-er, fair-er be.
feel the prom-ise is not vain That morn shall tear-less be.
from the ground there blossoms red Life that shall end-less be. A-MEN.

87 Let Me Come Closer to Thee, Jesus

J. L. LYNE

ORGANIST OF LLANTHONY ABBEY

1. Let me come clos-er to Thee, Je-sus, Oh, clos-er day by day;
2. Let me show forth Thy beau-ty, Je-sus, Like sunshine on the hills;
3. Yes, like a foun-tain, pre-cious Je-sus, Make me and let me be;
4. In all my heart and will, O Je-sus, Be al-to-geth-er King;
5. Thirsting and hungering for Thee, Je-sus, With bless-ed hun-ger here,

Let Me Come Closer to Thee, Jesus

Let me lean hard-er on Thee, Je - sus, Yes, hard-er all the way.
Oh, let my lips pour forth Thy sweetness In joy-ous spark-ling rills.
Keep me and use me dai - ly, Je - sus, For Thee, for on - ly Thee.
Make me a loy - al sub - ject, Je - sus, To Thee in ev - ery-thing.
Long-ing for home on Zi - on's mountain, No thirst, no hun-ger there. A - MEN.

88 In the Hour of Trial.

JAMES MONTGOMERY

SPENCER LANE

1. In the hour of tri - al, Je - sus, plead for me; Lest by base de-
2. With for - bid-den pleas-ures Would this vain world charm, Or its sor - did
3. Should Thy mer-cy send me Sor - row, toil, and woe, Or should pain at-
4. When my last hour com-eth, Fraught with strife and pain, When my dust re-

ni - al, I de-part from Thee. When Thou see'st me wa - ver, With a
treasures Spread to work me harm; Bring to my re-mem-brance Sad Geth-
tend me On my path be - low, Grant that I may nev - er Fail Thy
turn - eth To the dust a - gain; On Thy truth re - ly - ing, Thro' that

look re - call, Nor for fear or fa - vor Suf - fer me to fall.
sem - a - ne, Or, in dark-er semblance, Cross-crowned Cal-va-ry.
hand to see: Grant that I may ev - er Cast my care on Thee.
mor - tal strife: Je - sus, take me, dy - ing, To e - ter-nal life. A-MEN.

89 The Shepherd of Love

A. S. R.

Albert Simpson Reitz.

DUET.

1. The Shep-herd of Love is seek-ing the lost In paths that are
2. The Shep-herd of Love knows His sheep by name, And ten-der-ly
3. The Shep-herd of Love our ran-som hath paid, And of-fers sal-
4. The Shep-herd of Love now seek-eth His sheep, He seek-eth what-

rough and steep; He's call-ing the lambs that have gone a-stray,
leads the way; O wea-ry one, come to the Shepherd's fold,
va - tion free; He's pa-tient-ly wait-ing for thee to come,
e'er the cost; Be-hold, He is call-ing the wan-d'rer home,

rit.

CHORUS.

He's call-ing, call-ing His sheep.
He's call-ing, call-ing to-day.
He's call-ing, call-ing for thee.
He's call-ing, call-ing the lost.

Out of your dark-ness of

sin and shame, In-to His love, for-ev-er the same; Come to Him
call - ing, Call - ing, call - ing,

ad lib.

now, be-lieve on His name, O an-swer the call to-day.

Why Should He Love Me So?

R. H.

ROBERT HARKNESS

1. Love sent my Sav - ior to die in my stead, Why should He love me so?.. Meek - ly to Cal - va - ry's cross He was led,
2. Nails pierced His hands and His feet for my sin, Why should He love me so?.. He suf - fered sore my sal - va - tion to win,
3. O how He ag - o - nized there in my place, Why should He love me so?.. Noth - ing with - hold - ing my sin to ef - face,

CHORUS

Why should He love me so?.... Why should He love me so?..

Why should He love me so?..... Why should my Sav - ior to
love me so?

Cal - va - ry go? Why should He love me so?......
love me so?

91 According to Thy Gracious Word

JAMES MONTGOMERY   GREATOREX' "COLLECTION"

1. Ac - cord - ing to Thy gra-cious word, In meek hu - mil - i - ty,
2. Thy bod - y, bro - ken for my sake, My bread from heaven shall be;
3. When to the cross I turn my eyes, And rest on Cal - va - ry,
4. Re - mem - ber Thee, and all Thy pains, And all Thy love to me:
5. And when these fail-ing lips grow dumb, And mind and mem-ory flee,

This will I do, my dy - ing Lord, I will re - mem - ber Thee.
Thy tes - ta - men-tal cup I take, And thus re - mem - ber Thee.
O Lamb of God, my sac - ri - fice, I must re - mem - ber Thee.
Yea, while I breathe, a pulse re - mains Will I re - mem - ber Thee.
When Thou shalt in Thy King-dom come, Je - sus, re - mem - ber me.

92 On Calvary

G. W. B.   GEORGE W. BLOEMENDAL

1. Lord Je - sus, now at Thy re -quest We gath-er for the sup -per blest.
2. Lord Je - sus, may the cup and bread Re - mind us that Thy blood was shed
3. Lord Je - sus, let the Spir -it's power En-thrall our souls at this grave hour,
4. Lord Je - sus, ere we leave this place, In-crease our love to see Thy face.

Feed Thou our souls that we may see Thy match-less grace on Cal - va - ry.
To save us for e - ter - ni - ty. Great was Thy work on Cal - va - ry.
And help us live with tho'ts of Thee, Who bore our sins on Cal - va - ry.
Sal - va - tion soon com-plete shall be, Which Thou did'st win on Cal - va - ry.

93   Alas! and Did My Savior Bleed?

ISAAC WATTS   HUGH WILSON

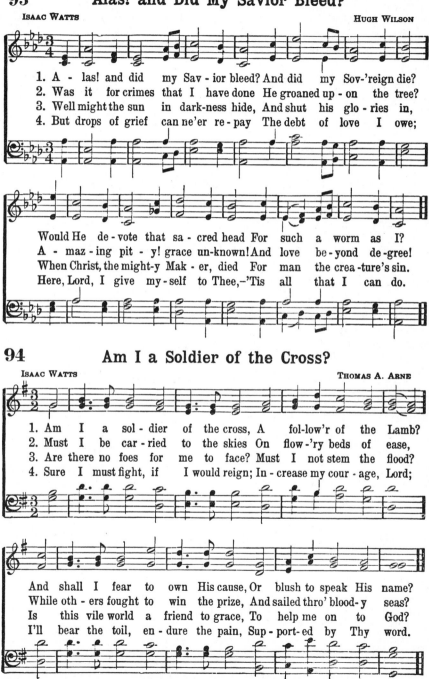

1. A - las! and did my Sav - ior bleed? And did my Sov - 'reign die?
2. Was it for crimes that I have done He groaned up - on the tree?
3. Well might the sun in dark-ness hide, And shut his glo - ries in,
4. But drops of grief can ne'er re - pay The debt of love I owe;

Would He de - vote that sa - cred head For such a worm as I?
A - maz - ing pit - y! grace un-known! And love be - yond de - gree!
When Christ, the might-y Mak - er, died For man the crea - ture's sin.
Here, Lord, I give my - self to Thee,—'Tis all that I can do.

94   Am I a Soldier of the Cross?

ISAAC WATTS   THOMAS A. ARNE

1. Am I a sol - dier of the cross, A fol-low'r of the Lamb?
2. Must I be car - ried to the skies On flow-'ry beds of ease,
3. Are there no foes for me to face? Must I not stem the flood?
4. Sure I must fight, if I would reign; In - crease my cour - age, Lord;

And shall I fear to own His cause, Or blush to speak His name?
While oth - ers fought to win the prize, And sailed thro' blood-y seas?
Is this vile world a friend to grace, To help me on to God?
I'll bear the toil, en - dure the pain, Sup - port - ed by Thy word.

Are You Washed In the Blood?

E. A. H.   ELISHA A. HOFFMAN

1. Have you been to Je - sus for the cleans-ing pow'r? Are you washed in the
2. Are you walk-ing dai - ly by the Sav - ior's side? Are you washed in the
3. When the Bridegroom cometh will your robes be white? Are you washed in the
4. Lay a - side the gar-ments that are stained with sin, Are you washed in the

blood of the Lamb? Are you ful - ly trust-ing in His grace this hour? Are you
blood of the Lamb? Do you rest each mo-ment in the Cru - ci - fied? Are you
blood of the Lamb? Will your soul be read - y for the mansions bright, And be
blood of the Lamb? There's a fountain flow-ing for the soul un-clean, O be

CHORUS

washed in the blood of the Lamb? Are you washed   in the blood,
                                  Are you washed   in the blood,

In the soul-cleans-ing blood of the Lamb?   Are your gar-ments
                         of the Lamb?

spot-less? Are they white as snow? Are you washed in the blood of the Lamb?

96 Calvary Covers It All

Mrs. WALTER G. TAYLOR   Mrs. WALTER G. TAYLOR

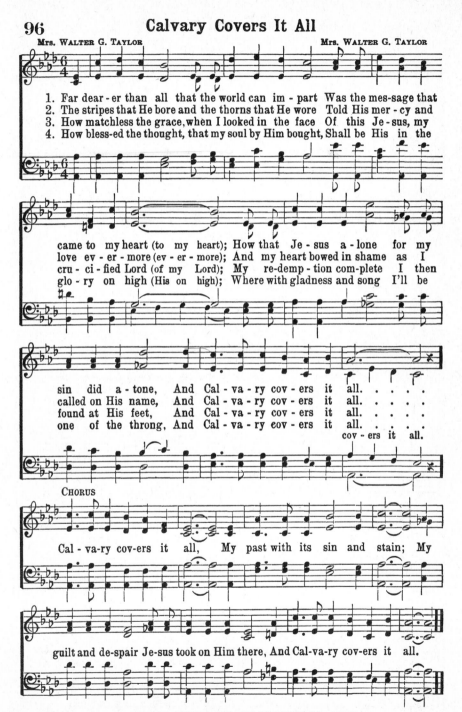

1. Far dear-er than all that the world can im-part Was the mes-sage that
2. The stripes that He bore and the thorns that He wore Told His mer-cy and
3. How matchless the grace, when I looked in the face Of this Je-sus, my
4. How bless-ed the thought, that my soul by Him bought, Shall be His in the

came to my heart (to my heart); How that Je-sus a-lone for my
love ev-er-more (ev-er-more); And my heart bowed in shame as I
cru-ci-fied Lord (of my Lord); My re-demp-tion com-plete I then
glo-ry on high (His on high); Where with gladness and song I'll be

sin did a-tone, And Cal-va-ry cov-ers it all. . . . . .
called on His name, And Cal-va-ry cov-ers it all. . . . . .
found at His feet, And Cal-va-ry cov-ers it all. . . . . .
one of the throng, And Cal-va-ry cov-ers it all. . . . .

cov-ers it all.

CHORUS

Cal-va-ry cov-ers it all, My past with its sin and stain; My

guilt and de-spair Je-sus took on Him there, And Cal-va-ry cov-ers it all.

97 Blessed Be the Fountain

E. R. LATTA

H. S. PERKINS

Moderato

1. Bless-ed be the Foun-tain of blood, To a world of sin-ners re-vealed;
2. Thorn-y was the crown that He wore, And the cross His bod-y o'er-came;
3. Fa-ther, I have wandered from Thee, Oft-en has my heart gone a-stray;

Bless-ed be the dear Son of God: On-ly by His stripes we are healed.
Griev-ous were the sor-rows He bore, But He suf-fered thus not in vain.
Crim-son do my sins seem to me— Wa-ter can-not wash them a-way.

Tho' I've wandered far from His fold, Bringing to my heart pain and woe,
May I to that Fountain be led, Made to cleanse my sins here be-low;
Je-sus, to that Fountain of Thine, Lean-ing on Thy prom-ise, I go;

Wash me in the blood of the Lamb, And I shall be whit-er than snow,
Wash me in the blood that He shed, And I shall be whit-er than snow.
Cleanse me by Thy wash-ing di-vine, And I shall be whit-er than snow.

CHORUS

Whit - - - - - er than the snow, ... Whit - - - - er
Whit - er than the snow, whit - er than the snow, Whit-er than the snow,

Blessed Be the Fountain

than the snow; . . . . Wash me in the blood of the
whit-er than the snow;

Lamb, ... And I shall be whit-er than snow. . . .
of the Lamb, than snow.

98 **O Happy Day**

PHILIP DODDRIDGE E. F. RIMBAULT

1. O hap-py day that fixed my choice On Thee, my Sav-ior and my God!
   Well may this glow-ing heart re-joice, And tell its rap-tures all a-broad.
2. O hap-py bond, that seals my vows To Him who mer-its all my love!
   Let cheer-ful an-thems fill His house, While to that sa-cred shrine I move.
3. 'Tis done: the great trans-ac-tion's done; I am my Lord's, and He is mine;
   He drew me, and I fol-lowed on, Charmed to confess the voice di-vine.
4. Now rest, my long-di-vid-ed heart; Fixed on this bliss-ful cen-tre, rest;
   Nor ev-er from my Lord de-part, With Him of ev-'ry good possessed.

FINE

Hap-py day, hap-py day, When Je-sus washed my sins a-way!

D. S.

He taught me how to watch and pray, And live re-joic-ing ev-'ry day;

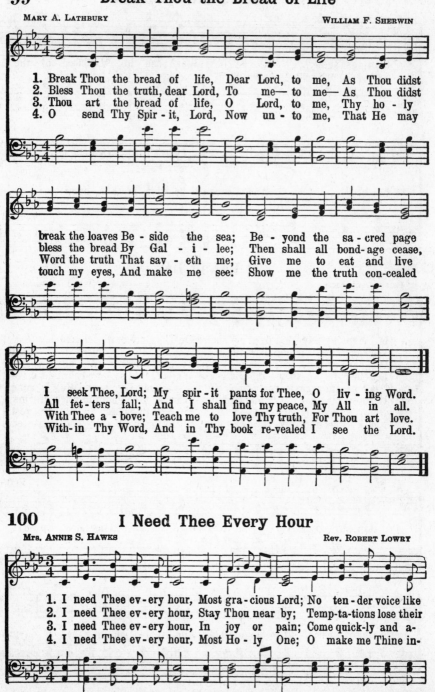

I Need Thee Every Hour

CHORUS

Thine Can peace af-ford.
power When Thou art nigh.   I need Thee, O, I need Thee; Ev-ery hour I
bide, Or life is vain.
deed, Thou bless-ed Son.

need Thee! O bless me now, my Sav-iour, I come to Thee!

101   Now the Day Is Over

SABINE BARING-GOULD   JOSEPH BARNBY

1. Now the day is o-ver, Night is draw-ing nigh,
2. Je-sus, give the wea-ry Calm and sweet re-pose;
3. Grant to lit-tle chil-dren Vi-sions bright of Thee;
4. Through the long night-watch-es, May Thine an-gels spread
5. When the morn-ing wak-ens, Then may I a-rise

Shad-ows of the eve-ning Steal a-cross the sky.
With Thy ten-derest bless-ing May our eye-lids close.
Guard the sail-ors toss-ing On the deep blue sea.
Their white wings a-bove me, Watch-ing round my bed.
Pure, and fresh, and sin-less In Thy ho-ly eyes. A-MEN.

eve-ning, Steal a-cross the sky.

Hail, Thou Once Despised

John Bakewell

Francois H. Barthelemon

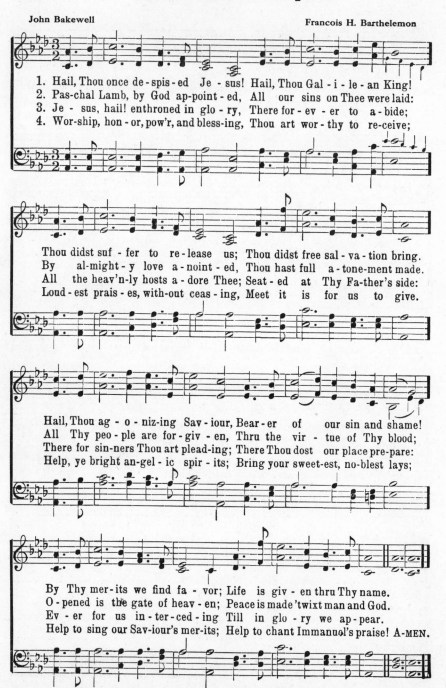

1. Hail, Thou once de-spis-ed Je - sus! Hail, Thou Gal - i - le - an King!
2. Pas-chal Lamb, by God ap-point - ed, All our sins on Thee were laid:
3. Je - sus, hail! enthroned in glo - ry, There for - ev - er to a - bide;
4. Wor-ship, hon - or, pow'r, and bless-ing, Thou art wor - thy to re-ceive;

Thou didst suf - fer to re-lease us; Thou didst free sal - va - tion bring.
By al-might - y love a - noint - ed, Thou hast full a - tone-ment made.
All the heav'n-ly hosts a - dore Thee; Seat - ed at Thy Fa-ther's side:
Loud - est prais - es, with-out ceas - ing, Meet it is for us to give.

Hail, Thou ag - o - niz-ing Sav - iour, Bear - er of our sin and shame!
All Thy peo - ple are for - giv - en, Thru the vir - tue of Thy blood;
There for sin-ners Thou art plead-ing; There Thou dost our place pre-pare:
Help, ye bright an-gel - ic spir - its; Bring your sweet-est, no-blest lays;

By Thy mer-its we find fa - vor; Life is giv - en thru Thy name.
O - pened is the gate of heav - en; Peace is made 'twixt man and God.
Ev - er for us in - ter-ced - ing Till in glo - ry we ap - pear.
Help to sing our Sav-iour's mer-its; Help to chant Immanuel's praise! A-MEN.

103 I Will Sing the Wondrous Story

F. H. Rowley

Peter P. Bilhorn

1. I will sing the won-drous sto - ry Of the Christ who died for me,
2. I was lost, but Je - sus found me, Found the sheep that went a - stray,
3. I was bruised, but Je - sus healed me; Faint was I from man-y a fall;
4. Days of dark-ness still come o'er me, Sor-row's paths I of - ten tread,
5. He will keep me till the riv - er Rolls its wa - ters at my feet;

How He left His home in glo - ry For the cross of Cal - va - ry.
Threw His lov - ing arms a - round me, Drew me back in - to His way.
Sight was gone, and fears pos-sessed me, But He freed me from them all.
But the Sav - iour still is with me; By His hand I'm safe - ly led.
Then He'll bear me safe - ly o - ver, Where the loved ones I shall meet.

CHORUS

Yes, I'll sing . . . . the won-drous sto - ry Of the
Yes, I'll sing the won-drous sto - ry

Christ . . . who died for me, Sing it with . . . . the saints in
Of the Christ who died for me, Sing it with

glo - - ry, Gath-ered by . . . . the crys-tal sea.
the saints in glo - ry, Gath-ered by the crys-tal sea.

104 Jesus Paid It All

Mrs. H. M. Hall

John T. Grape

1. I hear the Sav-ior say, "Thy strength in-deed is small, Child of
2. Lord, now in-deed I find Thy pow'r, and Thine a-lone, Can
3. For noth-ing good have I Where-by Thy grace to claim— I'll
4. And when, be-fore the throne, I stand in Him com-plete, "Je-sus

Chorus

weakness, watch and pray, Find in Me thine all in all."
change the lep-er's spots, And melt the heart of stone. Je-sus paid it all,
wash my garments white In the blood of Cal-v'ry's Lamb.
died my soul to save," My lips shall still re-peat.

All to Him I owe; Sin had left a crimson stain, He washed it white as snow.

105 Lord, I'm Coming Home

W. J. K.

Wm. J. Kirkpatrick

1. I've wan-dered far a-way from God, Now I'm com-ing home;
2. I've wast-ed man-y pre-cious years, Now I'm com-ing home;
3. I've tired of sin and stray-ing, Lord, Now I'm com-ing home;
4. My soul is sick, my heart is sore, Now I'm com-ing home;

Lord, I'm Coming Home

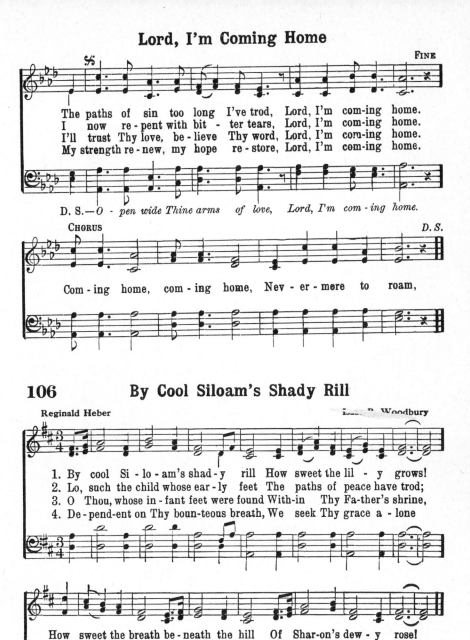

The paths of sin too long I've trod, Lord, I'm com-ing home.
I now re-pent with bit - ter tears, Lord, I'm com-ing home.
I'll trust Thy love, be - lieve Thy word, Lord, I'm com-ing home.
My strength re-new, my hope re - store, Lord, I'm com-ing home.

D. S.—O - pen wide Thine arms of love, Lord, I'm com - ing home.

CHORUS

Com - ing home, com - ing home, Nev - er - more to roam,

106   By Cool Siloam's Shady Rill

Reginald Heber   Isaac B. Woodbury

1. By cool Si - lo - am's shad - y rill How sweet the lil - y grows!
2. Lo, such the child whose ear - ly feet The paths of peace have trod;
3. O Thou, whose in - fant feet were found With-in Thy Fa-ther's shrine,
4. De - pend-ent on Thy boun-teous breath, We seek Thy grace a - lone

How sweet the breath be - neath the hill Of Shar-on's dew - y rose!
Whose se - cret heart, with in-fluence sweet, Is up-ward drawn to God.
Whose years, with changeless vir-tue crowned, Were all a - like di - vine.
In child-hood, man-hood, age, and death, To keep us still Thine own.

107 Jesus Put Himself in My Place

Author unknown
Arr. J. M. G.

HOMER HAMMONTREE

1. Shall I tell you what brought me to Je-sus, What caused me to
2. Oh, He felt all my load in the gar-den, My guilt He did
3. Soon He's com-ing a-gain from the glo-ry,—The proph-ets of

seek His bless-ed face? It was this, that, to save and to
car-ry to the tree; I was lost, and con-demned un-to
God on this a-gree; And till then this to oth-ers I'm

cleanse me, Je-sus put Him-self in my place....
judg-ment, But my Lord Him-self died for me....
tell-ing, That for them He died as for me. . . .

CHORUS

Je-sus put Him-self in my place, (O bless His name!) Yes, He put Him-

self in my place; (O bless His name!) This is the Gos-pel sto-ry,

Jesus Put Himself in My Place

To Je - sus be the glo - ry, For He put Him - self in my place.

108   Grace! 'Tis a Charming Sound

P. DODDRIDGE. 1, 3
A. M. TOPLADY. 2, 4, 5

IRA D. SANKEY

1. Grace! 'tis a charm-ing sound, Har - mo - ni - ous to the ear; Heav'n
2. 'Twas grace that wrote my name In life's e - ter - nal book; 'Twas
3. Grace taught my wand'ring feet To tread the heav'n-ly road; And
4. Grace taught my soul to pray, And made mine eyes o'er-flow; 'Twas
5. O let Thy grace in - spire My soul with strength di - vine: May

with the ech - o shall re-sound, And all the earth shall hear.
grace that gave me to the Lamb, Who all my sor - rows took.
new sup - plies each hour I meet, While press-ing on to God.
grace which kept me to this day, And will not let me go.
all my pow'rs to Thee as - pire, And all my days be Thine.

CHORUS

Saved by grace a - lone! This is all my plea:

Je - sus died for all man-kind, And Je - sus died for me.

109 My Redeemer

P. P. BLISS

JAMES McGRANAHAN

1. I will sing of my Re-deem-er And His won-drous love to me;
2. I will tell the won-drous sto-ry, How my lost es-tate to save,
3. I will praise my dear Re-deem-er, His tri-um-phant power I'll tell,
4. I will sing of my Re-deem-er, And His heaven-ly love to me;

On the cru-el cross He suf-fered, From the curse to set me free.
In His bound-less love and mer-cy, He the ran-som free-ly gave.
How the vic-to-ry He giv-eth O-ver sin, and death, and hell.
He from death to life hath brought me, Son of God, with Him to be.

CHORUS

Sing, oh, sing . . . . of my Re-deem-er, With His
Sing, oh, sing of my Re-deem-er, Sing, oh, sing of my Re-deem-er, With His

blood . . . . He pur-chased me, ... On the cross . . . . He sealed my
blood He purchased me, With His blood He purchased me, On the cross He sealed my pardon, On the

par-don, Paid the debt . . . . and made me free. . . . .
cross He sealed my par-don, Paid the debt and made me free, and made me free.

110 Seeking for Me

A. N.

E. E. HASTY

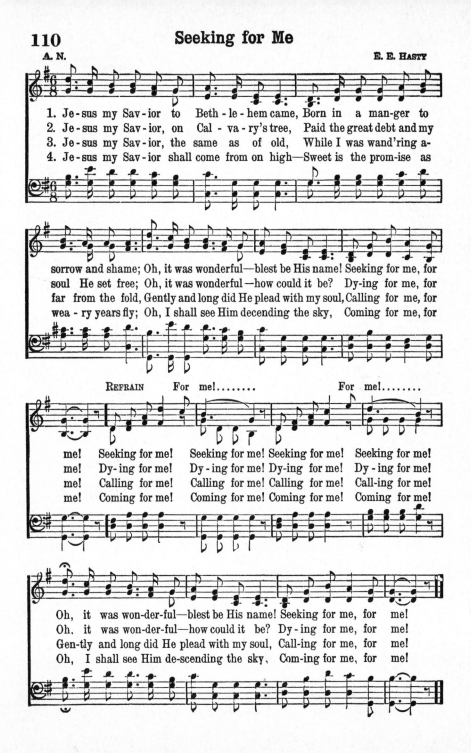

1. Je-sus my Sav-ior to Beth-le-hem came, Born in a man-ger to
2. Je-sus my Sav-ior, on Cal-va-ry's tree, Paid the great debt and my
3. Je-sus my Sav-ior, the same as of old, While I was wand'ring a-
4. Je-sus my Sav-ior shall come from on high—Sweet is the prom-ise as

sorrow and shame; Oh, it was wonderful—blest be His name! Seeking for me, for
soul He set free; Oh, it was wonderful—how could it be? Dy-ing for me, for
far from the fold, Gently and long did He plead with my soul, Calling for me, for
wea-ry years fly; Oh, I shall see Him decending the sky, Coming for me, for

REFRAIN For me!........ For me!........

me! Seeking for me! Seeking for me! Seeking for me! Seeking for me!
me! Dy-ing for me! Dy-ing for me! Dy-ing for me! Dy-ing for me!
me! Calling for me! Calling for me! Calling for me! Call-ing for me!
me! Coming for me! Coming for me! Coming for me! Coming for me!

Oh, it was won-der-ful—blest be His name! Seeking for me, for me!
Oh, it was won-der-ful—how could it be? Dy-ing for me, for me!
Gen-tly and long did He plead with my soul, Call-ing for me, for me!
Oh, I shall see Him de-scending the sky, Com-ing for me, for me!

111   O Sacred Head, Now Wounded

BERNARD OF CLAIRVAUX
Tr. JAMES W. ALEXANDER

H. L. HASSLER
Harmonized by J. S. BACH

To be sung slowly

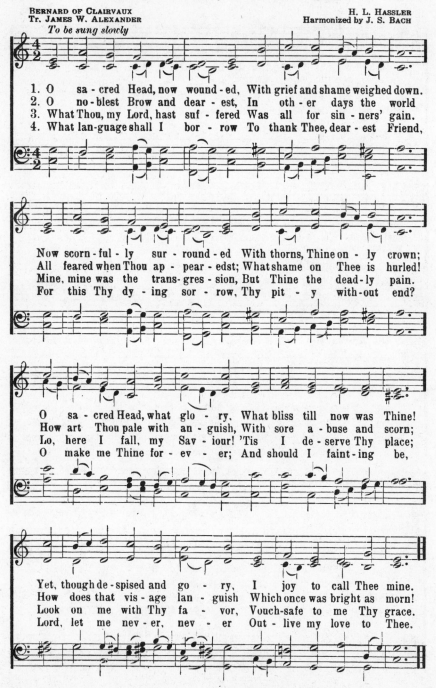

1. O sa - cred Head, now wound - ed, With grief and shame weighed down.
2. O no - blest Brow and dear - est, In oth - er days the world
3. What Thou, my Lord, hast suf - fered Was all for sin - ners' gain.
4. What lan-guage shall I bor - row To thank Thee, dear - est Friend,

Now scorn - ful - ly sur - round - ed With thorns, Thine on - ly crown;
All feared when Thou ap - pear - edst; What shame on Thee is hurled!
Mine, mine was the trans - gres - sion, But Thine the dead - ly pain.
For this Thy dy - ing sor - row, Thy pit - y with-out end?

O sa - cred Head, what glo - ry, What bliss till now was Thine!
How art Thou pale with an - guish, With sore a - buse and scorn;
Lo, here I fall, my Sav - iour! 'Tis I de - serve Thy place;
O make me Thine for - ev - er; And should I faint - ing be,

Yet, though de - spised and go - ry, I joy to call Thee mine.
How does that vis - age lan - guish Which once was bright as morn!
Look on me with Thy fa - vor, Vouch-safe to me Thy grace.
Lord, let me nev - er, nev - er Out - live my love to Thee.

Once for All

112

P. P. B.

P. P. Bliss

1. Free from the law, O hap-py con-di-tion, Je-sus hath
2. Now are we free—there's no con-dem-na-tion, Je-sus pro-
3. "Chil-dren of God," O glo-ri-ous call-ing, Sure-ly His

bled, and there is re-mis-sion; Cursed by the law and bruised by the
vides a per-fect sal-va-tion; "Come un-to Me," O hear His sweet
grace will keep us from fall-ing; Pass-ing from death to life at His

Chorus

fall, Grace hath redeemed us once for all.
call, Come, and He saves us once for all.
call, Bless-ed sal-va-tion once for all.

Once for all, O sin-ner, re-

ceive it; Once for all, O broth-er, be-lieve it; Cling to the

cross, the bur-den will fall, Christ hath re-deemed us once for all.

Tell Me the Story of Jesus

FANNY J. CROSBY

JNO. R. SWENEY

1. Tell me the sto-ry of Je-sus, Write on my heart ev-'ry word;
2. Fast-ing a-lone in the des-ert, Tell of the days that are past,
3. Tell of the cross where they nailed Him, Writh-ing in an-guish and pain;

CHO.—*Tell me the sto-ry of Je-sus, Write on my heart ev-'ry word;*

FINE

Tell me the sto-ry most pre-cious, Sweet-est that ev-er was heard.
How for our sins He was tempt-ed, Yet was tri-um-phant at last.
Tell of the grave where they laid Him, Tell how He liv-eth a-gain.

Tell me the sto-ry most pre-cious, Sweet-est that ev-er was heard.

Tell how the an-gels, in cho-rus, Sang as they welcomed His birth,
Tell of the years of His la-bor, Tell of the sor-row He bore,
Love in that sto-ry so ten-der, Clear-er than ev-er I see:

D. C. for Chorus

"Glo-ry to God in the high-est! Peace and good ti-dings to earth."
He was de-spised and af-flict-ed, Home-less, re-ject-ed and poor.
Stay, let me weep while you whis-per, Love paid the ran-som for me.

The Wonderful Story

C. H. G.

Chas. H. Gabriel.

1. O sweet is the sto-ry of Je-sus, The won-der-ful Sav-ior of men,
2. He came from the brightest of glo-ry; His blood as a ran-som He gave,
3. His mer-cy flows on like a riv-er; His love is un-meas-ured and free;

Who suf-fered and died for the sin-ner,—I'll tell it a-gain and a-gain!
To pur-chase e-ter-nal re-demp-tion; And O, He is might-y to save!
His grace is for-ev-er suf-fi-cient, It reach-es and pu-ri-fies me.

CHORUS.

O won - - der-ful, won-der-ful sto - - ry, The dear - - est that
O won-der-ful sto - - ry, O won-der-ful sto-ry, The dear-est that ev - - -

ev-er was told; . . . I'll re-peat it in glo - - ry, The won-der-ful
er, that ev-er was told; I'll re-peat it in glo-ry, The

sto - ry, Where I . . . shall His beau-ty be-hold. . . . A-MEN.
won-der-ful sto-ry, Where I shall His beau - ty, His beau-ty be-hold.

rit.

There is a Fountain

WILLIAM COWPER

LOWELL MASON

1. There is a foun-tain filled with blood Drawn from Im-man-uel's veins;
2. The dy-ing thief re-joiced to see That foun-tain in his day;
3. Dear dy-ing Lamb, Thy pre-cious blood Shall nev-er lose its pow'r,
4. E'er since, by faith, I saw the stream Thy flow-ing wounds sup-ply,
5. Then in a no-bler, sweet-er song, I'll sing Thy pow'r to save,

And sin-ners, plunged be-neath that flood, Lose all their guilt-y stains:
And there may I, though vile as he, Wash all my sins a-way:
Till all the ran-somed Church of God Be saved, to sin no more:
Re-deem-ing love has been my theme, And shall be till I die:
When this poor lisp-ing, stamm'ring tongue Lies si-lent in the grave:

Lose all their guilt-y stains, Lose all their guilt-y stains; And
Wash all my sins a-way, Wash all my sins a-way; And
Be saved, to sin no more, Be saved, to sin no more; Till
And shall be till I die, And shall be till I die; Re-
Lies si-lent in the grave, Lies si-lent in the grave; When

sin-ners, plunged be-neath that flood, Lose all their guilt-y stains.
there may I, though vile as he, Wash all my sins a-way.
all the ran-somed Church of God Be saved, to sin no more.
deem-ing love has been my theme, And shall be till I die.
this poor lisp-ing, stam-m'ring tongue Lies si-lent in the grave.

116   What a Wonderful Savior!

ELISHA A. HOFFMAN   ELISHA A. HOFFMAN

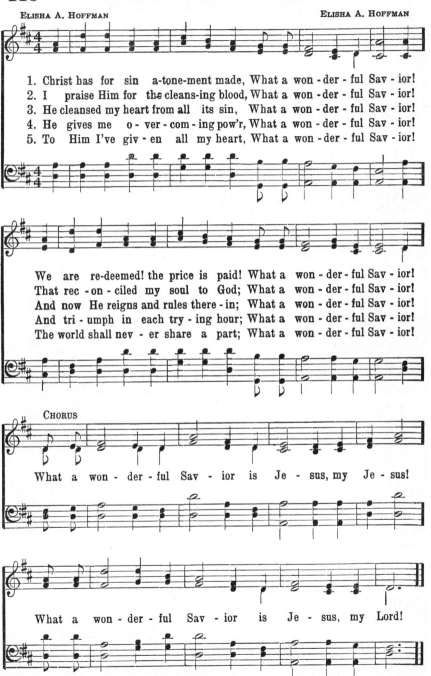

1. Christ has for sin a-tone-ment made, What a won - der - ful Sav - ior!
2. I praise Him for the cleans-ing blood, What a won - der - ful Sav - ior!
3. He cleansed my heart from all its sin, What a won - der - ful Sav - ior!
4. He gives me o - ver - com - ing pow'r, What a won - der - ful Sav - ior!
5. To Him I've giv - en all my heart, What a won - der - ful Sav - ior!

We are re-deemed! the price is paid! What a won - der - ful Sav - ior!
That rec - on - ciled my soul to God; What a won - der - ful Sav - ior!
And now He reigns and rules there - in; What a won - der - ful Sav - ior!
And tri - umph in each try - ing hour; What a won - der - ful Sav - ior!
The world shall nev - er share a part; What a won - der - ful Sav - ior!

CHORUS

What a won - der - ful Sav - ior is Je - sus, my Je - sus!

What a won - der - ful Sav - ior is Je - sus, my Lord!

All Your Anxiety

Andante con espress.

Words and air by Lieut. Col. E. H. JOY

1. Is there a heart o'er-bound by sor-row? Is there a life weighed down by care?
2. No oth-er Friend so keen to help you; No oth-er Friend so quick to hear;
3. Come then, at once, de-lay no long-er; Heed His en-treat-y, kind and sweet;

Come to the cross, each bur-den bear-ing, All your anx-i - e - ty—leave it there.
No oth-er place to leave your bur-den; No oth-er one to hear your prayer.
You need not fear a dis - ap-pointment, You shall find peace at the mer-cy-seat.

CHORUS

All your anx-i - e - ty, all your care. Bring to the Mer-cy-seat, leave it there;

Nev-er a bur-den He can-not bear, Nev-er a Friend like Je - sus.

118

He Is Mine

V. B.

VINCENT BENNETT

He is mine, . . . He is mine; . . .

He Is Mine

Seek-ing me, finding me, sav-ing me, keeping me, He   is   mine.

Thanks to God

119

Anon. (Swedish)
Tr. C. E. BACKSTROM

J. A. HULTMAN

1. Thanks to God for my Re-deem - er, Thanks for all Thou dost pro - vide!
2. Thanks for prayers that Thou hast answered, Thanks for what Thou dost de - ny!
3. Thanks for ros - es by the way - side, Thanks for thorns their stems contain!

Thanks for times now but   a   mem-'ry, Thanks for Je - sus by   my side!
Thanks for storms that I have weathered, Thanks for all Thou dost sup - ply!
Thanks for home and thanks for fire-side, Thanks for hope, that sweet re-frain!

Thanks for pleas-ant, balm - y springtime, Thanks for dark and drear-y   fall!
Thanks for pain, and thanks for pleas-ure, Thanks for com - fort in de - spair!
Thanks for joy   and thanks for sor - row, Thanks for heav'nly peace with Thee!

Thanks for tears   by   now for - got - ten, Thanks for peace with-in my   soul!
Thanks for grace that none can meas-ure, Thanks for love be-yond com - pare!
Thanks for hope in   the   to - mor - row, Thanks thro' all   e - ter - ni - ty!

120 When I See the Blood

JOHN

J. G. F.

1. Christ our Re-deem-er died on the cross, Died for the sin-ner,
2. Chief-est of sin-ners, Je-sus can save, As He has prom-ised,
3. Judg-ment is com-ing, all will be there, Who have re-ject-ed,
4. Oh, what com-pas-sion, oh, bound-less love! Je-sus hath pow-er,

paid all his due; All who re-ceive Him need nev-er fear,
so will He do; Oh, sin-ner, hear Him, trust in His Word,
who have re-fused? Oh, sin-ner, has-ten, let Je-sus in,
Je-sus is true; All who be-lieve are safe from the storm,

CHORUS

Yes, He will pass, will pass o-ver you.
Then He will pass, will pass o-ver you. When I see the
Then God will pass, will pass o-ver you.
Oh, He will pass, will pass o-ver you. When I

blood, When I see the blood, When I see the
see the blood, When I see the blood, When I

rit.

blood, I will pass, I will pass o-ver you.
see the blood, o-ver you.

121 Christt Arose

ROBERT LOWRY

ROBERT LOWRY

1. Low in the grave He lay— Je - sus my Sav - ior! Wait-ing the com-ing day —
2. Vain-ly they watch His bed—Je - sus my Sav - ior! Vain-ly they seal the dead—
3. Death cannot keep his prey— Je - sus my Sav - ior! He tore the bars a - way—

REFRAIN *Faster*

Je - sus my Lord! Up from the grave He a - rose, (He a-rose,) With a

might-y tri-umph o'er His foes; (He a-rose!) He a - rose a Vic - tor from the

dark do - main, And He lives for - ev - er with His saints to reign. He a-

rose! He a - rose! Hal - le - lu - jah! Christ a - rose!

He a - rose!

He a - rose!

122   **Christ the Lord Is Risen Today**

CHARLES WESLEY

From "Lyra Davidica"

1. Christ the Lord is risen to - day, Al - - - le - lu - ia!
2. Lives a - gain our glo - rious King: Al - - - le - lu - ia!
3. Love's re - deem-ing work is done, Al - - - le - lu - ia!
4. Soar we now, where Christ has led, Al - - - le - lu - ia!

Sons of men and an - gels say: Al - - - le - lu - ia!
Where, O death, is now thy sting? Al - - - le - lu - ia!
Fought the fight, the bat - tle won; Al - - - le - lu - ia!
Fol - lowing our ex - alt - ed Head; Al - - - le - lu - ia!

Raise your joys and tri - umphs high, Al - - - le - lu - ia!
Dy - ing once, He all doth save: Al - - - le - lu - ia!
Death in vain for - bids Him rise; Al - - - le - lu - ia!
Made like Him, like Him we rise; Al - - - le - lu - ia!

Sing, ye heavens, and earth, re - ply, Al - - - le - lu - ia!
Where thy vic - to - ry, O grave? Al - - - le - lu - ia!
Christ has o - pened Par - a - dise. Al - - - le - lu - ia!
Ours the cross, the grave, the skies. Al - - - le - lu - ia!

123

He Lives On High

Words by
B. B. McKinney

Arr. by B. B. McKinney
From Hawaiin Folk Song

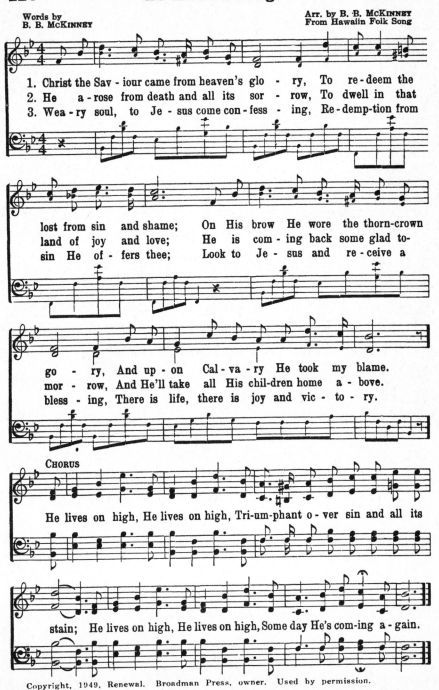

1. Christ the Sav-iour came from heaven's glo - ry, To re-deem the lost from sin and shame; On His brow He wore the thorn-crown go - ry, And up-on Cal-va-ry He took my blame.

2. He a-rose from death and all its sor - row, To dwell in that land of joy and love; He is com-ing back some glad to-mor - row, And He'll take all His chil-dren home a-bove.

3. Wea-ry soul, to Je-sus come con-fess - ing, Re-demp-tion from sin He of-fers thee; Look to Je-sus and re-ceive a bless - ing, There is life, there is joy and vic-to-ry.

CHORUS

He lives on high, He lives on high, Tri-um-phant o-ver sin and all its stain; He lives on high, He lives on high, Some day He's com-ing a-gain.

124 He Lives

A. H. ACKLEY

A. H. ACKLEY

1. I serve a ris-en Sav-ior, He's in the world to-day; I know that He is
2. In all the world a-round me I see His lov-ing care, And tho' my heart grows
3. Re-joice, rejoice, O Christian, lift up your voice and sing E-ter-nal hal-le-

liv-ing, what-ev-er men may say; I see His hand of mer-cy, I
wea-ry I nev-er will de-spair; I know that He is lead-ing, thro'
lu-jahs to Je-sus Christ the King! The Hope of all who seek Him, the

hear His voice of cheer, And just the time I need Him He's al-ways near.
all the storm-y blast, The day of His ap-pear-ing will come at last.
Help of all who find, None oth-er is so lov-ing, so good and kind.

REFRAIN *Spirited*

He lives, He lives, Christ Je-sus lives to-day! He walks with me and
He lives, He lives,

talks with me a-long life's nar-row way. He lives, He lives, sal-
He lives, He lives,

He Lives

va-tion to im - part! You ask me how I know He lives? He lives within my heart.

---

125   Move Forward!

G. W. CROFTS   D. B. TOWNER

1. Move forward! val-iant men and strong, Ye who have prayed and labored long;
2. Move forward! each and ev - er - y one; The gold - en har - vest is be - gun,
3. Move forward! reap-ing as you move! An-gels are watching from a - bove!
4. Move forward! day will die full soon; How quick-ly eve - ning fol - lows noon!

The time has come for you to rise, For lo! the sun rolls up the skies.
Ye reap-ers, come from glen and glade, And wield the sick - le's glittering blade.
A - round are wit-ness - es a host; A - rouse ye now and save the lost.
Now is the time to work and pray; Let glo - ry crown the dy - ing day.

CHORUS

Move for - ward, move for - ward, All a - long the line,
Move forward, move forward, move forward,

Move for - ward, move for - ward, The light be-gins to shine.
Move for-ward, move for-ward,

126 **Beyond the Sunset**

VIRGIL P. BROCK

BLANCHE KERR BROCK

1. Be-yond the sun - set, O bliss-ful morn - ing, When with our
2. Be-yond the sun - set no clouds will gath - er, No storms will
3. Be-yond the sun - set a hand will guide me To God, the
4. Be-yond the sun - set, O glad re - un - ion, With our dear

Sav - iour heav'n is be - gun. Earth's toiling end - ed, O glorious
threat - en, no fears an - noy; O day of glad - ness, O day un-
Fa - ther, whom I a - dore; His glorious pres - ence, His words of
loved ones who've gone be - fore; In that fair homeland we'll know no

dawn - ing; Be-yond the sun - set, when day is done.
end - ing, Be-yond the sun - set, e - ter - nal joy!
wel - come, Will be my por - tion on that fair shore.
par - ting, Bey-ond the sun - set for ev - er - more!

127 **Praise Ye the Triune God!**

Author unknown

F. F. FLEMMING

1. Praise ye the Fa - ther! for His lov - ing kind-ness, Ten - der - ly
2. Praise ye the Sav - iour! great is His com - pas - sion, Gra - cious - ly
3. Praise ye the Spir - it! Com - fort - er of Is - rael, Sent of the

Praise Ye the Triune God

cares He for His err-ing chil-dren; Praise Him, ye an-gels,
cares He for His cho-sen peo-ple; Young men and maid-ens,
Fa-ther and the Son to bless us; Praise ye the Fa-ther,

praise Him in the heav-ens, Praise ye Je-ho-vah!
ye old men and chil-dren, Praise ye the Sav-iour!
Son and Ho-ly Spir-it, Praise ye the Tri-une God! A-MEN.

128   Searcher of Hearts

GEORGE P. MORRIS   JOHN B. DYKES

1. Search-er of hearts, from mine e-rase All tho'ts that should not be,
2. Hear-er of prayer, O guide a-right Each word and deed of mine;
3. Giv-er of all—for ev-'ry good In the Re-deem-er came—
4. Fa-ther, and Son, and Ho-ly Ghost, Thou glo-rious Three in One,

And in its deep re-cess-es trace My grat-i-tude to Thee.
Life's bat-tle teach me how to fight, And be the vic-t'ry Thine.
For rai-ment, shel-ter, and for food, I thank Thee in His name.
Thou know-est best what I need most, And let Thy will be done. A-MEN.

129 Bringing Back the King

JAMES M. GRAY

JAMES McGRANAHAN

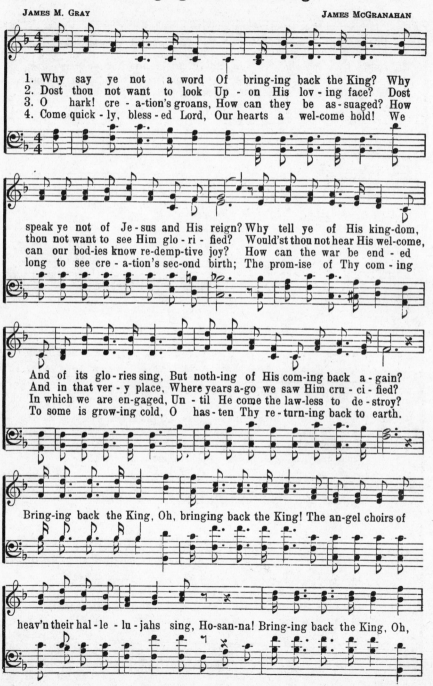

1. Why say ye not a word Of bring-ing back the King? Why
2. Dost thou not want to look Up - on His lov - ing face? Dost
3. O hark! cre - a-tion's groans, How can they be as-suaged? How
4. Come quick - ly, bless - ed Lord, Our hearts a wel-come hold! We

speak ye not of Je - sus and His reign? Why tell ye of His king-dom,
thou not want to see Him glo - ri - fied? Would'st thou not hear His wel-come,
can our bod-ies know re-demp-tive joy? How can the war be end - ed
long to see cre - a-tion's sec-ond birth; The prom-ise of Thy com - ing

And of its glo - ries sing, But noth-ing of His com-ing back a - gain?
And in that ver - y place, Where years a-go we saw Him cru - ci - fied?
In which we are en-gaged, Un - til He come the law-less to de - stroy?
To some is grow-ing cold, O has - ten Thy re - turn-ing back to earth.

Bring-ing back the King, Oh, bringing back the King! The an-gel choirs of

heav'n their hal - le - lu - jahs sing, Ho-san-na! Bring-ing back the King, Oh,

Bringing Back the King

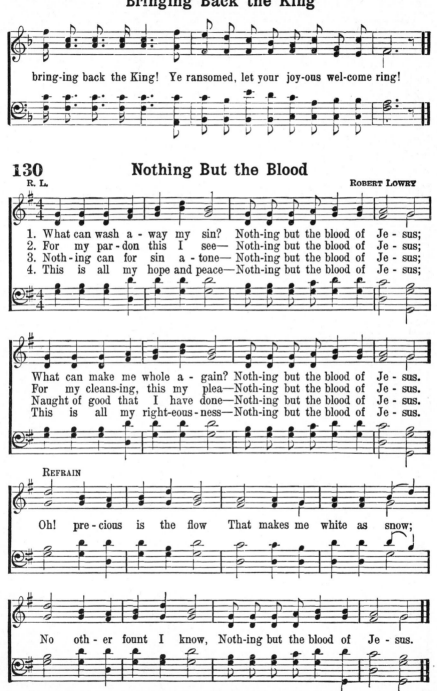

bring-ing back the King! Ye ransomed, let your joy-ous wel-come ring!

130
R. L.

Nothing But the Blood

ROBERT LOWRY

1. What can wash a - way my sin? Noth-ing but the blood of Je - sus;
2. For my par - don this I see— Noth-ing but the blood of Je - sus;
3. Noth - ing can for sin a - tone— Noth-ing but the blood of Je - sus;
4. This is all my hope and peace—Noth-ing but the blood of Je - sus;

What can make me whole a - gain? Noth-ing but the blood of Je - sus.
For my cleans-ing, this my plea—Noth-ing but the blood of Je - sus.
Naught of good that I have done—Noth-ing but the blood of Je - sus.
This is all my right-eous - ness—Noth-ing but the blood of Je - sus.

REFRAIN

Oh! pre - cious is the flow That makes me white as snow;

No oth - er fount I know, Noth-ing but the blood of Je - sus.

131

Christt Returneth

H. L. TURNER

JAMES McGRANAHAN

1. It may be at morn, when the day is a - wak-ing, When sunlight thro'
2. It may be at mid - day, it may be at twi-light, It may be, per-
3. While its hosts cry Hosanna, from heaven de-scend-ing, With glo - ri - fied
4. Oh, joy! oh, de-light! should we go with-out dy - ing, No sick-ness, no

dark - ness and shad - ow is break-ing, That Je - sus will come in the
chance, that the black-ness of mid-night Will burst in - to light in the
saints and the an - gels at - tend - ing, With grace on His brow, like a
sad - ness, no dread and no cry - ing, Caught up thro' the clouds with our

full - ness of glo - ry, To re - ceive from the world "His own."
blaze of His glo - ry, When Je - sus re - ceives "His own."
ha - lo of glo - ry, Will Je - sus re - ceive "His own."
Lord in - to glo - ry, When Je - sus re - ceives "His own."

CHORUS

O Lord Je - sus, how long, how long Ere we shout the glad song, Christ re-

rit.

turn-eth! Hal - le - lu-jah! hal - le - lu - jah! A - men, Hal - le - lu-jah! A - men.

132   Is It the Crowning Day?

GEORGE WALKER WHITCOMB

CHARLES H. MARSH

1. Je - sus may come to - day, Glad day! Glad day! And I would
2. I may go home to - day, Glad day! Glad day! Seem-eth I
3. Why should I anx-ious be? Glad day! Glad day! Lights ap - pear
4. Faithful I'll be to - day, Glad day! Glad day! And I will

see my Friend; Dan-gers and trou - bles would end If
hear their song; Hail to the ra - di - ant throng! If
on the shore, Storms will af - fright nev - er - more, For
free - ly tell Why I should love Him so well, For

CHORUS

Je - sus should come to - day.
I should go home to - day.   Glad day! Glad day! Is it the crowning
He is "at hand" to - day.
He is my all to - day.

day? I'll live for to - day, nor anx - ious be, Je - sus, my Lord, I

rit.

soon shall see; Glad day! Glad day! Is it the crown-ing day?

133 He Is Coming Again

M. J. C.

MABEL JOHNSTON CAMP

1. Lift up your heads, Pil-grims a-wea-ry, See day's ap-proach Now
2. Dark was the night, Sin warred a-gainst us; Heav-y the load Of
3. O bless-ed hope! O bliss-ful prom-ise! Fill-ing our hearts With
4. E-ven so, come, Pre-cious Lord Je-sus; Cre-a-tion waits Re-

crim-son the sky; Night shad-ows flee, And your Be-lov-ed, A-
sor-row we bore; But now we see Signs of His com-ing; Our
rap-ture di-vine; O day of days! Hail Thy ap-pear-ing! Thy
demp-tion to see; Caught up in clouds, Soon we shall meet Thee; O

CHORUS

wait-ed with long-ing, At last draw-eth nigh.
hearts glow with-in us, Joy's cup run-neth o'er! He is com-ing a-
tran-scend-ent glo-ry For-ev-er shall shine.
bless-ed as-sur-ance, For-ev-er with Thee!

gain, He is com-ing a-gain, The ver-y same Je-sus, Re-

ject-ed of men; He is com-ing a-gain, He is com-ing a-gain,

He Is Coming Again

With pow'r and great glo - ry, He is com-ing a - gain!
is com-ing a - gain!

134 Fill Me Now

E. R. STOKES.   JNO. R. SWENEY

1. Hov - er o'er me, Ho - ly Spir - it, Bathe my trem-bling heart and brow;
2. Thou canst fill me, gra-cious Spir - it, Though I can - not tell Thee how;
3. I am weak-ness, full of weak-ness, At Thy sa - cred feet I bow;
4. Cleanse and com-fort, bless and save me, Bathe, O bathe my heart and brow;

Fill me with Thy hal-lowed pres-ence, Come, O come and fill me now.
But I need Thee, great-ly need Thee, Come, O come and fill me now.
Blest, di - vine, e - ter - nal Spir - it, Fill with pow'r, and fill me now.
Thou art com-fort-ing and sav - ing, Thou art sweet - ly fill - ing now.

CHORUS

Fill me now, fill me now, Je - sus, come and fill me now;

Fill me with Thy hal-lowed pres-ence, Come, O come and fill me now.

135 Jesus Is Coming

JAMES M. GRAY

J. C. TROWBRIDGE

1. The Sav-iour who loves me and suf-fered the loss Of heav-en-ly
2. The an-gels, re-joic-ing and sing-ing His praise To Beth-le-hem
3. The saints will be with Him, O heav-en-ly bliss! How tear-ful the
4. O hearts that are wea-ry, and sin-ful, and sad, We car-ry the

glo-ry to die on the cross, The Babe of the man-ger, though
shep-herds of ear-li-er days, Will come in the glo-ry, at-
part-ing from fac-es we miss! But clouds are de-scend-ing, and
ti-dings that make us so glad; We pub-lish the Sav-iour o'er

born with-out stain, This Je-sus is com-ing, is com-ing a-gain!
tend-ing His train, When Je-sus, my Sav-iour, is com-ing a-gain!
we who re-main Are caught up to meet them with Je-sus a-gain!
moun-tain and plain; The Lord who re-deemed us is com-ing a-gain!

CHORUS

Je-sus is com-ing, is com-ing, is com-ing! Je-sus is com-ing a-gain!

rit.

My heart is so hap-py, my soul is so glad, For Je-sus is com-ing a-gain!

136 Some Golden Daybreak

C. A. BLACKMORE

CARL BLACKMORE

1. Some glo-rious morn-ing sor - row will cease, Some glo-rious morn-ing
2. Sad hearts will glad - den, all shall be bright, Good-bye for - ev - er
3. Oh, what a meet-ing, there in the skies, No tears nor cry - ing

all will be peace; Heart-aches all end - ed, school-days all done,
to earth's dark night; Changed in a mo - ment, like Him to be,
shall dim our eyes; Loved ones u - nit - ed e - ter - nal - ly,

rit   CHORUS

Heav - en will o - pen— Je - sus will come.
Oh, glo-rious day-break, Je - sus I'll see, Some gold - en day-break
Oh, what a day-break that morn will be.

Je - sus will come; Some gold-en day-break, bat-tles all won, He'll shout the

vic - t'ry, break thro' the blue, Some gold-en day-break, for me, for you.

137 One Day!

Dr. J. Wilbur Chapman

Chas. H. Marsh

1. One day when heav-en was filled with His prais-es, One day when sin was as black as could be,... Je-sus came forth to be born of a vir-gin—Dwelt amongst men, my ex-am-ple is He!...
2. One day they led Him up Cal-va-ry's moun-tain, One day they nailed Him to die on the tree;.. Suf-fer-ing an-guish, de-spised and re-ject-ed: Bear-ing our sins, my Re-deem-er is He!...
3. One day they left Him a-lone in the gar-den, One day He rest-ed, from suf-fer-ing free;.. An-gels came down o'er His tomb to keep vig-il; Hope of the hope-less, my Sav-ior is He!...
4. One day the grave could con-ceal Him no lon-ger, One day the stone rolled a-way from the door; Then He a-rose, o-ver death He had con-quered; Now is as-cend-ed, my Lord ev-er-more!.
5. One day the trump-et will sound for His com-ing, One day the skies with His glo-ries will shine; Won-der-ful day, my be-lov-ed ones bring-ing; Glo-ri-ous Sav-ior, this Je-sus is mine!.

CHORUS

Liv-ing, He loved me; dy-ing, He saved me; Bur-ied, He car-ried my sins far a-way;.. Ris-ing, He jus-ti-fied

One Day!

free-ly for - ev - er: One day He's com - ing— oh, glo - ri - ous day!

138   Must I Go Empty-Handed?

C. C. LUTHER

GEORGE C. STEBBINS

1. "Must I go, and emp - ty-hand - ed," Thus my dear Re-deem - er meet?
2. Not at death I shrink nor fal - ter, For my Sav - ior saves me now;
3. O the years in sin - ning wast - ed, Could I but re - call them now.
4. O ye saints, a-rouse, be ear - nest, Up and work while yet 'tis day;

Not one day of serv - ice give Him, Lay no tro - phy at His feet?
But to meet Him emp - ty-hand - ed, Tho't of that now clouds my brow.
I would give them to my Sav - ior, To His will I'd glad - ly bow.
Ere the night of death o'er-take thee, Strive for souls while still you may.

CHORUS

"Must I go, and emp - ty-hand-ed?" "Must I meet my Sav - ior so?

Not one soul with which to greet Him: Must I emp - ty-hand - ed go?

What a Gathering!

FANNY J. CROSBY

IRA D. SANKEY

1. On that bright and gold-en morn-ing, when the Son of man shall
2. When the blest, who sleep in Je-sus, at His bid-ding shall a-
3. When our eyes be-hold the cit-y, with its man-y man-sions
4. O the King is sure-ly com-ing, and the time is draw-ing

come, And the ra-diance of His glo-ry we shall see;
rise From the si-lence of the grave, and from the sea,
bright, And its riv-er, calm and rest-ful, flow-ing free;
nigh, When the bless-ed day of prom-ise we shall see;

When from ev-'ry clime and na-tion He shall call His peo-ple
And with bod-ies all ce-les-tial they shall meet Him in the
When the friends that death hath part-ed shall in bliss a-gain u-
Then the chang-ing "in a mo-ment," "in the twin-kling of an

home, What a gath-'ring of the ran-somed that will be!
skies, What a gath-'ring and re-joic-ing there will be!
nite, What a gath-'ring and a greet-ing there will be!
eye," And for-ev-er in His pres-ence we shall be.

What a Gathering!

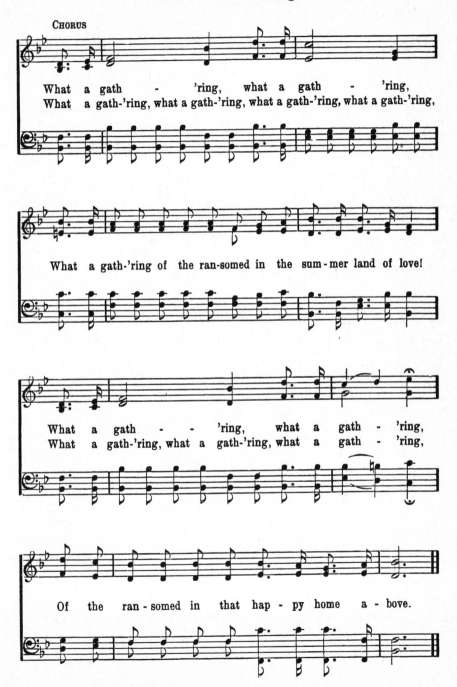

140 Will Jesus Find Us Watching?

FANNY J. CROSBY

W. H. DOANE

1. When Je-sus comes to re-ward His serv-ants, Wheth-er it be
2. If, at the dawn of the ear.-ly morn-ing, He shall call us
3. Have we been true to the trust He left us? Do we seek to
4. Bless-ed are those whom the Lord finds watch-ing, In His glo-ry

noon or night, Faith-ful to Him will He find us watch-ing,
one by one, When to the Lord we re-store our tal-ents,
do our best? If in our hearts there is naught con-demns us,
they shall share; If He shall come at the dawn or mid-night,

rit.

With our lamps all trimmed and bright?
Will He an-swer thee— Well done?
We shall have a glo-rious rest.
Will He find us watch-ing there?

CHORUS

O can we say we are

read-y, broth-er? Read-y for the soul's bright home? Say, will He

find you and me still watch-ing, Wait-ing, wait-ing when the Lord shall come?

141 Breathe On Me, Breath of God

EDWIN HATCH   ROBERT JACKSON

1. Breathe on me, Breath of God, Fill me with life a-new, That I may
2. Breathe on me, Breath of God, Un-til my heart is pure, Un-til with
3. Breathe on me, Breath of God, Till I am whol-ly Thine, Till all this
4. Breathe on me, Breath of God, So shall I nev-er die, But live with

love what Thou dost love, And do what Thou wouldst do.
Thee I will one will, To do or to en-dure.
earth-ly part of me, Glows with Thy fire di-vine.
Thee the per-fect life Of Thine e-ter-ni-ty. A-MEN.

142 Thy Holy Spirit, Lord, Alone

HENRIETTA E. BLAIR   WM. J. KIRKPATRICK, by per.

1. Thy Ho-ly Spir-it, Lord, a-lone Can turn our hearts from sin;
2. Thy Ho-ly Spir-it, Lord, a-lone Can deep-er love in-spire;
3. Thy Ho-ly Spir-it, Lord, can bring The gifts we seek in pray'r;
4. Thy Ho-ly Spir-it, Lord, can give The grace we need this hour;

His pow'r a-lone can sanc-ti-fy And keep us pure with-in.
His pow'r a-lone with-in our souls Can light the sa-cred fire.
His voice can words of com-fort speak And still each wave of care.
And while we wait, O Spir-it, come In sanc-ti-fy-ing pow'r.

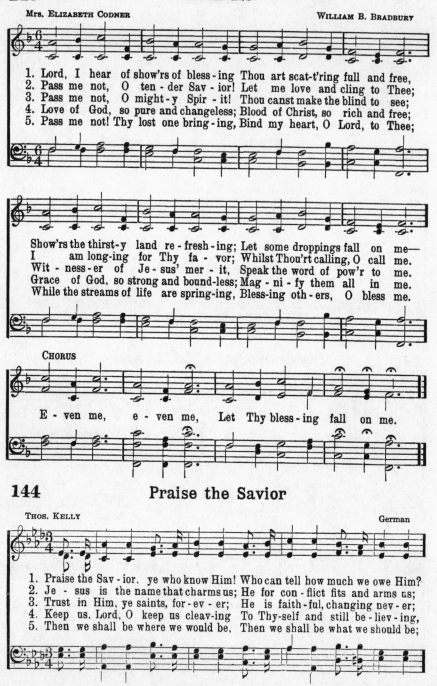

143

Even Me

Mrs. Elizabeth Codner

William B. Bradbury

1. Lord, I hear of show'rs of bless-ing Thou art scat-t'ring full and free,
2. Pass me not, O ten - der Sav - ior! Let me love and cling to Thee;
3. Pass me not, O might-y Spir - it! Thou canst make the blind to see;
4. Love of God, so pure and changeless; Blood of Christ, so rich and free;
5. Pass me not! Thy lost one bring-ing, Bind my heart, O Lord, to Thee;

Show'rs the thirst-y land re - fresh-ing; Let some droppings fall on me—
I am long-ing for Thy fa - vor; Whilst Thou'rt calling, O call me.
Wit - ness-er of Je - sus' mer - it, Speak the word of pow'r to me.
Grace of God, so strong and bound-less; Mag - ni - fy them all in me.
While the streams of life are spring-ing, Bless-ing oth - ers, O bless me.

Chorus

E - ven me, e - ven me, Let Thy bless-ing fall on me.

144

Praise the Savior

Thos. Kelly

German

1. Praise the Sav - ior, ye who know Him! Who can tell how much we owe Him?
2. Je - sus is the name that charms us; He for con - flict fits and arms us;
3. Trust in Him, ye saints, for - ev - er; He is faith - ful, changing nev - er;
4. Keep us, Lord, O keep us cleav-ing To Thy-self and still be - liev - ing,
5. Then we shall be where we would be, Then we shall be what we should be;

Praise the Savior

Glad-ly let us ren-der to Him All we are and have.
Noth-ing moves and noth-ing harms us While we trust in Him.
Nei-ther force nor guile can sev-er Those He loves from Him.
Till the hour of our re-ceiv-ing Prom-ised joys with Thee.
Things that are not now, nor could be, Soon shall be our own.

145 More Love to Thee

Elizabeth Prentiss

W. H. Doane

1. More love to Thee, O Christ, More love to Thee! Hear Thou the
2. Once earth-ly joy I craved, Sought peace and rest; Now Thee a-
3. Let sor-row do its work, Send grief and pain; Sweet are Thy
4. Then shall my lat-est breath Whis-per Thy praise; This be the

prayer I make On bend-ed knee; This is my ear-nest plea:
lone I seek, Give what is best; This all my prayer shall be:
mes-sen-gers, Sweet their re-frain, When they can sing with me,
part-ing cry My heart shall raise; This still its prayer shall be:

More love, O Christ, to Thee, More love to Thee, More love to Thee!

146 Holy Ghost, with Light Divine

ANDREW REED

L. GOTTSCHALK

1. Ho - ly Ghost, with light di - vine, Shine up - on this heart of mine;
2. Ho - ly Ghost, with power di - vine, Cleanse this guilt - y heart of mine;
3. Ho - ly Ghost, with joy di - vine, Cheer this sad-dened heart of mine;
4. Ho - ly Spir - it, all di - vine, Dwell with - in this heart of mine;

Chase the shades of night a - way, Turn my dark-ness in - to day.
Long hath sin with-out con - trol, Held do - min - ion o'er my soul.
Bid my man - y woes de - part, Heal my wound-ed, bleed-ing heart.
Cast down ev - ery i - dol-throne, Reign su-preme—and reign a - lone.

147 Fade, Fade, Each Earthly Joy

JANE C. BONAR

THEODORE E. PERKINS

1. Fade, fade, each earth-ly joy; Je - sus is mine. Break ev - ery
2. Tempt not my soul a - way; Je - sus is mine. Here would I
3. Fare - well, ye dreams of night; Je - sus is mine. Lost in this
4. Fare - well, mor - tal - i - ty; Je - sus is mine. Wel - come, e-

ten - der tie; Je - sus is mine. Dark is the wil - der-ness,
ev - er stay; Je - sus is mine. Per - ish-ing things of clay,
dawn-ing bright, Je - sus is mine. All that my soul has tried
ter - ni - ty; Je - sus is mine. Wel - come, O loved and blest,

Fade, Fade, Each Earthly Joy

Earth has no rest-ing-place, Je - sus a - lone can bless; Je - sus is mine.
Born but for one brief day, Pass from my heart a - way; Je - sus is mine.
Left but a dis - mal void; Je - sus has sat - is - fied; Je - sus is mine.
Wel - come, sweet scenes of rest, Welcome, my Saviour's breast; Je - sus is mine.

148   Nearer, My God, to Thee

SARAH F. ADAMS   LOWELL MASON

1. Near - er, my God, to Thee, Near - er to Thee! E'en though it
2. Though like the wan - der - er, The sun gone down, Dark - ness be
3. There let the way ap - pear, Steps un - to heaven: All that Thou
4. Then with my wak-ing thoughts Bright with Thy praise, Out of my
5. Or if on joy - ful wing, Cleav-ing the sky, Sun, moon, and

be a cross That rais - eth me; Still all my song shall be,
o - ver me, My rest a stone; Yet in my dreams I'd be
send - est me, In mer - cy given: An - gels to beck - on me
ston - y griefs Beth - el I'll raise; So by my woes to be
stars for - got, Up - ward I fly, Still all my song shall be,

Near - er, my God, to Thee, Near-er, my God, to Thee, Near-er to Thee!

Pentecostal Power

CHARLOTTE G. HOMER   CHAS. H. GABRIEL

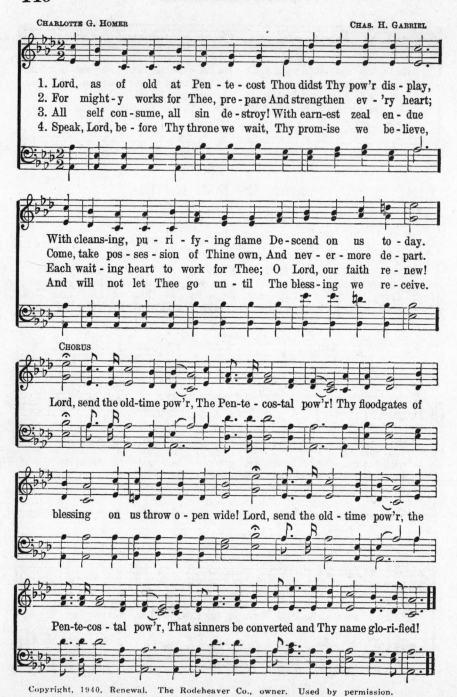

1. Lord, as of old at Pen - te - cost Thou didst Thy pow'r dis - play,
2. For might - y works for Thee, pre - pare And strengthen ev - 'ry heart;
3. All self con - sume, all sin de - stroy! With earn - est zeal en - due
4. Speak, Lord, be - fore Thy throne we wait, Thy prom-ise we be - lieve,

With cleans-ing, pu - ri - fy - ing flame De - scend on us to - day.
Come, take pos - ses - sion of Thine own, And nev - er - more de - part.
Each wait - ing heart to work for Thee; O Lord, our faith re - new!
And will not let Thee go un - til The bless-ing we re - ceive.

CHORUS

Lord, send the old-time pow'r, The Pen - te - cos - tal pow'r! Thy floodgates of

blessing on us throw o - pen wide! Lord, send the old - time pow'r, the

Pen - te - cos - tal pow'r, That sinners be converted and Thy name glo - ri - fied!

150 Revive Thy Work

ALFRED MIDLANE

JAMES MCGRANAHAN

1. Re - vive Thy work, O Lord! Thy might - y arm make bare;
2. Re - vive Thy work, O Lord! Dis - turb this sleep of death;
3. Re - vive Thy work, O Lord! Cre - ate soul-thirst for Thee;
4. Re - vive Thy work, O Lord! Ex - alt Thy pre - cious name;

Speak with the voice that wakes the dead, And make Thy peo - ple hear.
Quick - en the smoul-d'ring em - bers now By Thine al - might - y breath.
But hun-g'ring for the bread of life, Oh, may our spir - its be!
And, by the Ho - ly Ghost, our love For Thee and Thine in - flame.

CHORUS

Re - vive! ... re - vive! ... And give re - fresh-ing show'rs;
Re - vive Thy work! re - vive Thy work! And give, oh, give re - fresh - ing show'rs;

The glo - ry shall be all Thine own; The bless-ing shall be ours.

151 Spirit of God, Descend Upon My Heart

GEORGE CROLY

FREDERICK C. ATKINSON

1. Spir - it of God, de - scend up - on my heart;
2. Hast Thou not bid us love Thee, God and King?
3. Teach me to feel that Thou art al - ways nigh;
4. Teach me to love Thee as Thine an - gels love,

Wean it from earth, through all its puls - es move;
All, all Thine own, soul, heart and strength and mind;
Teach me the strug - gles of the soul to bear,
One ho - ly pas - sion fill - ing all my frame;

Stoop to my weak - ness, might - y as Thou art,
I see Thy cross— there teach my heart to cling:
To check the ris - ing doubt, the reb - el sigh;
The bap - tism of the heav'n - de - scend - ed Dove,

And make me love Thee as I ought to love.
O let me seek Thee, and O let me find.
Teach me the pa - tience of un - an - swered prayer.
My heart an al - tar; and Thy love the flame. A - MEN.

152 The Comforter Has Come

F. BOTTOME

WM. J. KIRKPATRICK

1. O spread the ti-dings 'round, wher-ev-er man is found, Wher-
2. The long, long night is past, the morn-ing breaks at last, And
3. Lo, the great King of kings, with heal-ing in His wings, To
4. O bound-less love di-vine! how shall this tongue of mine To

ev - er hu-man hearts and hu-man woes a-bound; Let ev-'ry Christian
hushed the dreadful wail and fu-ry of the blast, As o'er the gold-en
ev-'ry cap-tive soul a full de-liv'rance brings; And thro' the va-cant
wond'ring mor-tals tell the matchless grace di-vine—That I, a child of

D.S.—*Ho-ly Ghost from Heav'n, The Fa-ther's promise giv'n; O spread the ti-dings*

FINE.

tongue pro-claim the joy-ful sound: The Com-fort-er has come!
hills the day ad-vanc-es fast! The Com-fort-er has come!
cells the song of tri-umph rings; The Com-fort-er has come!
hell, should in His im-age shine! The Com-fort-er has come!

'round, wher-ev-er man is found— The Com-fort-er has come!

CHORUS

D. S.

The Com-fort-er has come, The Com-fort-er has come! The

153

The Quiet Hour

SPEAK, LORD, IN THE STILLNESS

E. May Grimes

Arr. by Alfred B. Smith

1. Speak, Lord, in the still - ness, While I wait on Thee;
2. Speak, O bless - ed Mas - ter, In this qui - et hour,
3. For the words Thou speak - est, "They are life" in - deed;
4. All to Thee is yield - ed, I am Thine a - lone!
5. Fill me with the knowl - edge Of Thy glo - rious will;
6. Like "a wa - tered gar - den" Full of fra - grance rare,

Hush'd my heart to lis - ten, In ex - pect - an - cy.
Let me see Thy face, Lord, Feel Thy touch of pow'r.
Liv - ing Bread from heav - en, Now my spir - it feed!
Bliss - ful, glad sur - ren - der— I am Thine a - lone!
All Thine own good plea - sure In Thy child ful - fill.
Lin - g'ring in Thy pres - ence, Let my life ap - pear.

154

My Saviour

Dora Greenwell

Wm. J. Kirkpatrick

1. I am not skilled to un-der-stand What God hath willed, what God hath planned;
2. I take Him at His word indeed: "Christ died for sin - ners," this I read;
3. That He should leave His place on high And come for sin - ful man to die,
4. Yea, liv - ing, dy - ing, let me bring My strength, my sol-ace from this spring:

I on - ly know at His right hand Is One who is my Sav-iour!
For in my heart I find a need Of Him to be my Sav-iour!
You count it strange? so once did I, Be - fore I knew my Sav-iour!
That He who lives to be my King Once died to be my Sav-iour!

155 I Love to Tell the Story

CATHERINE HANKEY

WILLIAM G. FISCHER

1. I love to tell the sto - ry Of un - seen things a - bove, Of
2. I love to tell the sto - ry, More won - der - ful it seems Than
3. I love to tell the sto - ry, 'Tis pleas - ant to re - peat What
4. I love to tell the sto - ry, For those who know it best Seem

Je - sus and His glo - ry, Of Je - sus and His love. I love to
all the gold - en fan - cies Of all our gold - en dreams. I love to
seems, each time I tell it, More won - der - ful - ly sweet. I love to
hun - ger - ing and thirst - ing To hear it like the rest. And when, in

tell the sto - ry, Be - cause I know 'tis true; It sat - is - fies my
tell the sto - ry, It did so much for me; And that is just the
tell the sto - ry, For some have nev - er heard The mes - sage of sal -
scenes of glo - ry, I sing the new, new song, 'Twill be the old, old

CHORUS

longings As noth - ing else can do.
rea - son I tell it now to thee.   I love to tell the sto - ry, 'Twill
va - tion From God's own ho - ly Word.
sto - ry That I have loved so long.

be my theme in glo - ry To tell the old, old sto - ry Of Jesus and His love.

156   O Word of God Incarnate

WILLIAM W. HOW

Würtemberg Gesangbuch

1. O Word of God in-car-nate, O Wis-dom from on high,
2. The Church from her dear Mas-ter Re-ceived the gift di-vine,
3. It float-eth like a ban-ner Be-fore God's host un-furled;
4. O make Thy Church, dear Sav-iour, A lamp of pur-est gold,

O Truth un-changed, un-chang-ing, O Light of our dark sky;
And still that light she lift-eth O'er all the earth to shine.
It shin-eth like a bea-con A-bove the dark-ling world.
To bear be-fore the na-tions Thy true light, as of old.

We praise Thee for the ra-diance That from the hal-lowed page,
It is the gold-en cask-et, Where gems of truth are stored;
It is the chart and com-pass That o'er life's surg-ing sea,
O teach Thy wan-dring pil-grims By this their path to trace,

A lan-tern to our foot-steps, Shines on from age to age.
It is the heaven-drawn pic-ture Of Christ, the liv-ing Word.
'Mid mists and rocks and quick-sands, Still guides, O Christ, to Thee.
Till, clouds and dark-ness end-ed, They see Thee face to face. A-MEN.

157 Tell Me the Old, Old Story

KATE HANKEY

W. H. DOANE

1. Tell me the Old, Old Sto-ry, Of un-seen things a-bove, Of Je-sus
2. Tell me the sto-ry slow-ly, That I may take it in— That won-der-
3. Tell me the sto-ry soft-ly, With ear-nest tones and grave; Re-mem-ber
4. Tell me the same old sto-ry, When you have cause to fear That this world's

and His glo-ry, Of Je-sus and His love; Tell me the sto-ry
ful re-demp-tion, God's rem-e-dy for sin; Tell me the sto-ry
I'm the sin-ner Whom Je-sus came to save; Tell me the sto-ry
emp-ty glo-ry Is cost-ing me too dear; Yes, and when that world's

sim-ply, As to a lit-tle child, For I am weak and wea-ry,
oft-en, For I for-get so soon, The "ear-ly dew" of morn-ing
al-ways, If you would real-ly be, In an-y time of troub-le,
glo-ry is dawn-ing on my soul, Tell me the Old, Old Sto-ry:

CHORUS

And help-less and de-filed.
Has passed a-way at noon. Tell me the Old, Old Sto-ry, Tell me the
A com-fort-er to me.
"Christ Je-sus makes thee whole."

Old, Old Sto-ry, Tell me the Old, Old Sto-ry Of Je-sus and His love.

158 Thy Word Have I Hid In My Heart

Adapted by E. O. S.

E. O. SELLERS

1. Thy Word is a lamp to my feet, A light to my path al - way,
2. For - ev - er, O Lord, is Thy Word Es - tab - lished and fixed on high;
3. At morn - ing, at noon, and at night I ev - er will give Thee praise;
4. Thro' Him whom Thy Word hath foretold, The Sav - ior and Morn - ing Star,

To guide and to save me from sin, And show me the heav'n - ly way.
Thy faith - ful - ness un - to all men A - bid - eth for - ev - er nigh.
For Thou art my por - tion, O Lord, And shall be thro' all my days!
Sal - va - tion and peace have been bro't To those who have strayed a - far.

CHORUS—Ps. 119: 11.

Thy Word have I hid in my heart (in my heart), That I might not

sin a - gainst Thee (a - gainst Thee); That I might not sin, That

ad lib.

I might not sin, Thy Word have I hid in my heart.

159 My Name's Written There

M. A. K. and B. B. McK.

FRANK M. DAVIS

1. I am bought not with rich-es, Nei-ther sil-ver nor gold; But
2. My sins, they were man-y, Like the sands of the sea, But the
3. Oh! that beau-ti-ful cit-y, With its man-sions of light, With its

Christ hath redeemed me, I am safe in His fold; In the Book of His
blood of my Sav-iour Is suf-fi-cient for me; For His prom-ise is
glo-ri-fied be-ings, In pure gar-ments of white; Where no e-vil thing

king-dom, With its pag-es so fair, Through Je-sus my Sav-iour, My
writ-ten, In bright let-ters that glow, "Tho' your sins be as scar-let, I will
com-eth To de-spoil what is fair; Where the angels are watching, My

REFRAIN

name's writ-ten there.
make them like snow." My name's writ-ten there, On the page white and fair;
name's writ-ten there.

In the Book of God's king-dom, My name's writ-ten there.

160 Only a Step

FANNY J. CROSBY   W. H. DOANE

1. On - ly a step to Je - sus! Then why not take it now?
2. On - ly a step to Je - sus! Be - lieve, and thou shalt live;
3. On - ly a step to Je - sus! A step from sin to grace;
4. On - ly a step to Je - sus! O why not come and say:

Come, and thy sin con - fess - ing, To Him, thy Sav - iour, bow.
Lov - ing - ly now He's wait - ing, And read - y to for - give.
What has thy heart de - cid - ed— The mo - ments fly a - pace?
"Glad - ly to Thee my Sav - iour, I give my - self a - way?"

CHORUS

On - ly a step, on - ly a step; Come, He waits for thee;

Come, and thy sin con - fess - ing, Thou shalt re - ceive a bless - ing;

Do not re - ject the mer - cy He free - ly of - fers thee.

161 Let Him In

J. B. ATCHINSON

E. O. EXCELL

1. There's a Stran-ger at the door,   Let   Him in;
2. O - pen now to Him your heart,   Let   Him in;
3. Hear you now His lov - ing voice?   Let   Him in;
4. Now ad - mit the heav'n-ly Guest,   Let   Him in;

Let the Sav-ior in,   Let the Sav-ior in;

He has been there oft be - fore,   Let   Him in;
If you wait He will de - part,   Let   Him in;
Now, oh, now make Him your choice,   Let   Him in;
He will make for you a feast,   Let   Him in;

Let the Sav-ior in,   Let the Sav-ior in;

Let Him in, ere He is gone, Let Him in, the Ho - ly One, Je - sus
Let Him in, He is your Friend, He your soul will sure de - fend, He will
He is stand-ing at your door, Joy to you He will re - store, And His
He will speak your sins for-giv'n, And when earth ties all are riv'n, He will

Christ, the Fa - ther's Son,   Let   Him in.
keep you to the end,   Let   Him in.
name you will a - dore,   Let   Him in.
take you home to heav'n,   Let   Him in.

Let the Sav-ior in,   Let the Sav-ior in.

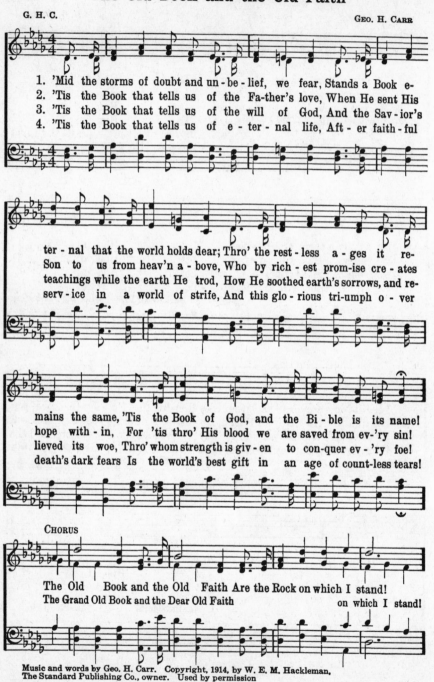

162 The Old Book and the Old Faith

G. H. C.

GEO. H. CARR

1. 'Mid the storms of doubt and un-be-lief, we fear, Stands a Book e-
2. 'Tis the Book that tells us of the Fa-ther's love, When He sent His
3. 'Tis the Book that tells us of the will of God, And the Sav-ior's
4. 'Tis the Book that tells us of e-ter-nal life, Aft-er faith-ful

ter-nal that the world holds dear; Thro' the rest-less a-ges it re-
Son to us from heav'n a-bove, Who by rich-est prom-ise cre-ates
teachings while the earth He trod, How He soothed earth's sorrows, and re-
serv-ice in a world of strife, And this glo-rious tri-umph o-ver

mains the same, 'Tis the Book of God, and the Bi-ble is its name!
hope with-in, For 'tis thro' His blood we are saved from ev-'ry sin!
lieved its woe, Thro' whom strength is giv-en to con-quer ev-'ry foe!
death's dark fears Is the world's best gift in an age of count-less tears!

CHORUS

The Old Book and the Old Faith Are the Rock on which I stand!
The Grand Old Book and the Dear Old Faith on which I stand!

Music and words by Geo. H. Carr. Copyright, 1914, by W. E. M. Hackleman,
The Standard Publishing Co., owner. Used by permission

The Old Book and the Old Faith

The Old Book and the Old Faith Are the bul-wark of the land!
The Grand Old Book and the Dear Old Faith

Thro' storm and stress they stand the test, In ev-'ry clime and na-tion blest;

The Old Book and the Old Faith Are the hope of ev-'ry land!
The Grand Old Book and the Dear Old Faith

GRAND CHORUS AT CLOSE (*May be omitted*)

Oh, the Grand Old Book and the Dear Old Faith Are the Rock on which I stand!

rit.

Oh, the Grand Old Book and the Dear Old Faith Are the hope of ev-'ry land!

163 Wonderful Words of Life

P. P. B.

P. P. BLISS

1. Sing them o - ver a - gain to me, Won-der-ful words of Life;
2. Christ, the bless-ed One, gives to all, Won-der-ful words of Life;
3. Sweet - ly ech - o the gos - pel call, Won-der-ful words of Life;

Let me more of their beau - ty see, Won-der - ful words of Life.
Sin - ner, list to the lov - ing call, Won-der - ful words of Life.
Of - fer par - don and peace to all, Won-der - ful words of Life.

Words of life and beau - ty, Teach me faith and du - ty;
All so free - ly giv - en, Woo - ing us to heav - en:
Je - sus, on - ly Sav - iour, Sanc - ti - fy for - ev - er:

REFRAIN

Beau-ti-ful words, won-der-ful words, Won-der-ful words of Life. Life.

164 Ye Christian Heralds!

B. H. DRAPER

H. C. ZEUNER

1. Ye Chris-tian her-alds! go pro-claim Sal - va-tion thro' Im-man-uel's name;
2. He'll shield you with a wall of fire, With flaming zeal your hearts in-spire,
3. And when our la - bors all are o'er, Then shall we meet to part no more—

Ye Christian Heralds!

To dis-tant climes the ti-dings bear, And plant the Rose of Shar-on there.
Bid rag-ing winds their fu - ry cease, And hush the tempest in - to peace.
Meet with the blood-bo't throng to fall, And crown our Je-sus—Lord of all.

165   Lead On, O King Eternal

ERNEST W. SHURTLEFF   HENRY SMART

1. Lead on, O King E-ter-nal, The day of march has come; Henceforth in fields of
2. Lead on, O King E-ter-nal, Till sin's fierce war shall cease, And ho - li-ness shall
3. Lead on, O King E-ter-nal, We fol-low, not with fears; For gladness breaks like

con - quest Thy tents shall be our home. Thro' days of prep-a - ra - tion Thy
whis - per The sweet A-men of peace; For not with swords loud clashing, Nor
morn-ing Where'er Thy face ap-pears; Thy cross is lift - ed o'er us; We

grace has made us strong, And now, O King E - ter - nal, We lift our bat-tle song.
roll   of stir-ring drums; With deeds of love and mercy, The heavenly kingdom comes.
jour - ney in its light: The crown awaits the conquest; Lead on, O God of might.

166 A Mighty Fortress Is Our God

MARTIN LUTHER
Tr. F. H. HEDGE

MARTIN LUTHER

1. A might-y for-tress is our God, A bul-wark nev-er fail - ing;
2. Did we in our own strength confide, Our striv-ing would be los - ing;
3. And tho' this world, with dev-ils filled, Should threaten to un-do us;
4. That word a - bove all earthly pow'rs—No thanks to them—a-bid - eth:

Our help-er He, a - mid the flood Of mor-tal ills pre-vail - ing.
Were not the right Man on our side, The Man of God's own choos - ing.
We will not fear, for God hath willed His truth to tri-umph through us.
The Spir-it and the gifts are ours Thro' Him who with us sid - eth.

For still our an-cient foe Doth seek to work us woe; His craft and pow'r are
Dost ask who that may be? Christ Je-sus, it is He; Lord Sabaoth is His
The prince of darkness grim—We tremble not for him; His rage we can en-
Let goods and kin-dred go, This mor-tal life al - so; The bod - y they may

great, And, armed with cru-el hate, On earth is not his e - qual.
name, From age to age the same, And He must win the bat - tle.
dure, For lo! his doom is sure, One lit - tle word shall fell him.
kill: God's truth a - bid - eth still, His king-dom is for - ev - er.

167 As a Volunteer

W. S. Brown

Chas. H. Gabriel

1. A call for loy-al sol-diers Comes to one and all; Sol-diers for the con-flict,
2. Yes, Jesus calls for sol-diers Who are filled with pow'r, Sol-diers who will serve Him
3. He calls you, for He loves you With a heart most kind, He whose heart was broken,
4. And when the war is o-ver, And the vic-t'ry won, When the true and faithful

Will you heed the call? Will you an-swer quick-ly, With a read-y cheer,
Ev-'ry day and hour; He will not for-sake you, He is 'ev-er near;
Bro-ken for man-kind; Now, just now He calls you, Calls in ac-cents clear,
Gath-er one by one, He will crown with glo-ry All who there ap-pear;

CHORUS

Will you be en-list-ed as a vol-un-teer? A vol-un-teer for Je-sus, A

sol-dier true! Oth-ers have en-list-ed, Why not you? Je-sus is the
Oh, why not?

Cap-tain, We will nev-er fear; Will you be en-list-ed As a vol-un-teer?

168 Hold the Fort

P. P. B.

P. P. BLISS

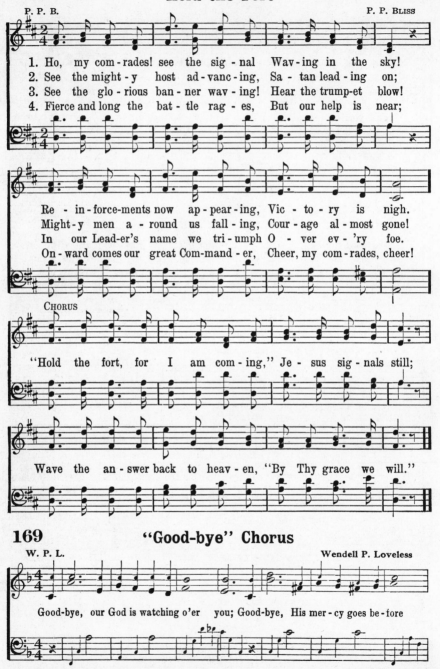

1. Ho, my com-rades! see the sig-nal Wav-ing in the sky!
2. See the might-y host ad-vanc-ing, Sa-tan lead-ing on;
3. See the glo-rious ban-ner wav-ing! Hear the trump-et blow!
4. Fierce and long the bat-tle rag-es, But our help is near;

Re-in-force-ments now ap-pear-ing, Vic-to-ry is nigh.
Might-y men a-round us fall-ing, Cour-age al-most gone!
In our Lead-er's name we tri-umph O-ver ev-'ry foe.
On-ward comes our great Com-mand-er, Cheer, my com-rades, cheer!

CHORUS

"Hold the fort, for I am com-ing," Je-sus sig-nals still;

Wave the an-swer back to heav-en, "By Thy grace we will."

169 "Good-bye" Chorus

W. P. L.

Wendell P. Loveless

Good-bye, our God is watching o'er you; Good-bye, His mer-cy goes be-fore

"Good-bye" Chorus

you; Good-bye, and we'll be pray-ing for you; So good-bye, may God bless you.....

170   **He Rolled the Sea Away**

Rev. H. J. Zelley   H. L. Gilmour

1. When Is - rael out of bond-age came, A sea be-fore them lay;
2. Be - fore me was a sea of sin, So great I feared to pray;
3. When sor-rows dark, like storm - y waves, Were dash-ing o'er my way;
4. And when I reach the sea of death, For need - ed grace I'll pray;

My Lord reached down His might-y hand, And rolled the sea a - way.
My heart's de - sire the Sav - ior read, And rolled the sea a - way.
A - gain the Lord in mer - cy came, And rolled the sea a - way.
I know the Lord will quick-ly come, And roll the sea a - way.

CHORUS

Then for-ward still, 'tis Je - ho-vah's will, Tho' the bil-lows dash and spray;

With a con-qu'ring tread we will push a - head, He'll roll the sea a - way.

Faith Is the Victory

JOHN H. YATES

IRA D. SANKEY

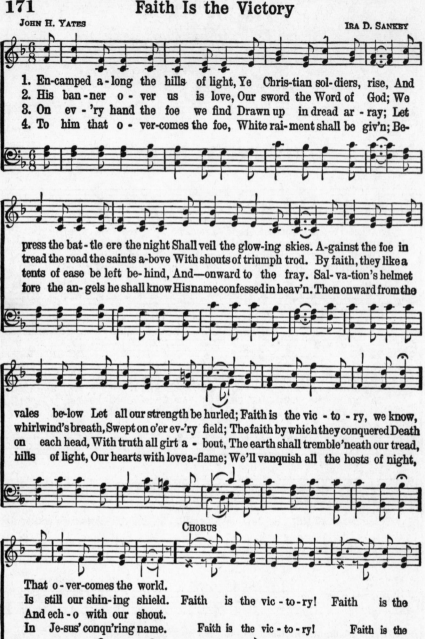

1. En-camped a-long the hills of light, Ye Chris-tian sol-diers, rise, And
2. His ban-ner o - ver us is love, Our sword the Word of God; We
3. On ev-'ry hand the foe we find Drawn up in dread ar - ray; Let
4. To him that o - ver-comes the foe, White rai-ment shall be giv'n; Be-

press the bat - tle ere the night Shall veil the glow-ing skies. A-gainst the foe in
tread the road the saints a-bove With shouts of triumph trod. By faith, they like a
tents of ease be left be-hind, And—onward to the fray. Sal-va-tion's helmet
fore the an - gels he shall know His name confessed in heav'n. Then onward from the

vales be-low Let all our strength be hurled; Faith is the vic - to - ry, we know,
whirlwind's breath, Swept on o'er ev-'ry field; The faith by which they conquered Death
on each head, With truth all girt a - bout, The earth shall tremble 'neath our tread,
hills of light, Our hearts with love a-flame; We'll vanquish all the hosts of night,

CHORUS

That o - ver-comes the world.
Is still our shin-ing shield. Faith is the vic - to - ry! Faith is the
And ech - o with our shout.
In Je-sus' conqu'ring name. Faith is the vic - to - ry! Faith is the

Faith Is the Victory

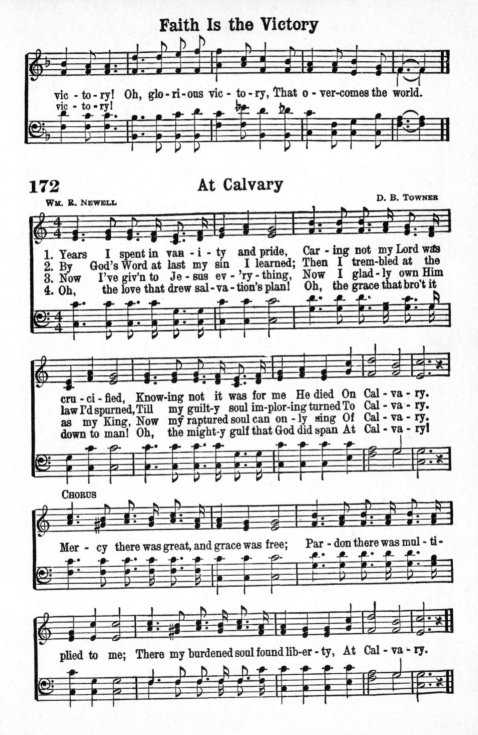

vic - to - ry! Oh, glo - ri - ous vic - to - ry, That o - ver-comes the world.

vic - to - ry!

172   **At Calvary**

WM. R. NEWELL

D. B. TOWNER

1. Years I spent in van - i - ty and pride, Car - ing not my Lord was
2. By God's Word at last my sin I learned; Then I trem-bled at the
3. Now I've giv'n to Je - sus ev - 'ry - thing, Now I glad - ly own Him
4. Oh, the love that drew sal - va - tion's plan! Oh, the grace that bro't it

cru - ci - fied, Know-ing not it was for me He died On Cal - va - ry.
law I'd spurned, Till my guilt-y soul im-plor-ing turned To Cal - va - ry.
as my King, Now my raptured soul can on - ly sing Of Cal - va - ry.
down to man! Oh, the might-y gulf that God did span At Cal - va - ry!

CHORUS

Mer - cy there was great, and grace was free; Par - don there was mul - ti-

plied to me; There my burdened soul found lib-er - ty, At Cal - va - ry.

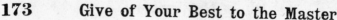

173 **Give of Your Best to the Master**

H. B. G.

Mrs. Charles Barnard

1. Give of your best to the Mas - ter; Give of the strength of your youth;
2. Give of your best to the Mas - ter; Give Him first place in your heart;
3. Give of your best to the Mas - ter; Naught else is wor-thy His love;

Ref.—*Give of your best to the Mas - ter; Give of the strength of your youth;*

FINE

Throw your soul's fresh, glowing ar - dor In - to the bat - tle for truth.
Give Him first place in your serv-ice, Con - se-crate ev - 'ry part.
He gave Him-self for your ran-som, Gave up His glo - ry a - bove:

Clad in sal - va-tion's full ar - mor, Join in the bat-tle for truth.

Je - sus has set the ex - am - ple; Dauntless was He, young and brave;..
Give, and to you shall be giv - en; God His be - lov - ed Son gave;..
Laid down His life with-out mur - mur, You from sin's ru - in to save;...

rall. D. C.

Give Him your loy - al de - vo - tion, Give Him the best that you have.....
Grate-ful - ly seek-ing to serve Him, Give Him the best that you have.....
Give Him your heart's ad-o - ra - tion, Give Him the best that you have.....

174 Loyalty to Christ

DR. E. T. CASSEL

FLORA H. CASSEL

1. From o-ver hill and plain There comes the signal strain, 'Tis loy-al-ty, loy-al-ty,
2. O hear, ye brave, the sound That moves the earth around, 'Tis loy-al-ty, loy-al-ty,
3. Come, join our loy-al throng, We'll rout the giant wrong, 'Tis loy-al-ty, loy-al-ty,
4. The strength of youth we lay At Je-sus' feet to-day, 'Tis loy-al-ty, loy-al-ty,

loy - al - ty to Christ; Its mu - sic rolls a - long, The hills take up the song,
loy - al - ty to Christ; A - rise to dare and do, Ring out the watch-word true,
loy - al - ty to Christ; Where Satan's banners float We'll send the bu-gle note,
loy - al - ty to Christ; His gos-pel we'll pro-claim Thro'-out the world's domain,

CHORUS.

Of loy-al-ty, loy-al-ty, Yes, loy-al-ty to Christ. "On to vic-to-ry! On to

vic-to-ry!" Cries our great Commander; "On!" . . . We'll move at His command,
great Commander; "On!"

We'll soon possess the land, Thro' loyalty, loyalty, Yes, loy-al-ty to Christ. A-MEN.

175 "Are Ye Able," Said the Master

EARL MARLATT

HARRY S. MASON

1. "Are ye a - ble," said the Mas - ter, "To be cru - ci - fied with Me?"
2. "Are ye a - ble," to re - mem - ber, When a thief lifts up his eyes,
3. "Are ye a - ble," when the shad - ows Close a - round you with the sod,
4. "Are ye a - ble," still the Mas - ter Whis - pers down e - ter - ni - ty,

"Yea," the conquering Christians answered, "To the death we fol - low Thee."
That his par - doned soul is wor - thy Of a place in Par - a - dise?
To be - lieve that spir - it tri - umphs, To com - mend your soul to God?
And he - ro - ic spir - its an - swer, Now, as then in Gal - i - lee.

REFRAIN

"Lord, we are a - ble," Our spir - its are Thine, Re - mold them,

make us like Thee, di - vine: Thy guid - ing ra - diance a - bove

rit - - - -

us shall be A bea - con to God, To love and loy - al - ty.

176 Sail On!

C. H. G.

Chas. H. Gabriel.

1. Up-on a wide and stormy sea, Thou'rt sail-ing to e-ter-ni-ty,
2. Art far from shore, and wea-ry-worn—The sky o'er-cast, the can-vas torn?
3. Do comrades trem-ble and re-fuse To fur-ther dare the taunting hues?
4. Do snarling waves thy craft as-sail? Art pow'rless, drift-ing with the gale?

Ad lib.

And thy great Ad-m'ral or-ders Thee:—"Sail on! sail on! sail on!"
Hark ye! a voice to thee is borne:—"Sail on! sail on! sail on!"
No oth-er course is thine to choose, Sail on! sail on! sail on!
Take heart! God's word shall nev-er fail! Sail on! sail on! sail on!

CHORUS.

Sail on! sail on! the storms will soon be past, The dark-ness

will not al-ways last; Sail on! sail on! God

Sail on! sail on!

Rit. e dim pp

lives! and He commands: "Sail on! sail on!"

on! sail on! sail on sail on!

Copyright, 1909, Renewal 1937. The Rodeheaver Co., owner.

177 Onward, Christian Soldiers

SABINE BARING-GOULD

ARTHUR SULLIVAN

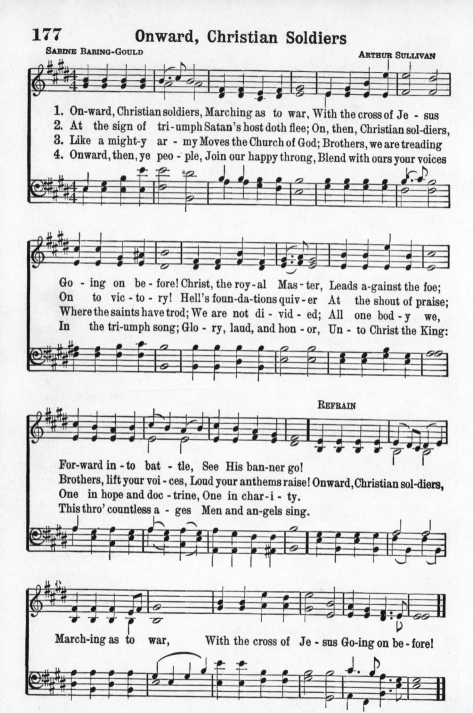

1. On-ward, Christian soldiers, Marching as to war, With the cross of Je - sus
2. At the sign of tri-umph Satan's host doth flee; On, then, Christian sol-diers,
3. Like a might-y ar - my Moves the Church of God; Brothers, we are treading
4. Onward, then, ye peo - ple, Join our happy throng, Blend with ours your voices

Go - ing on be - fore! Christ, the roy-al Mas-ter, Leads a-gainst the foe;
On to vic - to - ry! Hell's foun-da-tions quiv-er At the shout of praise;
Where the saints have trod; We are not di - vid-ed; All one bod - y we,
In the tri-umph song; Glo - ry, laud, and hon - or, Un - to Christ the King:

REFRAIN

For-ward in - to bat - tle, See His ban-ner go!
Brothers, lift your voi - ces, Loud your anthems raise! Onward, Christian sol-diers,
One in hope and doc - trine, One in char - i - ty.
This thro' countless a - ges Men and an-gels sing.

March-ing as to war, With the cross of Je - sus Go-ing on be - fore!

Sound the Battle Cry

W. F. S.   WM. F. SHERWIN

1. Sound the bat-tle cry! See, the foe is nigh; Raise the standard high
2. Strong to meet the foe, Marching on we go, While our cause we know,
3. O! Thou God of all, Hear us when we call, Help us one and all

For the Lord; Gird your ar-mor on, Stand firm, ev-'ry one; Rest your
Must pre-vail; Shield and banner bright, Gleam-ing in the light; Bat-tling
By Thy grace; When the bat-tle's done, And the vic-t'ry's won, May we

CHORUS ff

cause up-on His ho-ly word.
for the right We ne'er can fail.   Rouse, then, sol-diers, ral-ly round the
wear the crown Be-fore Thy face.

ban-ner, Read-y, stead-y, pass the word a-long;   On-ward, for-ward,

shout a-loud Ho-san-na! Christ is Cap-tain of the might-y throng.

179 Stand Up, Stand Up for Jesus

GEORGE DUFFIELD

ADAM GEIBEL

Unison

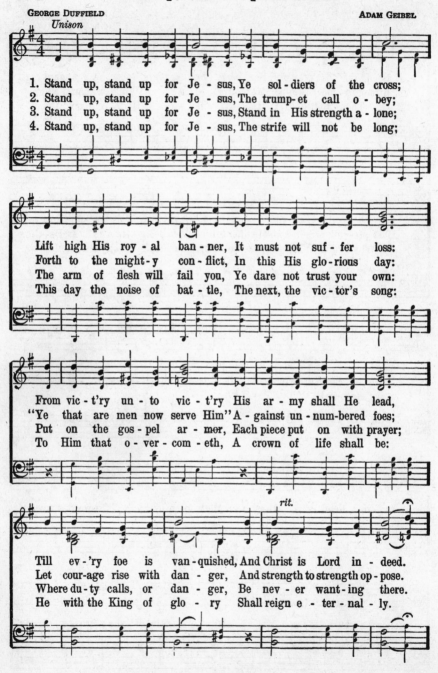

1. Stand up, stand up for Je - sus, Ye sol - diers of the cross;
2. Stand up, stand up for Je - sus, The trump- et call o - bey;
3. Stand up, stand up for Je - sus, Stand in His strength a - lone;
4. Stand up, stand up for Je - sus, The strife will not be long;

Lift high His roy - al ban - ner, It must not suf - fer loss:
Forth to the might - y con - flict, In this His glo - rious day:
The arm of flesh will fail you, Ye dare not trust your own:
This day the noise of bat - tle, The next, the vic - tor's song:

From vic - t'ry un - to vic - t'ry His ar - my shall He lead,
"Ye that are men now serve Him" A - gainst un - num-bered foes;
Put on the gos - pel ar - mor, Each piece put on with prayer;
To Him that o - ver - com - eth, A crown of life shall be:

rit.

Till ev - 'ry foe is van - quished, And Christ is Lord in - deed.
Let cour-age rise with dan - ger, And strength to strength op - pose.
Where du - ty calls, or dan - ger, Be nev - er want - ing there.
He with the King of glo - ry Shall reign e - ter - nal - ly.

Stand Up, Stand Up for Jesus

CHORUS

Stand up for Je - sus, Ye sol - diers of the cross; ...
Stand up, stand up for Je - sus,

Lift high His roy - al ban - ner, It must not, It must not suf - fer loss.

180 Stand Up for Jesus

G. DUFFIELD

G. J. WEBB

1. Stand up, stand up for Je - sus, Ye sol - diers of the cross, Lift high His
2. Stand up, stand up for Je - sus, The trump-et call o - bey; Forth to the
3. Stand up, stand up for Je - sus, Stand in His strength a - lone; The arm of

roy - al ban - ner, It must not suf - fer loss; From vic - t'ry un - to vic - t'ry, His
might - y con - flict, In this His glorious day. "Ye that are men now serve Him," A-
flesh will fail you—Ye dare not trust your own; Put on the gos - pel ar - mor, Each

ar - my shall He lead, Till ev - 'ry foe is vanquished And Christ is Lord in-deed.
gainst unnumbered foes; Let courage rise with danger, And strength to strength oppose.
piece put on with prayer, Where du - ty calls, or dan - ger, Be nev - er want-ing there.

181 Ten Thousand Times Ten Thousand

Henry Alford

John B. Dykes

1. Ten thou - sand times ten thou - sand In spar-kling rai - ment bright,
2. What rush of al - le - lu - ias Fills all the earth and sky!
3. O then what rap - tured greet-ings On Ca-naan's hap - py shore!
4. Bring near Thy great sal - va - tion, Thou Lamb for sin - ners slain;

The ar - mies of the ransomed saints Throng up the steeps of light:
What ring - ing of a thou-sand harps Be - speaks the tri - umph nigh!
What knit-ting sev-ered friend-ships up, Where part-ings are no more!
Fill up the roll of Thine e - lect, Then take Thy pow'r and reign:

'Tis fin - ished, all is fin-ished, Their fight with death and sin:
O day, for which cre - a - tion And all its tribes were made;
Then eyes with joy shall spar - kle, That brimmed with tears of late,
Ap - pear, De-sire of na - tions, Thine ex - iles long for home;

Fling o - pen wide the gold - en gates, And let the vic - tors in.
O joy, for all its for - mer woes A thou - sand-fold re - paid!
Or-phans no lon - ger fa - ther-less, Nor wid - ows des - o - late.
Show in the heav'ns Thy prom-ised sign; Thou Prince and Sav-ior, come.

182 The Banner of the Cross

D. W. WHITTLE   JAMES McGRANAHAN

1. There's a roy - al ban - ner giv - en for dis - play To the sol - diers
2. Though the foe may rage and gath - er as the flood, Let the stand - ard
3. O - ver land and sea, wher - ev - er man may dwell, Make the glo - rious
4. When the glo - ry dawns—'tis draw-ing ver - y near—It is has-tening

of the King; As an en - sign fair we lift it up to - day,
be dis - played; And be-neath its folds, as sol-diers of the Lord,
ti - dings known; Of the crim - son ban - ner now the sto - ry tell,
day by day— Then be-fore our King the foe shall dis - ap-pear,

CHORUS

While as ran-somed ones we sing.
For the truth be not dis - mayed! March-ing on, ... march-ing
While the Lord shall claim His own!
And the cross the world shall sway! on, on,

on, . . . For Christ count ev - ery-thing but loss! . . . . . And to
on, on, ev - ery-thing, ev - ery-thing but loss!

crown Him King, toil and sing 'Neath the ban - ner of the cross!
we'll Be - neath

183 The Son of God Goes Forth to War

REGINALD HEBER

HENRY S. CUTLER

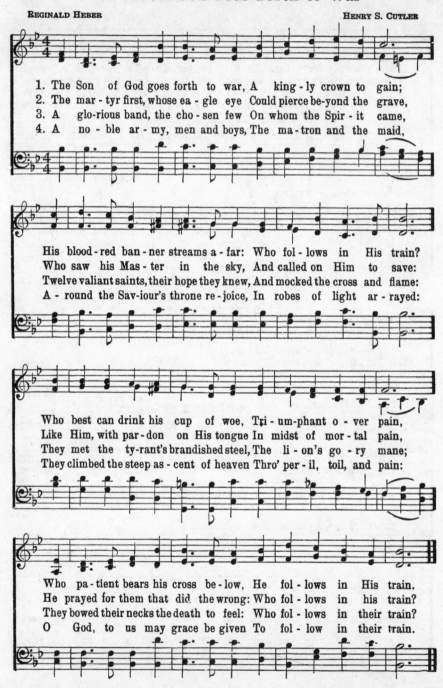

1. The Son of God goes forth to war, A king-ly crown to gain;
2. The mar-tyr first, whose ea-gle eye Could pierce be-yond the grave,
3. A glo-rious band, the cho-sen few On whom the Spir-it came,
4. A no-ble ar-my, men and boys, The ma-tron and the maid,

His blood-red ban-ner streams a-far: Who fol-lows in His train?
Who saw his Mas-ter in the sky, And called on Him to save:
Twelve valiant saints, their hope they knew, And mocked the cross and flame:
A-round the Sav-iour's throne re-joice, In robes of light ar-rayed:

Who best can drink his cup of woe, Tri-um-phant o-ver pain,
Like Him, with par-don on His tongue In midst of mor-tal pain,
They met the ty-rant's brandished steel, The li-on's go-ry mane;
They climbed the steep as-cent of heaven Thro' per-il, toil, and pain:

Who pa-tient bears his cross be-low, He fol-lows in His train.
He prayed for them that did the wrong: Who fol-lows in his train?
They bowed their necks the death to feel: Who fol-lows in their train?
O God, to us may grace be given To fol-low in their train.

184 True-Hearted, Whole-Hearted

FRANCES R. HAVERGAL

GEO. C. STEBBINS

1. True-hearted, whole-hearted, faith-ful and loy-al, King of our lives, by Thy
2. True-hearted, whole-hearted, full-est al-le-giance Yielding henceforth to our
3. True-hearted, whole-hearted, Sav-ior all-glo-rious! Take Thy great pow-er and

grace we will be; Un-der the standard ex-alt-ed and roy-al, Strong in Thy
glo-ri-ous King; Val-iant en-deav-or and lov-ing o-be-dience, Free-ly and
reign there a-lone, O-ver our wills and af-fec-tions vic-to-rious, Free-ly sur-

CHORUS

strength we will bat-tle for Thee. Peal out the watch-word! si-lence it nev-er!
joy-ous-ly now would we bring.
ren-dered and whol-ly Thine own. Peal out the watch-word! si-lence it nev-er!

Song of our spir-its, re-joic-ing and free; Peal out the watch-word!
Song of our spir-its, re-joic-ing and free; Peal out the watch-word!

loy-al for-ev-er, King of our lives, by Thy grace we will be.
loy-al for-ev-er, King of our lives, by Thy grace we will be.

185 Victory Through Grace

SALLIE MARTIN

JNO. R. SWENEY

1. Con-quer-ing now and still to con-quer, Rid-eth a King in His might,
2. Con-quer-ing now and still to con-quer, Who is this won-der-ful King?
3. Con-quer-ing now and still to con-quer, Je-sus, Thou Ru-ler of all,

Lead-ing the host of all the faith-ful In - to the midst of the fight;
Whence are the ar-mies which He lead-eth, While of His glo - ry they sing?
Thrones and their scepters all shall per-ish, Crowns and their splendor shall fall,

See them with cour - age ad - vanc - ing, Clad in their bril-liant ar - ray,
He is our Lord and Re - deem - er, Sav - ior and Mon - arch di - vine;
Yet shall the ar - mies Thou lead - est, Faith-ful and true to the last,

FINE.

Shout-ing the name of their Lead-er, Hear them ex - ult - ing - ly say:
They are the stars that for - ev - er Bright in His King-dom will shine.
Find in Thy man-sions e - ter - nal Rest, when their warfare is past.

D.S.—Yet to the true and the faith-ful Vic-t'ry is prom-ised thro' grace.

CHORUS

D. S.

Not to the strong is the bat - tle, Not to the swift is the race,

186 Who Is On the Lord's Side

FRANCES R. HAVERGAL

Arranged by JOHN GOSS

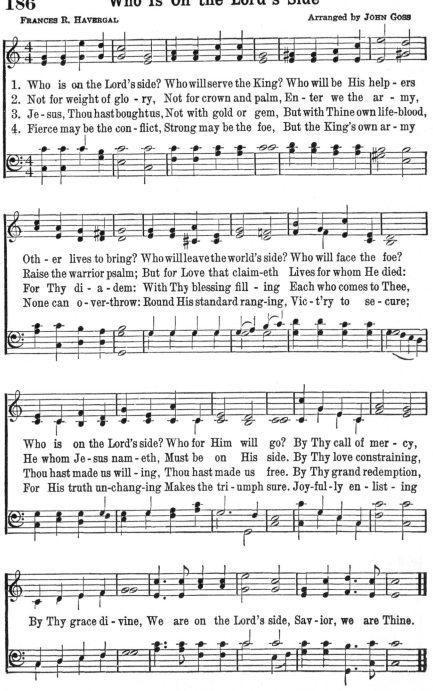

1. Who is on the Lord's side? Who will serve the King? Who will be His help - ers
2. Not for weight of glo - ry, Not for crown and palm, En - ter we the ar - my,
3. Je - sus, Thou hast bought us, Not with gold or gem, But with Thine own life-blood,
4. Fierce may be the con - flict, Strong may be the foe, But the King's own ar - my

Oth - er lives to bring? Who will leave the world's side? Who will face the foe?
Raise the warrior psalm; But for Love that claim-eth Lives for whom He died:
For Thy di - a - dem: With Thy blessing fill - ing Each who comes to Thee,
None can o - ver-throw: Round His standard rang-ing, Vic - t'ry to se - cure;

Who is on the Lord's side? Who for Him will go? By Thy call of mer - cy,
He whom Je - sus nam - eth, Must be on His side. By Thy love constraining,
Thou hast made us will - ing, Thou hast made us free. By Thy grand redemption,
For His truth un-chang-ing Makes the tri - umph sure. Joy-ful-ly en - list - ing

By Thy grace di - vine, We are on the Lord's side, Sav - ior, we are Thine.

187

P. P. B.

Almost Persuaded

P. P. BLISS

1. "Al - most per-suad - ed," now to be - lieve; "Al - most per-suad - ed,"
2. "Al - most per-suad - ed," come, come to - day; "Al - most per-suad - ed,"
3. "Al - most per-suad - ed," har - vest is past! "Al - most per-suad - ed,"

Christ to re - ceive; Seems now some soul to say, "Go, Spir - it,
turn not a - way; Je - sus in - vites you here, An - gels are
doom comes at last! "Al - most" can-not a - vail; "Al - most" is

go Thy way, Some more con - ven - ient day On Thee I'll call."
lin-g'ring near, Prayers rise from hearts so dear, O wan-d'rer, come.
but to fail! Sad, sad, that bit - ter wail, "Al - most," but lost!

188

J. H. S.

Only Trust Him

J. H. Stockton

1. Come, ev - 'ry soul by sin op-pressed, There's mer-cy with the Lord,
2. For Je - sus shed His pre-cious blood, Rich bless-ings to be - stow;
3. Yes, Je - sus is the Truth, the Way, That leads you in - to rest:

And He will sure - ly give you rest By trust-ing in His Word.
Plunge now in - to the crim - son flood That wash-es white as snow.
Be - lieve in Him with-out de - lay, And you are ful - ly blest.

Only Trust Him

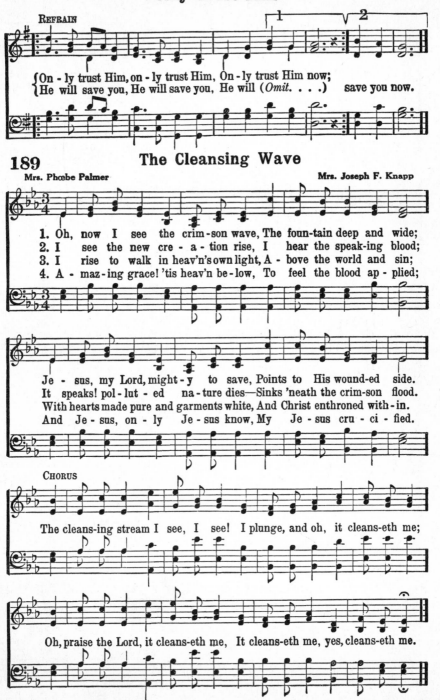

REFRAIN

{ On - ly trust Him, on - ly trust Him, On - ly trust Him now;
{ He will save you, He will save you, He will (*Omit.* . . .) save you now.

189

The Cleansing Wave

Mrs. Phœbe Palmer

Mrs. Joseph F. Knapp

1. Oh, now I see the crim-son wave, The foun-tain deep and wide;
2. I see the new cre - a - tion rise, I hear the speak-ing blood;
3. I rise to walk in heav'n's own light, A - bove the world and sin;
4. A - maz-ing grace! 'tis heav'n be-low, To feel the blood ap - plied;

Je - sus, my Lord, might - y to save, Points to His wound-ed side.
It speaks! pol - lut - ed na - ture dies—Sinks 'neath the crim-son flood.
With hearts made pure and garments white, And Christ enthroned with - in.
And Je - sus, on - ly Je - sus know, My Je - sus cru - ci - fied.

CHORUS

The cleans-ing stream I see, I see! I plunge, and oh, it cleans-eth me;

Oh, praise the Lord, it cleans-eth me, It cleans-eth me, yes, cleans-eth me.

Arr. from Neumaster, 1671

James McGranahan

1. Sin - ners Je - sus will re - ceive; Sound this word of grace to all
2. Come, and He will give you rest; Trust Him, for His word is plain;
3. Now my heart con-demns me not, Pure be - fore the law I stand;
4. Christ re - ceiv - eth sin - ful men, E - ven me with all my sin;

Who the heav'n - ly path-way leave, All who lin - ger, all who fall.
He will take the sin - ful - est; Christ re - ceiv - eth sin - ful men.
He who cleansed me from all spot, Sat - is - fied its last de-mand.
Purged from ev - 'ry spot and stain, Heav'n with Him I en - ter in.

REFRAIN

Sing it o'er . . . . . . and o'er a - gain; . . . . . . Christ re-
Sing it o'er a-gain, Sing it o'er a-gain; Christ re-

ceiv - - - eth sin-ful men; . . . . . Make the mes - - - sage
ceiv-eth sin - ful men, Christ re-ceiv-eth sin - ful men; Make the message plain,

clear and plain: . . . . . . Christ re - ceiv - eth sin - ful men.
Make the mes-sage plain:

191 Have You Counted the Cost?

A. J. H.

A. J. Hodge

1. There's a line that is drawn by re-ject-ing our Lord, Where the call of His
2. You may bar-ter your hope of e-ter-ni-ty's morn, For a mo-ment of
3. While the door of His mer-cy is o-pen to you, Ere the depth of His

Spir-it is lost,..... And you hur-ry along with the pleasure-mad throng—
joy at the most,.... For the glit-ter of sin and the things it will win—
love you ex-haust,... Won't you come and be healed, won't you whisper, I yield—

rit. *p*

CHORUS.

rit.

Have you counted, have you counted the cost?
Have you counted, have you counted the cost? Have you counted the cost, if your
I have counted, I have counted the cost.

pp   *a tempo*

soul should be lost, Tho' you gain the whole world for your own?..... E-ven

rit. *p*

now it may be that the line you have crossed, Have you counted, have you counted the cost?

He is Able to Deliver Thee

W. A. O.

W. A. OGDEN

1. 'Tis the grand-est theme thro' the a-ges rung; 'Tis the grandest theme for a
2. 'Tis the grand-est theme in the earth or main; 'Tis the grandest theme for a
3. 'Tis the grand-est theme, let the ti-dings roll, To the guilt-y heart, to the

mor - tal tongue; 'Tis the grandest theme that the world e'er sung, "Our God is
mor - tal strain; 'Tis the grandest theme, tell the world a - gain, "Our God is
sin - ful soul; Look to God in faith, He will make thee whole, "Our God is

CHORUS.

a - ble to de - liv - er thee." He is a - - - ble to de - liv - er thee,
a - ble, He is a - ble

He is a - - - ble to de - liv - er thee; Tho' by sin op-prest,
a - ble, He is a - ble

Go to Him for rest; "Our God is a - ble to de - liv - er thee." A - MEN.

193 Him That Cometh Unto Me

E. E. HEWITT

WM. J. KIRKPATRICK

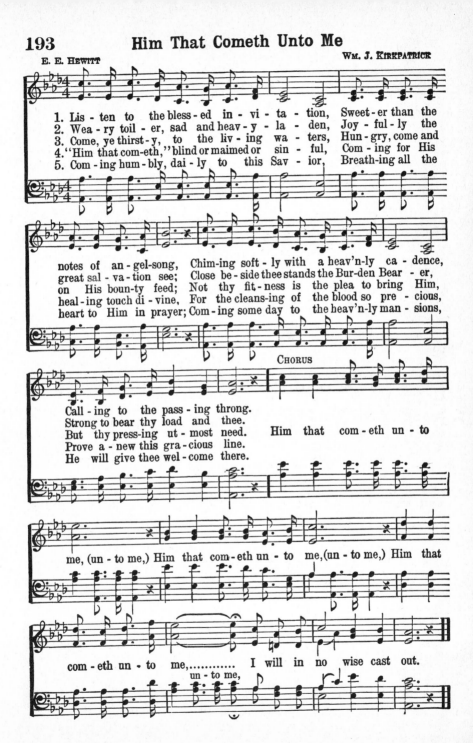

1. Lis - ten to the bless - ed in - vi - ta - tion, Sweet - er than the
2. Wea - ry toil - er, sad and heav - y - la - den, Joy - ful - ly the
3. Come, ye thirst - y, to the liv - ing wa - ters, Hun - gry, come and
4. "Him that com - eth," blind or maimed or sin - ful, Com - ing for His
5. Com - ing hum - bly, dai - ly to this Sav - ior, Breath - ing all the

notes of an - gel-song, Chim - ing soft - ly with a heav'n-ly ca - dence,
great sal - va - tion see; Close be - side thee stands the Bur - den Bear - er,
on His boun - ty feed; Not thy fit - ness is the plea to bring Him,
heal - ing touch di - vine, For the cleans - ing of the blood so pre - cious,
heart to Him in prayer; Com - ing some day to the heav'n-ly man - sions,

Call - ing to the pass - ing throng.
Strong to bear thy load and thee.
But thy press - ing ut - most need.
Prove a - new this gra - cious line.
He will give thee wel - come there.

CHORUS

Him that com - eth un - to me, (un - to me,) Him that com - eth un - to me, (un - to me,) Him that com - eth un - to me,............ un - to me, I will in no wise cast out.

194 I Am Coming Home

A. H. ACKLEY

B. D. ACKLEY

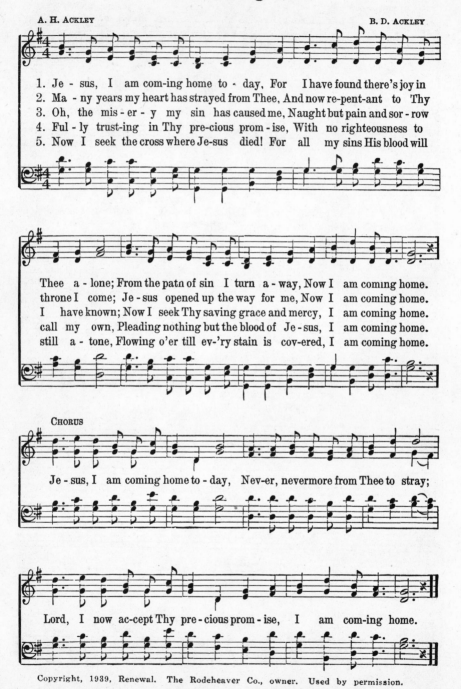

1. Je - sus, I am com-ing home to - day, For I have found there's joy in
2. Ma - ny years my heart has strayed from Thee, And now re-pent-ant to Thy
3. Oh, the mis - er - y my sin has caused me, Naught but pain and sor - row
4. Ful - ly trust-ing in Thy pre-cious prom - ise, With no righteousness to
5. Now I seek the cross where Je-sus died! For all my sins His blood will

Thee a - lone; From the path of sin I turn a - way, Now I am coming home.
throne I come; Je - sus opened up the way for me, Now I am coming home.
I have known; Now I seek Thy saving grace and mercy, I am coming home.
call my own, Pleading nothing but the blood of Je - sus, I am coming home.
still a - tone, Flowing o'er till ev-'ry stain is cov-ered, I am coming home.

CHORUS

Je - sus, I am coming home to - day, Nev-er, nevermore from Thee to stray;

Lord, I now ac-cept Thy pre-cious prom - ise, I am com-ing home.

195 I Am Praying For You

S. O'MALEY CLUFF

IRA D. SANKEY

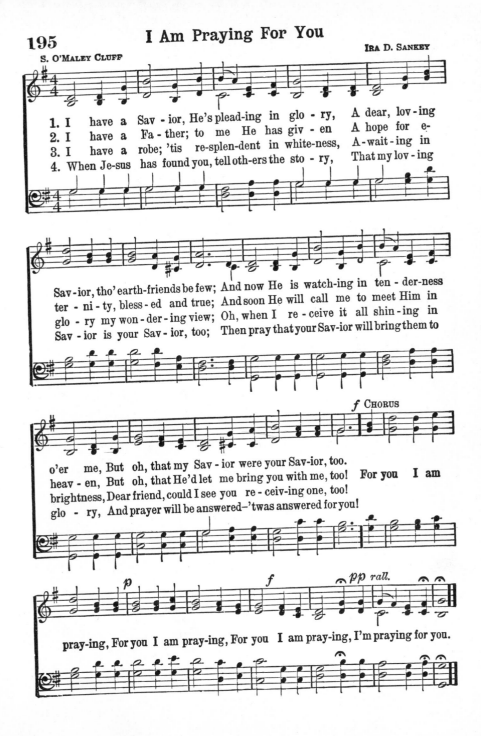

1. I have a Sav-ior, He's plead-ing in glo-ry, A dear, lov-ing Sav-ior, tho' earth-friends be few; And now He is watch-ing in ten-der-ness o'er me, But oh, that my Sav-ior were your Sav-ior, too.

2. I have a Fa-ther; to me He has giv-en A hope for e-ter-ni-ty, bless-ed and true; And soon He will call me to meet Him in heav-en, But oh, that He'd let me bring you with me, too!

3. I have a robe; 'tis re-splen-dent in white-ness, A-wait-ing in glo-ry my won-der-ing view; Oh, when I re-ceive it all shin-ing in brightness, Dear friend, could I see you re-ceiv-ing one, too!

4. When Je-sus has found you, tell oth-ers the sto-ry, That my lov-ing Sav-ior is your Sav-ior, too; Then pray that your Sav-ior will bring them to glo-ry, And prayer will be answered—'twas answered for you!

f CHORUS

For you I am pray-ing, For you I am pray-ing, For you I am pray-ing, I'm praying for you.

196 Jesus, I Come

WM. T. SLEEPER

GEO. C. STEBBINS

1. Out of my bond-age, sor-row and night, Je-sus, I come, Je-sus, I come;
2. Out of my shame-ful fail-ure and loss, Je-sus, I come, Je-sus, I come;
3. Out of un-rest and ar-ro-gant pride, Je-sus, I come, Je-sus, I come;
4. Out of the fear and dread of the tomb, Je-sus, I come, Je-sus, I come;

In-to Thy free-dom, glad-ness and light, Je-sus, I come to Thee.
In-to the glo-rious gain of Thy cross, Je-sus, I come to Thee.
In-to Thy bless-ed will to a-bide, Je-sus, I come to Thee.
In-to the joy and light of Thy home, Je-sus, I come to Thee.

Out of my sick-ness in-to Thy health, Out of my want and in-to Thy wealth,
Out of earth's sorrows in-to Thy balm, Out of life's storms and in-to Thy calm,
Out of my-self to dwell in Thy love, Out of de-spair in-to raptures a-bove,
Out of the depths of ru-in un-told, In-to the peace of Thy sheltering fold,

Out of my sin and in-to Thy-self, Je-sus, I come to Thee.
Out of dis-tress to ju-bi-lant psalm, Je-sus, I come to Thee.
Up-ward for aye on wings like a dove, Je-sus, I come to Thee.
Ev-er Thy glo-rious face to be-hold, Je-sus, I come to Thee.

197 Jesus Is Calling

FANNY J. CROSBY

GEO. C. STEBBINS

1. Je-sus is ten-der-ly call-ing thee home—Call-ing to-day,
2. Je-sus is call-ing the wea-ry to rest—Call-ing to-day,
3. Je-sus is wait-ing; O come to Him now—Wait-ing to-day,
4. Je-sus is plead-ing; O list to His voice: Hear Him to-day,

call-ing to-day; Why from the sun-shine of love wilt thou roam
call-ing to-day; Bring Him thy bur-den and thou shalt be blest:
wait-ing to-day; Come with thy sins; at His feet low-ly bow;
hear Him to-day; They who be-lieve on His name shall re-joice;

REFRAIN

Far-ther and far-ther a-way?
He will not turn thee a-way.
Come, and no lon-ger de-lay.
Quick-ly a-rise and a-way.

Call - - ing to-day, ...
Call-ing, call-ing to-day, to-day,

Call - - ing to-day, ...
Call-ing, call-ing to-day, to-day,

Je - - - - sus is
Je-sus is ten-der-ly

call - - - - ing, is ten-der-ly call-ing to-day.
call-ing to-day,

198 Just As I Am

CHARLOTTE ELLIOTT

WILLIAM B. BRADBURY

1. Just as I am, with-out one plea, But that Thy blood was shed for me,
2. Just as I am, and wait-ing not To rid my soul of one dark blot,
3. Just as I am, though tossed a-bout With many a con-flict, many a doubt,
4. Just as I am—poor, wretched, blind; Sight, rich-es, heal-ing of the mind,
5. Just as I am—Thou wilt re-ceive, Wilt welcome, pardon, cleanse, relieve,

And that Thou bidd'st me come to Thee, O Lamb of God, I come! I come!
To Thee whose blood can cleanse each spot, O Lamb of God, I come! I come!
Fightings and fears with-in, with-out, O Lamb of God, I come! I come!
Yea, all I need in Thee to find, O Lamb of God, I come! I come!
Be-cause Thy prom-ise I be-lieve, O Lamb of God, I come! I come!

199 I Heard the Voice of Jesus Say

HORATIUS BONAR

Old English Air
Arr. by B. B. McKINNEY

1. I heard the voice of Je-sus say, "Come un-to Me and rest;
2. I heard the voice of Je-sus say, "Be-hold, I free-ly give
3. I heard the voice of Je-sus say, "I am this dark world's Light;

Lay down, thou wear-y one, lay down Thy head up-on My breast."
The liv-ing wa-ter; thirst-y one, Stoop down and drink, and live."
Look un-to Me, thy morn shall rise, And all thy day be bright."

I Heard the Voice of Jesus Say

DUET

I came to Je-sus as I was, Wea-ry and worn and sad,
I came to Je-sus and I drank Of that life-giv-ing stream;
I looked to Je-sus and I found In Him my Star, my Sun;

PARTS

I found in Him a rest-ing-place, And He has made me glad.
My thirst was quenched, my soul re-vived, And now I live in Him.
And in that light of life I'll walk, Till traveling days are done.

200 Where He Leads Me

E. W. BLANDLY   J. S. NORRIS

1. I can hear my Sav-iour call-ing, I can hear my Sav-iour call-ing,
2. I'll go with Him through the garden, I'll go with Him through the garden,
3. I'll go with Him through the judgment, I'll go with Him through the judgment,
4. He will give me grace and glo-ry, He will give me grace and glo-ry,

REF.—*Where He leads me I will fol-low, Where He leads me I will fol-low,*

I can hear my Sav-iour call-ing, "Take thy cross and fol-low, fol-low Me."
I'll go with Him through the gar-den, I'll go with Him, with Him all the way.
I'll go with Him through the judgment, I'll go with Him, with Him all the way.
He will give me grace and glo-ry, And go with me, with me all the way.

Where He leads me I will fol-low, I'll go with Him, with Him all the way.

Softly and Tenderly

W. L. T.   WILL L. THOMPSON

1. Soft - ly and ten-der - ly Je - sus is call-ing, Call - ing for you and for me;
2. Why should we tarry when Jesus is plead-ing, Pleading for you and for me?
3. Time is now fleeting, the moments are passing, Passing from you and from me;
4. Oh! for the won-der-ful love He has promised, Promised for you and for me;

See, on the portals He's waiting and watching, Watching for you and for me.
Why should we linger and heed not His mercies, Mer-cies for you and for me?
Shadows are gathering, death-beds are coming, Com-ing for you and for me.
Tho' we have sinned, He has mercy and pardon, Par-don for you and for me.

CHORUS

Come home,.. come home,...... Ye who are wear-y, come home;...
Come home, come home,

Ear-nest-ly, ten-der-ly, Je - sus is call-ing, Call-ing, O sin-ner, come home!

The Nail-Scarred Hand

B. B. McK.

B. B. McKinney

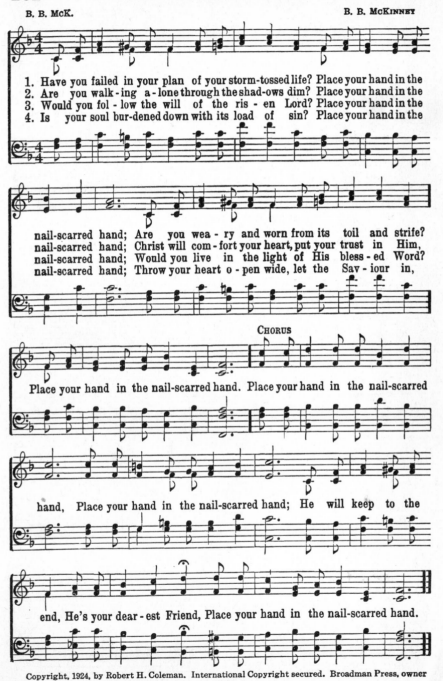

1. Have you failed in your plan of your storm-tossed life? Place your hand in the
2. Are you walk-ing a-lone through the shad-ows dim? Place your hand in the
3. Would you fol-low the will of the ris-en Lord? Place your hand in the
4. Is your soul bur-dened down with its load of sin? Place your hand in the

nail-scarred hand; Are you wea-ry and worn from its toil and strife?
nail-scarred hand; Christ will com-fort your heart, put your trust in Him,
nail-scarred hand; Would you live in the light of His bless-ed Word?
nail-scarred hand; Throw your heart o-pen wide, let the Sav-iour in,

CHORUS

Place your hand in the nail-scarred hand. Place your hand in the nail-scarred
hand, Place your hand in the nail-scarred hand; He will keep to the
end, He's your dear-est Friend, Place your hand in the nail-scarred hand.

Open Wide the Door

W. Kitching.

John H. Burke.

1. Je - sus knocks; He calls to thee; "Wea - ry one, O come to me;"
2. Je - sus knocks, He comes to save, 'Twas for thee His life He gave;
3. Je - sus knocks, is knock-ing still; Yield to Him at once thy will;
4. Je - sus knocks; the mo-ments fly; While sal - va - tion yet is nigh;

He can save, and on - ly He; O - - pen wide the door.
He hath tri-umphed o'er the grave;
He with joy thy heart can fill;
Ere the Sav - ior pass - eth by, O - pen, o - pen wide the door.

CHORUS.

O - - - - - pen wide the door,
O - pen, o - pen wide, O - pen wide the door,

O - - - pen wide the door, He can save, and
O - pen, o - pen wide, o - pen wide the door,

on - ly He;— O - - pen wide the door.
O - pen, o - pen wide the door. o - pen wide the door.

204 He the Pearly Gates Will Open

Fred Blom
Authorized Tr. by N. Carlson

Elsie Ahlwen
Arranged

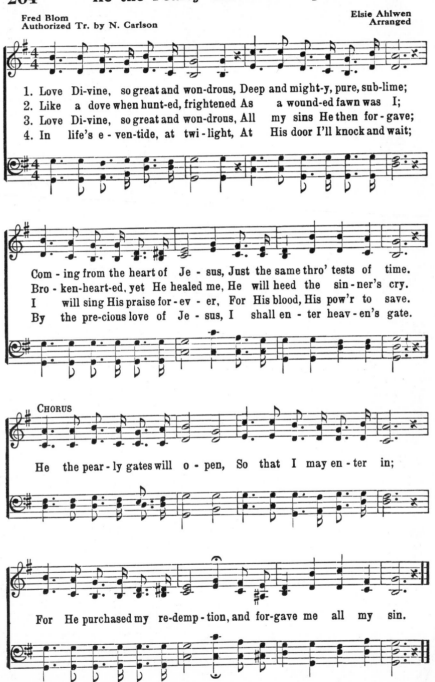

1. Love Di-vine, so great and won-drous, Deep and might-y, pure, sub-lime;
2. Like a dove when hunt-ed, frightened As a wound-ed fawn was I;
3. Love Di-vine, so great and won-drous, All my sins He then for-gave;
4. In life's e-ven-tide, at twi-light, At His door I'll knock and wait;

Com - ing from the heart of Je - sus, Just the same thro' tests of time.
Bro - ken-heart-ed, yet He healed me, He will heed the sin-ner's cry.
I will sing His praise for-ev - er, For His blood, His pow'r to save.
By the pre-cious love of Je - sus, I shall en - ter heav-en's gate.

CHORUS

He the pear - ly gates will o - pen, So that I may en - ter in;

For He purchased my re-demp - tion, and for-gave me all my sin.

Verily, Verily

G. M. J.

James McGranahan

1. Oh, what a Sav-ior, that He died for me! From con-dem-
2. All my in-iq-ui-ties on Him were laid, All my in-
3. Though poor and need-y I can trust my Lord, Though weak and
4. Though all un-wor-thy, yet I will not doubt, For him that

na-tion He hath made me free; "He that be-liev-eth on the
debt-ed-ness by Him was paid; All who be-lieve on Him, the
sin-ful I be-lieve His Word; Oh, glad mes-sage! ev-'ry
com-eth, He will not cast out; "He that be-liev-eth," oh, the

CHORUS

Son," saith He, "Hath ev-er-last-ing life."
Lord hath said, "Hath ev-er-last-ing life." "Ver-i-ly, ver-i-ly,
child of God "Hath ev-er-last-ing life."
good news shout, "Hath ev-er-last-ing life!"

I say un-to you," "Ver-i-ly, ver-i-ly," mes-sage ev-er new;

"He that be-liev-eth on the Son," "'tis true, "Hath ev-er-last-ing life"

206 "Whosoever Will"

P. P. B.

P. P. BLISS

1. "Who-so-ev-er hear - eth," shout, shout the sound! Spread the bless-ed ti-dings
2. Who-so-ev-er com - eth, need not de - lay, Now the door is o - pen,
3. "Who-so-ev-er will," the prom-ise is se - cure; "Who-so-ev - er will," for-

all the world a-round; Tell the joy - ful news wher - ev - er man is found,
en - ter while you may; Je - sus is the true, the on - ly Liv - ing Way:
ev - er must en-dure; "Who-so - ev - er will," 'tis life for - ev - er - more;

CHORUS

"Who-so-ev - er will may come." "Who-so-ev - er will, who - so-ev - er will!"

Send the proc - la - ma - tion o - ver vale and hill; 'Tis a lov - ing

Fa - ther calls the wan-d'rer home: "Who-so - ev - er will may come."

207 Why Not Now?

EL NATHAN

C. C. CASE

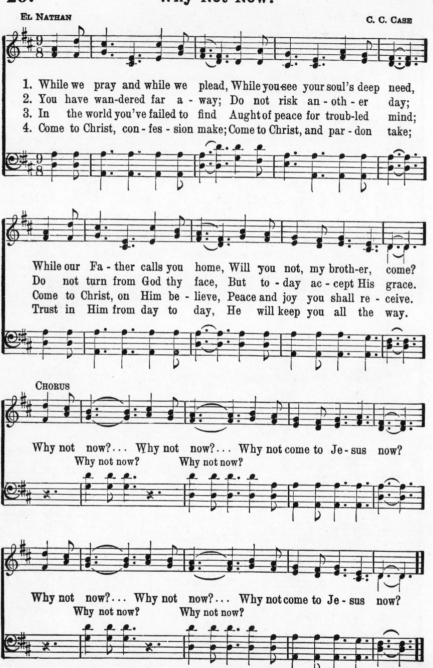

1. While we pray and while we plead, While you see your soul's deep need,
2. You have wan-dered far a - way; Do not risk an - oth - er day;
3. In the world you've failed to find Aught of peace for troub-led mind;
4. Come to Christ, con - fes - sion make; Come to Christ, and par - don take;

While our Fa - ther calls you home, Will you not, my broth-er, come?
Do not turn from God thy face, But to - day ac - cept His grace.
Come to Christ, on Him be - lieve, Peace and joy you shall re - ceive.
Trust in Him from day to day, He will keep you all the way.

CHORUS

Why not now?... Why not now?... Why not come to Je - sus now?
Why not now? Why not now?

Why not now?... Why not now?... Why not come to Je - sus now?
Why not now? Why not now?

208 You Must Open the Door

Ina Duley Ogdon

Homer A. Rodeheaver

1. There's a Sav-iour who stands at the door of your heart, He is
2. He has come from the Fa-ther sal-va-tion to bring, And His
3. He is lov-ing and kind, full of in-fi-nite grace, In your
4. He will lead you at last to that bless-ed a-bode, To the

long-ing to en-ter—why let Him de-part? He has pa-tient-ly
name is called Je-sus, Re-deem-er and King; To save you and
heart, in your life, will you give Him a place? He is wait-ing to
cit-y of God, at the end of the road, Where the night nev-er

called you so oft-en be-fore, But you must o-pen the door.
keep you He pleads ev-er-more, But you must o-pen the door.
bless you, your soul to re-store, But you must o-pen the door.
falls, when life's jour-ney is o'er, But you must o-pen the door.

CHORUS

You must o-pen the door, You must o-pen the door, When

Je-sus comes in, He will save you from sin, But you must o-pen the door.

209

Why Do You Wait?

G. F. R.

Geo. F. Root

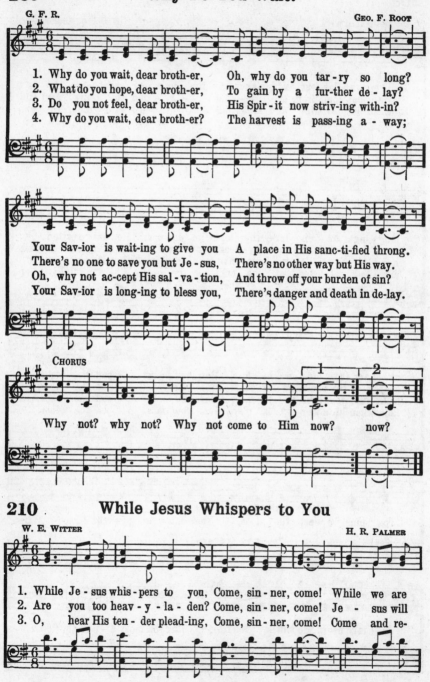

1. Why do you wait, dear broth-er,   Oh, why do you tar-ry so long?
2. What do you hope, dear broth-er,   To gain by a fur-ther de-lay?
3. Do you not feel, dear broth-er,   His Spir-it now striv-ing with-in?
4. Why do you wait, dear broth-er?   The harvest is pass-ing a-way;

Your Sav-ior is wait-ing to give you   A place in His sanc-ti-fied throng.
There's no one to save you but Je-sus, There's no other way but His way.
Oh, why not ac-cept His sal-va-tion,   And throw off your burden of sin?
Your Sav-ior is long-ing to bless you, There's danger and death in de-lay.

Chorus

Why not? why not? Why not come to Him now?   now?

210

While Jesus Whispers to You

W. E. Witter

H. R. Palmer

1. While Je-sus whis-pers to you, Come, sin-ner, come! While we are
2. Are you too heav-y-la-den? Come, sin-ner, come! Je-sus will
3. O, hear His ten-der plead-ing, Come, sin-ner, come! Come and re-

While Jesus Whispers to You

pray-ing for you, Come, sin - ner, come! Now is the time to own Him,
bear your bur-den, Come, sin - ner, come! Je - sus will not de-ceive you,
ceive the bless-ing, Come, sin - ner, come! While Je - sus whis-pers to you,

Come, sin-ner, come! Now is the time to know Him, Come, sin-ner, come!
Come, sin-ner, come! Je - sus can now re-ceive you, Come, sin-ner, come!
Come, sin-ner, come! While we are pray-ing for you, Come, sin-ner, come!

211 Oh, How I Love Jesus

1. There is a name I love to hear, I love to sing its worth; It sounds like
2. It tells me of a Sav-ior's love, Who died to set me free; It tells me
3. It tells me what my Fa-ther hath In store for ev - 'ry day, And tho' I
4. It tells of One whose loving heart Can feel my deep-est woe, Who in each

CHORUS

mu - sic in mine ear, The sweetest name on earth.
of His precious blood, The sin-ner's per-fect plea. Oh, how I love Je - sus,
tread a darksome path, Yields sunshine all the way.
sor - row bears a part, That none can bear be-low.

Oh, how I love Je - sus, Oh, how I love Je - sus, Be-cause He first loved me!

212 Crown Him with Many Crowns

MATTHEW BRIDGES

GEORGE J. ELVEY

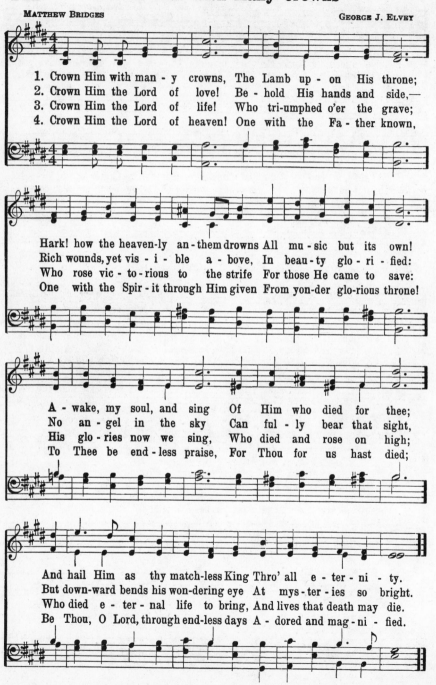

1. Crown Him with man - y crowns, The Lamb up - on His throne;
2. Crown Him the Lord of love! Be - hold His hands and side,—
3. Crown Him the Lord of life! Who tri-umphed o'er the grave;
4. Crown Him the Lord of heaven! One with the Fa - ther known,

Hark! how the heaven-ly an - them drowns All mu - sic but its own!
Rich wounds, yet vis - i - ble a - bove, In beau-ty glo - ri - fied:
Who rose vic - to - rious to the strife For those He came to save:
One with the Spir - it through Him given From yon-der glo-rious throne!

A - wake, my soul, and sing Of Him who died for thee;
No an - gel in the sky Can ful - ly bear that sight,
His glo - ries now we sing, Who died and rose on high;
To Thee be end - less praise, For Thou for us hast died;

And hail Him as thy match-less King Thro' all e - ter - ni - ty.
But down-ward bends his won-dering eye At mys - ter - ies so bright.
Who died e - ter - nal life to bring, And lives that death may die.
Be Thou, O Lord, through end-less days A - dored and mag-ni - fied.

213 Glorious Things of Thee Are Spoken

JOHN NEWTON

FRANZ JOSEPH HAYDN

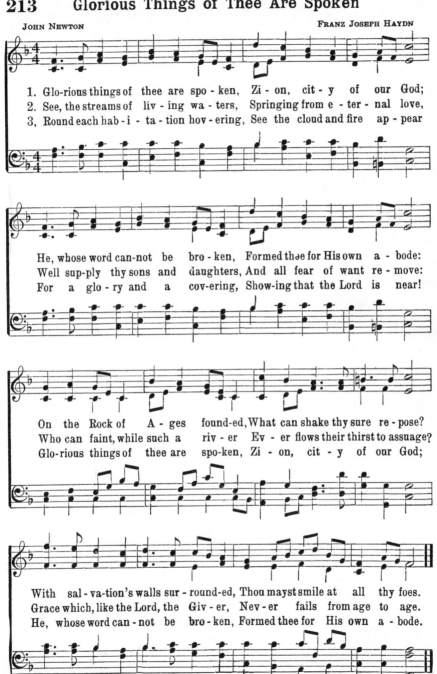

1. Glo-rious things of thee are spo - ken, Zi - on, cit - y of our God;
2. See, the streams of liv - ing wa - ters, Springing from e - ter - nal love,
3. Round each hab - i - ta - tion hov - ering, See the cloud and fire ap - pear

He, whose word can-not be bro - ken, Formed thee for His own a - bode:
Well sup-ply thy sons and daughters, And all fear of want re - move:
For a glo - ry and a cov-ering, Show-ing that the Lord is near!

On the Rock of A - ges found-ed, What can shake thy sure re - pose?
Who can faint, while such a riv - er Ev - er flows their thirst to assuage?
Glo-rious things of thee are spo-ken, Zi - on, cit - y of our God;

With sal - va-tion's walls sur - round-ed, Thou mayst smile at all thy foes.
Grace which, like the Lord, the Giv - er, Nev - er fails from age to age.
He, whose word can - not be bro - ken, Formed thee for His own a - bode.

214 God the Omnipotent

HENRY F. CHORLEY
JOHN ELLERTON

ALEXIS F. LVOV

1. God the Om - nip - o - tent! King, who or - dain - est
2. God the All - mer - ci - ful! earth hath for - sak - en
3. God the All - right-eous One! man hath de - fied Thee;
4. So shall Thy peo - ple, with thank - ful de - vo - tion,

Thun - der Thy clar - ion, the light - ning Thy sword;
Meek - ness and mer - cy, and slight - ed Thy word;
Yet to e - ter - ni - ty stand - eth Thy word;
Praise Him who saved them from per - il and sword,

Show forth Thy pit - y on high where Thou reign - est;
Let not Thy wrath in its ter - rors a - wak - en;
False - hood and wrong shall not tar - ry be - side Thee;
Sing - ing in cho - rus from o - cean to o - cean

Give to us peace in our time, O Lord.
Give to us peace in our time, O Lord.
Give to us peace in our time, O Lord.
Peace to the na - tions, and praise to the Lord. A - MEN.

215 Golden Harps Are Sounding

FRANCES R. HAVERGAL

FRANCES R. HAVERGAL

1. Gold - en harps are sound-ing, An - gel voic - es ring, Pearl-y gates are
2. He who came to save us, He who bled and died, Now is crowned with
3. Pray - ing for His chil - dren In that bless-ed place, Call-ing them to

o - pened, O - pened for the King; Christ, the King of glo - ry,
glo - ry At His Fa-ther's side. Nev - er - more to suf - fer,
glo - ry, Send-ing them His grace; His bright home pre-par - ing,

Je - sus, King of love, Is gone up in tri - umph To His throne a - bove.
Nev - er-more to die, Je - sus, King of glo - ry, Is gone up on high.
Faith-ful ones, for you; Je - sus ev - er liv - eth, Ev - er lov - eth too.

REFRAIN

All His work is end - ed, Joy - ful - ly we sing;

Je - sus hath as - cend - ed: Glo - ry to our King! A - MEN.

Great God of Wonders

SAMUEL DAVIES

JOHN NEWTON

1. Great God of won-ders! all Thy ways Are match-less, God-like,
2. In won-der lost, with trem-bling joy We take the par-don
3. O may this strange, this match-less grace, This God-like mir-a-

and di-vine; But the fair glo-ries of Thy grace More God-like
of our God; Par-don for crimes of deep-est dye, A par-don
cle of love, Fill the whole earth with grate-ful praise, And all th'an-

and un-ri-valed shine, More God-like and un-ri-valed shine.
bought with Je-sus' blood; A par-don bought with Je-sus' blood:
gel-ic choirs a-bove, And all th'an-gel-ic choirs a-bove.

CHORUS

Who is a par-d'ning God like Thee? Or who has grace so

rich and free? Or who has grace so rich and free? A-MEN.

Holy is the Lord

FANNY J. CROSBY

WM. B. BRADBURY

1. Ho - ly, ho - ly, ho - ly is the Lord! Sing, O ye peo - ple,
2. Praise Him, praise Him, shout a - loud for joy! Watch-man of Zi - on,
3. King E - ter - nal, bless - ed be His name! So may His chil - dren

glad - ly a - dore Him; Let the moun - tains trem - ble at His word,
her - ald the sto - ry; Sin and death His king - dom shall de - stroy,
glad - ly a - dore Him; When in heav'n we join the hap - py strain,

Let the hills be joy - ful be - fore Him; Might - y in wis - dom,
All the earth shall sing of His glo - ry; Praise Him, ye an - gels,
When we cast our bright crowns be - fore Him; There in His like - ness

bound-less in mer - cy, Great is Je - ho - vah, King o - ver all.
ye who be - hold Him Robed in His splen - dor, match-less, di - vine.
joy - ful a - wak - ing, There we shall see Him, there we shall sing.

CHORUS

Ho - ly, ho - ly, ho - ly is the Lord, Let the hills be joy - ful be - fore Him.

Used by permission of The Biglow & Main Co.

218 Let Us Crown Him

E. PERRONET
Allegro

JAMES McGRANAHAN

1. All hail the pow'r of Je-sus' name! Let an-gels pros-trate fall;
2. Let ev-'ry kin-dred, ev-'ry tribe, On this ter-res-trial ball,
3. O that with yon-der sa-cred throng We at His feet may fall!

Bring forth the roy-al di-a-dem, And crown Him Lord of all.
To Him all maj-es-ty as-cribe, And crown Him Lord of all.
We'll join the ev-er-last-ing song, And crown Him Lord of all.

CHORUS

Let us crown Him, . . . Let us crown Him, . . . Let us
Him Lord of all,   Him Lord of all,

crown the great Re-deem-er Lord of all; . . . . Let us crown Him, ...
                                                    Him Lord of all,

Let us crown Him, . . . Let us crown Him Lord of all.
Him Lord of all,   the great Re-deem-er Lord of all.

219 O Thou My Soul, Bless God the Lord

Scotch Version

JAMES McGRANAHAN

1. O thou my soul, bless God the Lord, And all that in me is,
2. Bless, O my soul, the Lord thy God, And not for-get-ful be
3. All thy in-iq-ui-ties who doth Most gra-cious-ly for-give,
4. The Lord Je-ho-vah gra-cious is, And He is mer-ci-ful,
5. O bless the Lord, all ye His works, Wherewith the world is stored,

Be lift-ed up, His ho-ly name To mag-ni-fy and bless.
Of all His gra-cious ben-e-fits He hath be-stowed on thee.
Who thy dis-eas-es all and pains Doth heal and thee re-lieve.
Long-suf-fer-ing and slow to wrath, In kind-ness plen-ti-ful.
In His do-min-ions ev-'ry-where; My soul, bless thou the Lord.

CHORUS

Bless the Lord, Bless the Lord, Bless the Lord, O my
Bless the Lord, Bless the Lord,

soul, And all that is with-in me, Bless His ho - ly name.
Bless His ho-ly

220 Glory to Jesus

J. WAKEFIELD MACGILL

From BATISTE. Har. by C. W. and E. M.

1. Je - sus has loved me— won - der - ful Sav - ior! Je - sus has
2. Je - sus has saved me— won - der - ful Sav - ior! Je - sus has
3. Je - sus will lead me— won - der - ful Sav - ior! Je - sus will
4. Je - sus will crown me— won - der - ful Sav - ior! Je - sus will

CHO.—Glo - ry to Je - sus—won - der - ful Sav - ior! Glo - ry to

loved me, I can - not tell *why;* .... Came He to res - cue
saved me, I can - not tell *how;* .... All that I know is,
lead me, I can - not tell *where;* ... But I will fol - low,
crown me, I can - not tell *when;* ... White throne of splen - dor

Je - sus, the One I a - dore; .... *Glo - ry to Je - sus—*

D. C. for CHORUS

sin - ners all worth-less, My heart He conquered—for Him I would die.
He was my ran - som, Dy - ing on Cal-v'ry with thorns on His brow.
thro' joy or sor - row, Sun-shine or tem-pest, sweet peace or de - spair.
hail I with glad - ness, Crowned 'mid the plaudits of an - gels and men.

won - der - ful Sav - ior! Glo - ry to Je - sus, and praise ev - er - more.

221 On Jordan's Stormy Banks

SAMUEL STENNETT

Arr. by R. M. McINTOSH

1. On Jor-dan's storm-y banks I stand, And cast a wish-ful eye
2. All o'er those wide - ex - tend - ed plains Shines one e - ter - nal day;
3. No chill-ing winds, nor pois'nous breath, Can reach that health-ful shore;
4. When shall I reach that hap - py place, And be for - ev - er blest?

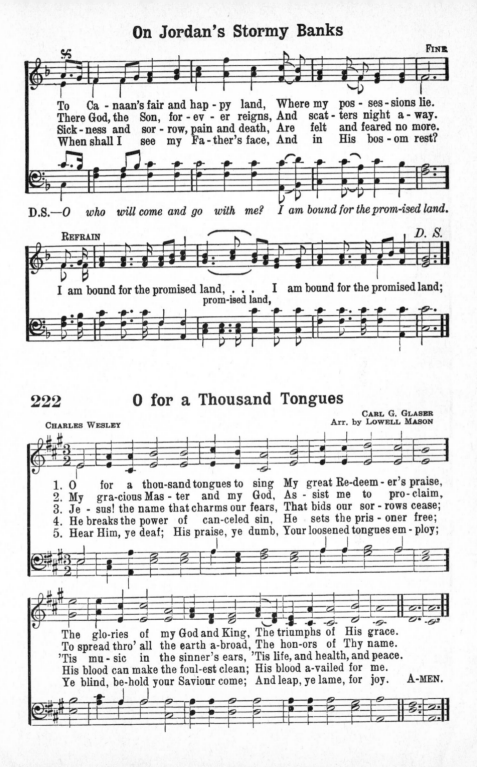

On Jordan's Stormy Banks

FINE

To Ca-naan's fair and hap-py land, Where my pos-ses-sions lie.
There God, the Son, for-ev-er reigns, And scat-ters night a-way.
Sick-ness and sor-row, pain and death, Are felt and feared no more.
When shall I see my Fa-ther's face, And in His bos-om rest?

D.S.—*O who will come and go with me? I am bound for the prom-ised land.*

REFRAIN

D. S.

I am bound for the promised land, . . . I am bound for the promised land;
prom-ised land,

222   **O for a Thousand Tongues**

CARL G. GLASER
Arr. by LOWELL MASON

CHARLES WESLEY

1. O for a thou-sand tongues to sing My great Re-deem-er's praise,
2. My gra-cious Mas-ter and my God, As-sist me to pro-claim,
3. Je-sus! the name that charms our fears, That bids our sor-rows cease;
4. He breaks the power of can-celed sin, He sets the pris-oner free;
5. Hear Him, ye deaf; His praise, ye dumb, Your loosened tongues em-ploy;

The glo-ries of my God and King, The triumphs of His grace.
To spread thro' all the earth a-broad, The hon-ors of Thy name.
'Tis mu-sic in the sinner's ears, 'Tis life, and health, and peace.
His blood can make the foul-est clean; His blood a-vailed for me.
Ye blind, be-hold your Saviour come; And leap, ye lame, for joy.   A-MEN.

Praise Him! Praise Him!

FANNY J. CROSBY

CHESTER G. ALLEN

1. Praise Him! praise Him! Je-sus, our bless-ed Re-deem-er! Sing, O Earth, His
2. Praise Him! praise Him! Je-sus, our bless-ed Re-deem-er! For our sins He
3. Praise Him! praise Him! Je-sus, our bless-ed Re-deem-er! Heavenly por-tals

won-der-ful love pro-claim! Hail Him! hail Him! highest archangels in glo-ry;
suffered, and bled, and died; He our Rock, our hope of e-ter-nal sal-va-tion,
loud with ho-san-nas ring! Je-sus, Sav-iour, reigneth for-ev-er and ev-er;

Strength and hon-or give to His ho-ly name! Like a shep-herd, Je-sus will
Hail Him! hail Him! Je-sus the Cru-ci-fied. Sound His prais-es! Je-sus who
Crown Him! crown Him! Prophet, and Priest, and King! Christ is com-ing! o-ver the

REFRAIN

guard His children, In His arms He carries them all day long: Praise Him! praise Him!
bore our sor-rows, Love unbounded, wonderful, deep and strong: Praise Him! praise Him!
world vic-to-rious, Power and glo-ry un-to the Lord be-long: Praise Him! praise Him!

tell of His ex-cel-lent greatness: Praise Him! praise Him! ev-er in joy-ful song!

224 Praise Ye the Lord, the Almighty

JOACHIM NEANDER
Trans. by CATHERINE WINKWORTH

"Stralsund Gesangbuch"
Arr. in "Praxis Pietatas Melica"

1. Praise ye the Lord, the Al-might-y, the King of cre-a-tion! O my soul, praise Him, for He is thy health and sal-va-tion! All ye who hear, Now to His tem-ple draw near; Join me in glad ad-o-ra——tion!

2. Praise ye the Lord, who o'er all things so won-drous-ly reign-eth, Shel-ters thee un-der His wings, yea, so gen-tly sus-tain-eth! Hast thou not seen How thy de-sires e'er have been Grant-ed in what He or-dain——eth?

3. Praise ye the Lord, who with mar-vel-ous wis-dom hath made thee! Decked thee with health, and with lov-ing hand guid-ed and stayed thee; How oft in grief Hath not He brought thee re-lief, Spread-ing His wings for to shade . . thee!

4. Praise ye the Lord! O let all that is in me a-dore Him! All that hath life and breath, come now with prais-es be-fore Him! Let the A-men Sound from His peo-ple a-gain: Glad-ly for aye we a-dore . . Him. A-MEN.

The Church's One Foundation

Samuel J. Stone   Samuel S. Wesley

1. The Church-'s one foun - da - tion Is Je - sus Christ her Lord;
2. E - lect from ev - 'ry na - tion, Yet one o'er all the earth,
3. 'Mid toil and trib - u - la - tion, And tu - mult of her war,
4. Yet she on earth hath un - ion With God the Three in One,

She is His new cre - a - tion By wa - ter and the word:
Her char - ter of sal - va - tion, One Lord, one faith, one birth;
She waits the con - sum - ma - tion Of peace for - ev - er - more;
And mys - tic sweet com - mun - ion With those whose rest is won:

From Heav'n He came and sought her To be His ho - ly bride; With
One ho - ly name she bless - es, Par-takes one ho - ly food, And
Till, with the vi - sion glo - rious, Her long - ing eyes are blest, And
O hap - py ones and ho - ly! Lord, give us grace that we, Like

His own blood He bought her, And for her life He died.
to one hope she press - es, With ev - 'ry grace en - dued.
the great church vic - to - rious Shall be the church at rest.
them, the meek and low - ly, On high may dwell with Thee. A-MEN.

226 The God of Abraham Praise

THOMAS OLIVERS   Hebrew Melody. Arr. by MEYER LEONI

1. The God of Abraham praise, Who reigns en-throned a - bove;
2. The God of Abraham praise, At whose su-preme com - mand
3. He by Him - self hath sworn, I on His oath de - pend;
4. The whole tri - um-phant host Give thanks to God on high;

An - cient of ev - er - last - ing days, And God of love.
From earth I rise, and seek the joys At His right hand.
I shall, on ea - gles' wings up - borne, To heav'n as - cend;
"Hail, Fa - ther, Son, and Ho - ly Ghost!" They ev - er cry.

Je - ho - vah, great I AM, By earth and heav'n con - fessed;
I all on earth for - sake, Its wis - dom, fame, and pow'r;
I shall be - hold His face, I shall His pow'r a - dore,
Hail, Abraham's God, and mine! I join the heav'n - ly lays;

I bow and bless the sa - cred Name, For - ev - er blest.
And Him my on - ly por - tion make, My shield and tow'r.
And sing the won - ders of His grace For - ev - er - more.
All might and maj - es - ty are Thine, And end - less praise.

To God Be the Glory

FANNY J. CROSBY

W. H. DOANE

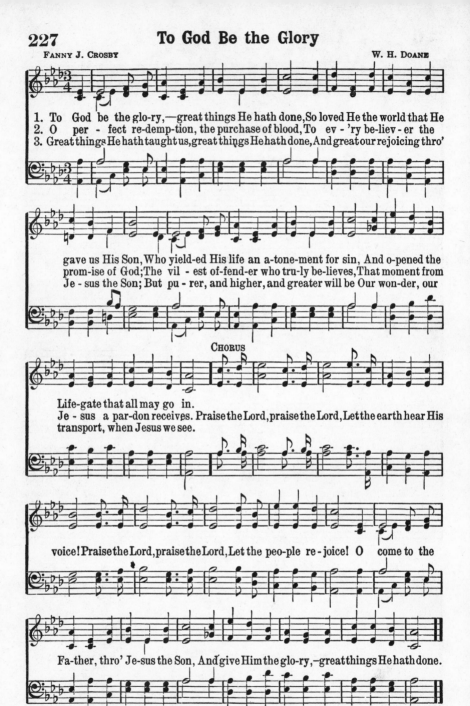

1. To God be the glo-ry,—great things He hath done, So loved He the world that He
2. O per - fect re-demp-tion, the purchase of blood, To ev - 'ry be-liev - er the
3. Great things He hath taught us, great things He hath done, And great our rejoicing thro'

gave us His Son, Who yield-ed His life an a-tone-ment for sin, And o-pened the
prom-ise of God; The vil - est of-fend-er who tru-ly be-lieves, That moment from
Je - sus the Son; But pu - rer, and higher, and greater will be Our won-der, our

CHORUS

Life-gate that all may go in.
Je - sus a par-don receives. Praise the Lord, praise the Lord, Let the earth hear His
transport, when Jesus we see.

voice! Praise the Lord, praise the Lord, Let the peo-ple re - joice! O come to the

Fa-ther, thro' Je-sus the Son, And give Him the glo-ry,—great things He hath done.

228   Jesus, Wondrous Saviour!

Arr. by ALFRED B. SMITH

Worshipfully

1. Je - sus, won - drous Sav - iour! Christ, of kings the King!
2. All earth's flow - ing plea - sures Were a win - try sea,
3. Life is death, if sev - ered From Thy throb - bing heart;
4. Je - sus! All per - fec - tions Rise and end in Thee;

An - gels fall be - fore Thee, Pros - trate, wor - ship - ing;
Heav'n it - self with - out Thee Dark as night would be.
Death with life a - bun - dant At Thy touch would start.
Bright-ness of God's glo - ry Thou, e - ter - nal - ly.

Fair - est they con - fess Thee In the Heav'n a - bove;
Lamb of God! Thy glo - ry Is the light a - bove;
Worlds and men and an - gels All con - sist in Thee;
Fa - vored be - yond mea - sure They Thy face who see;

We would sing Thee fair - est Here in hymns of love.
Lamb of God! Thy glo - ry Is the life of love.
Yet Thou cam - est to us In hu - mil - i - ty.
May, we, gra - cious Sav - iour, Share this ec - sta - sy.

229 We Praise Thee, O God, Our Redeemer

JULIA BULKLEY CADY

Netherlands Folksong from
The Collection by ANDRIANUS VALERIUS

1. We praise Thee, O God, our Re-deem-er, Cre-a-tor, In grate-ful de-
2. We wor-ship Thee, God of our fa-thers, we bless Thee; Thro' life's storm and
3. With voic-es u-nit-ed our prais-es we of-fer, To Thee, great Je-

vo-tion our trib-ute we bring. We lay it be-fore Thee, we kneel and a-
tem-pest our Guide hast Thou been. When per-ils o'er-take us, es-cape Thou wilt
ho-vah, glad anthems we raise. Thy strong arm will guide us, our God is be-

dore Thee, We bless Thy ho-ly Name, glad prais-es we sing.
make us, And with Thy help, O Lord, our bat-tles we win.
side us, To Thee, our great Re-deem-er, for ev-er be praise. A-MEN.

230 I Love Thy Kingdom, Lord

TIMOTHY DWIGHT

"WILLIAMS' Psalmody"

1. I love Thy King-dom, Lord, The house of Thine a-bode,
2. I love Thy Church, O God: Her walls be-fore Thee stand,
3. For her my tears shall fall, For her my prayers as-cend;
4. Be-yond my high-est joy I prize her heaven-ly ways,
5. Sure as Thy truth shall last, To Zi-on shall be given

I Love Thy Kingdom, Lord

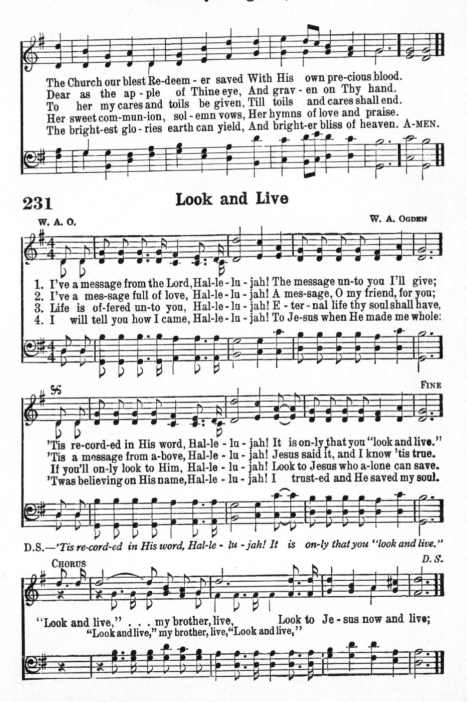

The Church our blest Re-deem - er saved With His own pre-cious blood.
Dear as the ap - ple of Thine eye, And grav - en on Thy hand.
To her my cares and toils be given, Till toils and cares shall end.
Her sweet com-mun-ion, sol - emn vows, Her hymns of love and praise.
The bright-est glo - ries earth can yield, And bright-er bliss of heaven. A-MEN.

231 Look and Live

W. A. O.

W. A. OGDEN

1. I've a message from the Lord, Hal-le - lu - jah! The message un-to you I'll give;
2. I've a mes-sage full of love, Hal-le - lu - jah! A mes-sage, O my friend, for you;
3. Life is of-fered un-to you, Hal-le - lu - jah! E - ter-nal life thy soul shall have,
4. I will tell you how I came, Hal-le - lu - jah! To Je-sus when He made me whole:

FINE

'Tis re-cord-ed in His word, Hal-le - lu - jah! It is on-ly that you "look and live."
'Tis a message from a-bove, Hal-le - lu - jah! Jesus said it, and I know 'tis true.
If you'll on-ly look to Him, Hal-le - lu - jah! Look to Jesus who a-lone can save.
'Twas believing on His name, Hal-le - lu - jah! I trust-ed and He saved my soul.

D.S.—'Tis re-cord-ed in His word, Hal-le - lu - jah! It is on-ly that you "look and live."

CHORUS

D. S.

"Look and live," . . . my brother, live, Look to Je - sus now and live;
"Look and live," my brother, live, "Look and live,"

232 All Creatures of Our God and King

ST. FRANCIS OF ASSISI
Tr. by WILLIAM H. DRAPER

Melody from GEISTLICHE KIRCHENGESÄNGE

In unison

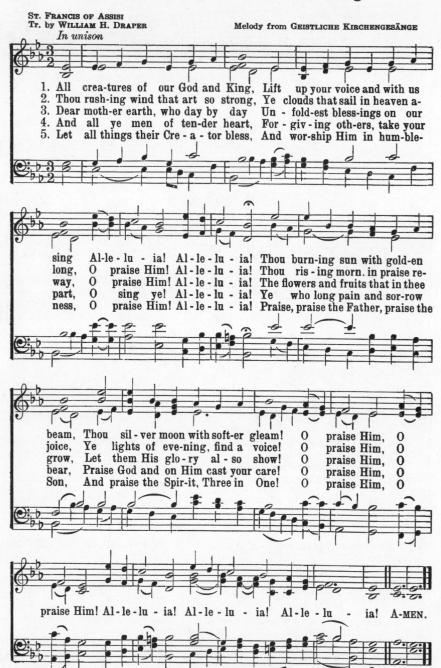

1. All crea-tures of our God and King, Lift up your voice and with us
2. Thou rush-ing wind that art so strong, Ye clouds that sail in heaven a-
3. Dear moth-er earth, who day by day Un - fold-est bless-ings on our
4. And all ye men of ten-der heart, For - giv-ing oth-ers, take your
5. Let all things their Cre - a - tor bless, And wor-ship Him in hum-ble-

sing Al-le-lu - ia! Al-le-lu - ia! Thou burn-ing sun with gold-en
long, O praise Him! Al-le-lu - ia! Thou ris - ing morn. in praise re-
way, O praise Him! Al-le-lu - ia! The flowers and fruits that in thee
part, O sing ye! Al-le-lu - ia! Ye who long pain and sor-row
ness, O praise Him! Al-le-lu - ia! Praise, praise the Father, praise the

beam, Thou sil - ver moon with soft-er gleam! O praise Him, O
joice, Ye lights of eve-ning, find a voice! O praise Him, O
grow, Let them His glo - ry al - so show! O praise Him, O
bear, Praise God and on Him cast your care! O praise Him, O
Son, And praise the Spir-it, Three in One! O praise Him, O

praise Him! Al-le-lu - ia! Al-le-lu - ia! Al-le-lu - ia! A-MEN.

233   I Am Trusting Thee, Lord Jesus

FRANCES R. HAVERGAL

E. W. BULLINGER

1. I am trust-ing Thee, Lord Je-sus! Trust-ing on-ly Thee!
2. I am trust-ing Thee, Lord Je-sus! At Thy feet I bow,
3. I am trust-ing Thee to guide me: Thou a-lone shalt lead,
4. I am trust-ing Thee, Lord Je-sus! Nev-er let me fall!

Trust-ing Thee for full sal-va-tion, Great and free.
For Thy grace and ten-der mer-cy, Trust-ing now!
Ev-'ry day and hour sup-ply-ing All my need.
I am trust-ing Thee for-ev-er, And for all.

234   My Heart's Prayer

H. P. Blanchard

Ralph E. Stewart

1. My new life I owe to Thee, Je-sus, Lamb of Cal-va-ry;
2. Hum-bly at Thy cross I'd stay, Je-sus, keep me there, I pray;
3. Grant me wis-dom, grace and pow'r, Lord I need Thee ev-'ry hour;
4. Sav-ior, Thou hast heard my plea, Thou art near—so near to me;

Sin was can-celed on the tree, Je-sus, bless-ed Je--sus.
Teach me more of Thee each day, Je-.sus, bless-ed Je--sus.
Let my will be lost in Thine, Je-sus, bless-ed Je--sus.
Now I feel Thy strength'ning pow'r, Je-sus, bless-ed Je--sus.

235 I've Found Real Joy

C. H. L.

C. Harold Lowden

1. Be-fore I met my Sav-iour, my heart was troub-led sore, I
2. In Him I'm ful-ly trust-ing each mo-ment of the day, With
3. I rev-el in His Pres-ence—such fel-low-ship is rare, He's

knew I was a sin-ner and doomed for-ev-er more; But one day in my
Him be-side to guide me, I nev-er lose my way; The things that once an-
with me when the storm breaks, and when the day is fair; Each joy-ous as-pir-

wan-d'ring, I heard a Voice Di-vine, And life has changed com-plete-ly,
noyed me, or caused me bit-ter pain, Are sanc-ti-fied for-ev-er
a-tion, each grief that bends me low, He shares with me each mo-ment,

Chorus

since I have claimed Him mine.
and changed from loss to gain.   I nev-er knew that life could be so won-der-ful,
as   on our way we go.

I nev-er knew that life could be so grand (so grand); But since I heard His call,

I've Found Real Joy

And yield - ed Him my all, I've found real joy and peace in trust-ing Je - sus.

236   I Shall Be Like Him

W. A. S.

REV. W. A. SPENCER

1. When I shall reach the more ex-cel-lent glo-ry, And all my tri-als are passed,
2. We shall not wait till the glo - ri-ous dawning Breaks on the vi-sion so fair,
3. More and more like Him, repeat the blest story, O - ver and o - ver a -gain,

I shall be like Him, O won-der-ful sto-ry! I shall be like Him at last.
Now we may welcome the heav-en-ly morning, Now we His image may bear.
Changed by His Spirit from glo-ry to glo-ry, I shall be sat-is-fied then.

CHORUS

I shall be like Him, I shall be like Him, And in His beau - ty shall shine,

I shall be like Him, wondrously like Him, Je-sus, my Sav-iour di - vine.

All Hail the Power

OLIVER HOLDEN

1. All hail the pow'r of Je-sus' name! Let an-gels pros-trate fall:
2. Ye cho-sen seed of Is-rael's race, Ye ran-somed from the fall,
3. Let ev-'ry kin-dred, ev-'ry tribe On this ter-res-trial ball,
4. O that with yon-der sa-cred throng We at His feet may fall!

Bring forth the roy-al di-a-dem, And crown Him Lord of all,
Hail Him who saves you by His grace, And crown Him Lord of all,
To Him all maj-es-ty as-cribe, And crown Him Lord of all,
We'll join the ev-er-last-ing song, And crown Him Lord of all,

Bring forth the roy-al di-a-dem, And crown Him Lord of all!
Hail Him who saves you by His grace, And crown Him Lord of all!
To Him all maj-es-ty as-cribe, And crown Him Lord of all!
We'll join the ev-er-last-ing song, And crown Him Lord of all!

238 Miles' Lane WILLIAM SHRUBSOLE

1. All hail the pow'r of Je-sus' name! Let an-gels pros-trate fall; Bring forth the roy-al

di-a-dem, And crown Him, crown Him, crown Him, Crown Him Lord of all!

239 All Hail the Power of Jesus' Name

E. PERRONET

JAMES ELLOR

1. All hail the pow'r of Je - sus' name! Let an - gels pros-trate fall,
2. Ye cho - sen seed of Is - rael's race, Ye ran-somed from the fall,
3. Let ev - 'ry kin - dred, ev - 'ry tribe, On this ter - res-trial ball,
4. O that with yon - der sa - cred throng We at His feet may fall,

Let an - gels pros-trate fall; Bring forth the roy - al di - a - dem,
Ye ran-somed from the fall, Hail Him who saves you by His grace,
On this ter - res-trial ball, To Him all maj - es - ty as - cribe,
We at His feet may fall! We'll join the ev - er - last - ing song,

And crown . . . . Him, Crown Him,

And crown Him, crown Him, crown Him, crown Him, And crown Him Lord of
And crown . . . . Him, Crown Him,

And crown Him, crown Him, crown Him, Crown . . . .

crown Him, crown Him;

all, crown Him; And crown Him Lord of all!
crown . . . . . Him;

. . . . Him; And crown Him Lord of all!

240 My Jesus, I Love Thee

WILLIAM R. FEATHERSTONE
Chorus by A. B. S.

Netherlands Melody

1. My Je - sus, I love Thee, I know Thou art mine; For Thee all the fol - lies
2. I love Thee be-cause Thou hast first lov-ed me, And purchased my par-don
3. I'll love Thee in life, I will love Thee in death, And praise Thee as long as
4. In man-sions of glo - ry and end - less de-light, I'll ev - er a - dore Thee

of sin I re-sign; My gra - cious Re - deem - er, my Sav-iour art Thou;
on Cal - va - ry's tree; I love Thee for wear - ing the thorns on Thy brow;
Thou lendest me breath; And say when the death-dew lies cold on my brow,
in heav - en so bright; I'll sing with the glit - ter - ing crown on my brow,

If ev - er I loved Thee, my Je - sus 'tis now.

CHORUS

Je - sus, Je - sus,
Name that I love, Blest Name of my Sav - iour, Who came from a - bove.

241 He Cannot Fail

C. E. M., JR.

C. E. MASON, JR.

He can-not fail for He is God, He can-not fail, He pledged His word

He Cannot Fail

Search Me, O God

243 The Old-Fashioned Way

Mrs. C. D. Martin

W. Stillman Martin

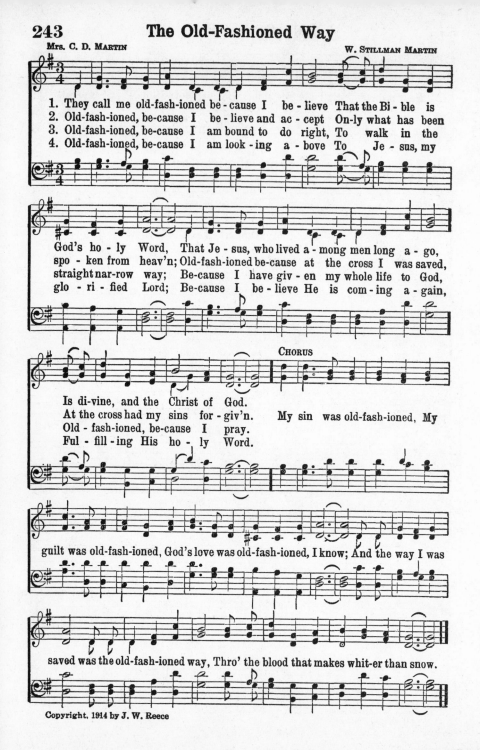

1. They call me old-fash-ioned be-cause I be-lieve That the Bi-ble is
2. Old-fash-ioned, be-cause I be-lieve and ac-cept On-ly what has been
3. Old-fash-ioned, be-cause I am bound to do right, To walk in the
4. Old-fash-ioned, be-cause I am look-ing a-bove To Je-sus, my

God's ho-ly Word, That Je-sus, who lived a-mong men long a-go,
spo-ken from heav'n; Old-fash-ioned be-cause at the cross I was saved,
straight nar-row way; Be-cause I have giv-en my whole life to God,
glo-ri-fied Lord; Be-cause I be-lieve He is com-ing a-gain,

CHORUS

Is di-vine, and the Christ of God.
At the cross had my sins for-giv'n. My sin was old-fash-ioned, My
Old-fash-ioned, be-cause I pray.
Ful-fill-ing His ho-ly Word.

guilt was old-fash-ioned, God's love was old-fash-ioned, I know; And the way I was

saved was the old-fash-ioned way, Thro' the blood that makes whit-er than snow.

244 ## Ashamed of Jesus

Joseph Griggs

E. O. Excell
Arr. by Herman Voss

1. Je - sus, and shall it ev - er be A mor - tal man a-
2. A - shamed of Je - sus! soon - er far Let eve - ning blush to
3. A - shamed of Je - sus! that dear Friend, On whom my hopes of
4. A - shamed of Je - sus! yes, I may, When I've no guilt to

shamed of Thee? A - shamed of Thee, whom an - gels praise, Whose
own a star; He sheds the beams of light di - vine O'er
heav'n de - pend! No! when I blush, be this my shame, That
wash a - way; No tear to wipe, no good to crave, No

glo - ries shine thro' end - less days.
this be - night - ed soul of mine.
I no more re - vere His name.
fears to quell, no soul to save.

CHORUS

A - shamed .... of
A-shamed of Je - sus, a-

Je - sus, I nev - er, I nev - er will be; ..... For
shamed of Je - sus, I nev - er will be; For

Je - - sus, my Sav - iour, is not a-shamed of me.
Je - sus, my Sav - iour, for Je-sus, my Sav-iour,

245 "Whosoever" Meaneth Me

J. E. M.   J. Edwin McConnell.

1. I am hap-py to-day and the sun shines bright, The clouds have been
2. All my hopes have been raised, O His name be praised, His glo-ry has
3. O what won-der-ful love, O what grace di-vine, That Je-sus should

rolled a-way; For the Sav-ior said, Who-so-ev-er will, May
filled my soul; I've been lift-ed up and from sin set free, His
die for me; I was lost in sin, for the world I pined, But

CHORUS.

come with Him to stay. (to stay.)
blood hath made me whole. (me whole.) "Who-so-ev-er," sure-ly mean-eth me,
now I am set free. (set free.)

Sure-ly mean-eth me, O sure-ly mean-eth me; "Who-so-ev-er,"

sure-ly mean-eth me, "Who-so-ev-er," mean-eth me.
                                                    mean-eth me.

246 **Jesus! Jesus! Jesus!** ABBEY HYMNS

Slowly

1. Je - sus! Je - sus! Je - sus! Sing a - loud the Name;
2. Je - sus! Name of cleans - ing, Wash-ing all our stains;
3. Je - sus! Name of bold - ness,— Mak - ing cow - ards brave;
4. Je - sus! Name of beau - ty, Beau - ty far too bright
5. Je - sus! be our joy - note In this vale of tears;

Till it soft - ly, slow - ly, Sets all hearts a - flame.
Je - sus! Name of heal - ing, Balm for all our pains.
Name! that in the bat - tle, Cer - tain - ly must save.
For our earth-born fan - cy, For our mor - tal sight.
Till we reach the home-land, And th' e - ter - nal years. A - MEN.

247 **The Old-Time Religion**

CHO.—'Tis the old - time re - lig - ion, 'Tis the old - time re - lig - ion,
1. It was good for our moth-ers, It was good for our moth-ers,
2. It has saved our . . fa - thers, It has saved our . . fa - thers,
3. Makes me love ev - 'ry - bod - y, Makes me love ev - 'ry - bod - y,
4. It will do when I am dy - ing, It will do when I am dy - ing,
5. It will take us all to heav - en, It will take us all to heav - en,

'Tis the old - time re - lig - ion, And it's good e-nough for me.
It was good for our moth - ers, And it's good e-nough for me.
It has saved our . . fa - thers, And it's good e-nough for me.
Makes me love ev - 'ry - bod - y, And it's good e-nough for me.
It will do when I am dy - ing, And it's good e-nough for me.
It will take us all to heav - en, And it's good e-nough for me.

248 A Child of the King

HATTIE E. BUELL

Rev. JOHN B. SUMMER, arr.

1. My Fa - ther is rich in hous - es and lands, He hold - eth the
2. My Fa-ther's own Son, the Sav - iour of men, Once wan-dered on
3. I once was an out - cast stran-ger on earth, A sin - ner by
4. A tent or a cot - tage, why should I care? They're build-ing a

wealth of the world in His hands! Of ru - bies and dia-monds, of
earth as the poor - est of them; But now He is plead-ing our
choice, and an al - ien by birth; But I've been a - dopt - ed, my
pal - ace for me o - ver there; Tho' ex - iled from home, yet,

sil - ver and gold, His cof - fers are full, He has rich - es un-told.
par - don on high, That we may be His when He comes by and by.
name's writ-ten down, An heir to a man - sion, a robe, and a crown.
still I may sing: All glo - ry to God, I'm a child of the King.

CHORUS

I'm a child of the King, A child of the King:

With Je - sus my Sav - iour I'm a child of the King.

249   And Can It Be That I Should Gain?

CHARLES WESLEY

Majestic (Not fast)

1. And can it be that I should gain An in - t'rest in the
2. He left His Fa-ther's throne a - bove, So free, so in - fi -
3. No con-dem-na - tion now I dread, I am my Lord's and

Sav-iour's blood? Died He for me, who caused His pain? For me, who
nite His grace! Emp-tied Him-self of all but love, And bled for
He is mine; A - live in Him, my liv - ing Head, And clothed in

CHORUS

Him to death pur - sued?
A - dam's help - less race?   A - maz-ing love! How can it be
right-eous-ness di - vine.

That Thou, my God, shouldst die for me? A - maz - ing love! How
A - maz-ing love!

rit.

can it be That Thou, my God, shouldst die for me?
How can it be That Thou, my God,

250 A New Name in Glory

C. A. M.   C. Austin Miles

1. I was once a sin-ner, but I came Par-don to re-ceive from my
2. I was humbly kneeling at the cross, Fearing naught but God's an-gry
3. In the Book 'tis written "Saved by Grace," O the joy that came to my

Lord: This was free-ly giv-en, and I found That He al-ways kept His
frown; When the heavens opened and I saw That my name was writ-ten
soul! Now I am for-giv-en and I know By the blood I am made

CHORUS

word (kept His word).
down (writ-ten down). There's a new name writ-ten down in glo-ry,
whole (am made whole).

And it's mine, O yes, it's mine! And the white-robed angels sing the
And it's mine, yes, it's mine!

sto - ry, "A sin-ner has come home." For there's a
has come home.

A New Name in Glory

new name written down in glo-ry, And it's mine, O yes, it's mine!
And it's mine, yes, it's mine!

With my sins for-giv-en I am bound for heav-en, Nev-er-more to roam.

251   Let the Lower Lights Be Burning

P. P. Bliss

P. P. Bliss

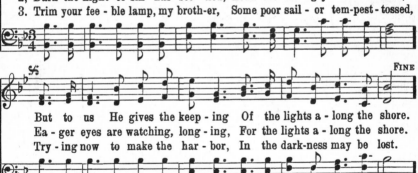

1. Bright-ly beams our Fa-ther's mer - cy From His light-house ev - er - more,
2. Dark the night of sin has set - tled, Loud the an - gry bil-lows roar;
3. Trim your fee - ble lamp, my broth-er, Some poor sail - or tem-pest - tossed,

Fine

But to us He gives the keep - ing Of the lights a - long the shore.
Ea - ger eyes are watching, long - ing, For the lights a - long the shore.
Try - ing now to make the har - bor, In the dark-ness may be lost.

D. S.–*Some poor fainting, struggling sea - man You may res-cue, you may save.*

Chorus

D. S.

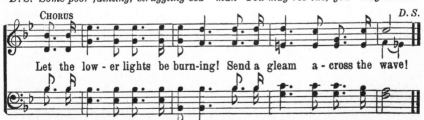

Let the low - er lights be burn-ing! Send a gleam a - cross the wave!

252 Footsteps of Jesus

MARY B. C. SLADE

A. B. EVERETT

1. Sweet-ly, Lord, have we heard Thee call-ing, Come, fol-low Me! And we
2. Though they lead o'er the cold, dark mountains, Seek-ing His sheep; Or a-
3. If they lead thre' the tem-ple ho-ly, Preaching the Word; Or in
4. Then at last, when on high He sees us, Our jour-ney done, We will

CHORUS.

see where Thy foot-prints falling Lead us to Thee.
long by Si - lo-am's fountains, Help-ing the weak: Foot-prints of Je-sus, that
homes of the poor and low-ly, Serv-ing the Lord:
rest where the steps of Je - sus End at His throne.

make the pathway glow; We will follow the steps of Je-sus wher-e'er they go.

253 I Hear the Words

HORATIUS BONAR

C. MALAN

1. I hear the words of love, I gaze up - on the blood,
2. 'Tis ev - er - last - ing peace! Sure as Je - ho - vah's name,
3. The clouds may go and come, And storms may sweep my sky;
4. My love is oft - times low, My joy still ebbs and flows,
5. I change, He chang-es not; The Christ can nev - er die:

I Hear the Words

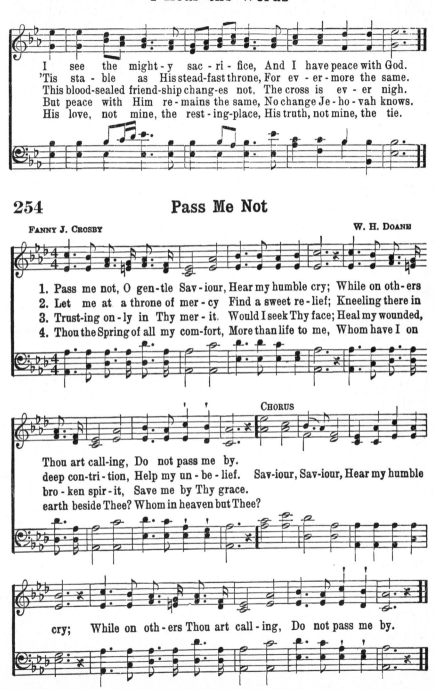

I see the might-y sac-ri-fice, And I have peace with God.
'Tis sta-ble as His stead-fast throne, For ev-er-more the same.
This blood-sealed friend-ship chang-es not, The cross is ev-er nigh.
But peace with Him re-mains the same, No change Je-ho-vah knows.
His love, not mine, the rest-ing-place, His truth, not mine, the tie.

254

Pass Me Not

FANNY J. CROSBY

W. H. DOANE

1. Pass me not, O gen-tle Sav-iour, Hear my humble cry; While on oth-ers
2. Let me at a throne of mer-cy Find a sweet re-lief; Kneeling there in
3. Trust-ing on-ly in Thy mer-it, Would I seek Thy face; Heal my wounded,
4. Thou the Spring of all my com-fort, More than life to me, Whom have I on

CHORUS

Thou art call-ing, Do not pass me by.
deep con-tri-tion, Help my un-be-lief.   Sav-iour, Sav-iour, Hear my humble
bro-ken spir-it, Save me by Thy grace.
earth beside Thee? Whom in heaven but Thee?

cry;   While on oth-ers Thou art call-ing, Do not pass me by.

255 He Hideth My Soul

FANNY J. CROSBY
Allegretto

WM. J. KIRKPATRICK

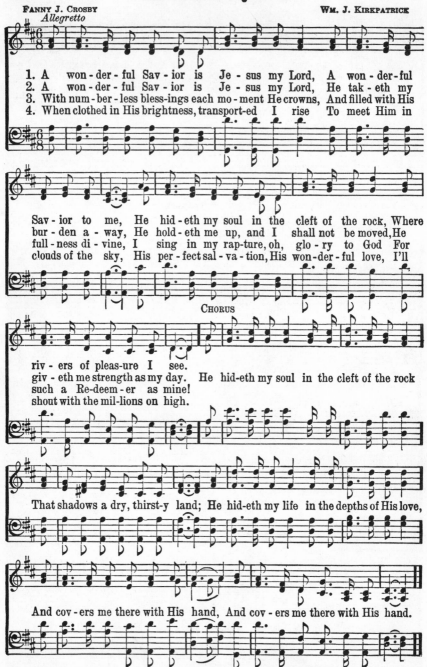

1. A won-der-ful Sav-ior is Je-sus my Lord, A won-der-ful
2. A won-der-ful Sav-ior is Je-sus my Lord, He tak-eth my
3. With num-ber-less bless-ings each mo-ment He crowns, And filled with His
4. When clothed in His brightness, transport-ed I rise To meet Him in

Sav-ior to me, He hid-eth my soul in the cleft of the rock, Where
bur-den a-way, He hold-eth me up, and I shall not be moved, He
full-ness di-vine, I sing in my rap-ture, oh, glo-ry to God For
clouds of the sky, His per-fect sal-va-tion, His won-der-ful love, I'll

riv-ers of pleas-ure I see.
giv-eth me strength as my day.
such a Re-deem-er as mine!
shout with the mil-lions on high.

CHORUS

He hid-eth my soul in the cleft of the rock

That shadows a dry, thirst-y land; He hid-eth my life in the depths of His love,

And cov-ers me there with His hand, And cov-ers me there with His hand.

256 He Included Me

REV. J. OATMAN, JR.   HAMP SEWELL

1. I am so hap-py in Christ to-day, That I go sing-ing a-long my way;
2. Glad-ly I read, "Who-so-ev-er may Come to the fountain of life to-day;"
3. Ever God's Spirit is saying, "Come!" Hear the Bride saying, "No longer roam;"
4. "Freely come drink," words the soul to thrill! O with what joy they my heart do fill!

Yes, I'm so hap-py to know and say, "Je-sus in-clud-ed me too."
But when I read it I al-ways say, "Je-sus in-clud-ed me too."
But I am sure while they're calling home, Je-sus in-clud-ed me too.
For when He said, "Who-so-ev-er will," Je-sus in-clud-ed me too.

CHORUS.

Je-sus in-clud-ed me, Yes, He in-clud-ed me, When the Lord said
"Who-so-ev-er," He in-clud-ed me; Je-sus in-clud-ed me, Yes, He in-
clud-ed me, When the Lord said "Who-so-ev-er," He included me. A-MEN.

257 He is Mine

C. Austin Miles   *Parts*   J. Lincoln Hall

Tenor and Basses, or all in unison, or solo.

1. There is a Shepherd who cares for His own, And He is mine; Nothing am I, He's a King on a throne, But He is mine; How He can love such a sin-ner as I, Tho' He is mine, I can-not fath-om tho' oft-en I try,
2. Je-sus left heaven my Sav-ior to be, And He is mine; I am not worth all He suffered for me, But He is mine; Tho' I'm not wor-thy He dwells in my heart, And He is mine; From Him I'll never, no, nev-er de-part,
3. There is a Com-fort-er come from a-bove, He, too, is mine, Com-ing to me to re-veal Je-sus' love, And that is mine; Shepherd and Savior, and Com-fort-er, too, They all are mine; That's why I know the old sto-ry is true,

Chorus

But He is mine. He is mine....... He
For He is mine.
They all are mine.   He is mine,

Tho' all un-wor-thy, I know He is mine, He

is mine; Tho' it is won-der-ful, yet it is true, That He is mine.
yes, He is mine;
is mine:

He is So Precious to Me

C. H. G.

CHAS. H. GABRIEL.

1. So pre-cious is Je-sus, my Sav-ior, my King, His praise all the day
2. He stood at my heart's door 'mid sunshine and rain, And pa-tient-ly wait-
3. I stand on the moun-tain of bless-ing at last, No cloud in the heav-
4. I praise Him be-cause He ap-point-ed a place Where, some day, thro' faith

long with rap-ture I sing; To Him in my weak-ness for strength I can cling,
ed an en-trance to gain; What shame that so long He en-treat-ed in vain,
ens a shad-ow to cast; His smile is up-on me, the val-ley is past,
in His won-der-ful grace, I know I shall see Him—shall look on His face,

CHORUS. *Faster.*

For He is so pre-cious to me. For He is so pre-cious to me, . . .
so pre-cious to me,

For He is so pre-cious to me; . . . . 'Tis Heav-en be-low
so pre-cious to me;

rit. . .

My Re-deem-er to know, For He is so pre-cious to me. A - MEN.

259　He's a Wonderful Saviour to Me

Virgil P. Brock

Blanche Kerr Brock

1. I was lost in sin but Je-sus res-cued me, He's a won-der-ful Sav-ior to me;
2. He's a Friend so true, so pa-tient and so kind, He's a won-der-ful Sav-ior to me; (So won-der-full)
3. He is al-ways near to com-fort and to cheer, He's a won-der-ful Sav-ior to me;
4. Dear-er grows the love of Je-sus day by day, He's a won-der-ful Sav-ior to me;

I was bound by fear but Je-sus set me free, He's a
Ev-'ry-thing I need in Him I al-ways find, He's a
He for-gives my sins, He dries my ev-'ry tear, He's a
Sweet-er is His grace while pressing on my way, He's a

won-der-ful Sav-ior to me.　So won-der-full!

Chorus

For He's a won-der-ful Sav-ior to me, won-der-full! He's a won-der-ful Sav-ior to me; won-der-full! I was lost in sin, but Je-sus took me in, He's a won-der-ful Sav-ior to me.

260   How Tedious and Tasteless the Hours

JOHN NEWTON   LEWIS EDSON

1. How te-dious and taste-less the hours When Je-sus no lon-ger I see!
2. His name yields the rich-est per-fume, And sweet-er than mu-sic His voice;
3. Con - tent with be-hold-ing His face, My all to His pleas-ure re-signed,
4. Dear Lord, if in-deed I am Thine, If Thou art my sun and my song,

Sweet prospects, sweet birds, and sweet flowers, Have all lost their sweetness to me.
His pres-ence dis-pers-es my gloom, And makes all with-in me re-joice:
No chang-es of sea-son or place Would make an-y change in my mind:
Say, why do I lan-guish and pine, And why are my win-ters so long?

The mid-sum-mer sun shines but dim; The fields strive in vain to look gay;
I should, were He al-ways thus nigh, Have noth-ing to wish or to fear;
While blest with a sense of His love, A pal-ace a toy would ap-pear;
Oh, drive these dark clouds from my sky; Thy soul-cheer-ing pres-ence re-store;

But when I am hap-py with Him, De-cem-ber's as pleas-ant as May.
No mor-tal so hap-py as I; My sum-mer would last all the year.
And pris-ons would pal-a-ces prove, If Je-sus would dwell with me there.
Or take me un-to Thee on high, Where win-ter and clouds are no more.

261 I Am His, and He Is Mine

Rev. WADE ROBINSON

Rev. J. MOUNTAIN

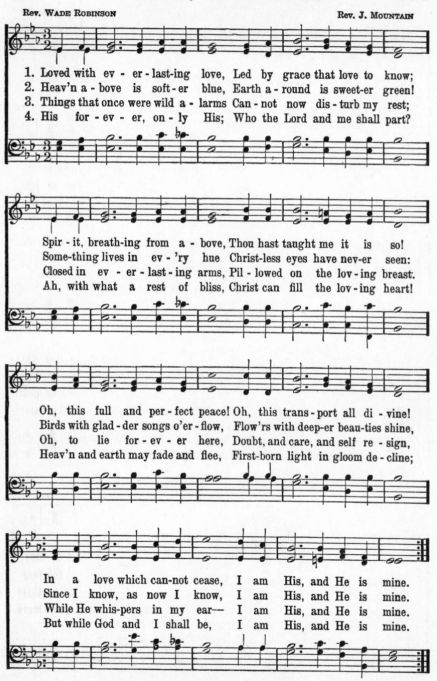

1. Loved with ev - er - last-ing love, Led by grace that love to know;
2. Heav'n a - bove is soft - er blue, Earth a - round is sweet-er green!
3. Things that once were wild a - larms Can - not now dis - turb my rest;
4. His for - ev - er, on - ly His; Who the Lord and me shall part?

Spir - it, breath-ing from a - bove, Thou hast taught me it is so!
Some-thing lives in ev - 'ry hue Christ-less eyes have nev-er seen:
Closed in ev - er - last - ing arms, Pil - lowed on the lov-ing breast.
Ah, with what a rest of bliss, Christ can fill the lov-ing heart!

Oh, this full and per - fect peace! Oh, this trans - port all di - vine!
Birds with glad - der songs o'er - flow, Flow'rs with deep-er beau-ties shine,
Oh, to lie for - ev - er here, Doubt, and care, and self re - sign,
Heav'n and earth may fade and flee, First-born light in gloom de - cline;

In a love which can-not cease, I am His, and He is mine.
Since I know, as now I know, I am His, and He is mine.
While He whis-pers in my ear— I am His, and He is mine.
But while God and I shall be, I am His, and He is mine.

262 Jesus, I Am Resting

JEAN SOPHIE PIGOTT

J. MOUNTAIN

1. Je - sus, I am rest-ing, rest-ing In the joy of what Thou art;
2. Sim - ply trust-ing Thee, Lord Je - sus, I be-hold Thee as Thou art,
3. Ev - er lift Thy face up - on me, As I work and wait for Thee;

CHO. —*Je - sus, I am rest - ing, rest - ing, In the joy of what Thou art,*

FINE.

I am find - ing out the great-ness Of Thy lov - ing heart.
And Thy love, so pure, so change-less, Sat - is - fies my heart;
Rest-ing 'neath Thy smile, Lord Je - sus, Earth's dark shad-ows flee.

I am find - ing out the great - ness Of Thy lov - ing heart.

p

Thou hast bid me gaze up - on Thee, And Thy beau-ty fills my soul,
Sat - is - fies its deep-est long-ings, Meets, sup-plies its ev - 'ry need,
Bright-ness of my Fa-ther's glo - ry, Sun-shine of my Fa-ther's face,

Cres.　　　　　　　　　　　　　*p*　　　　D.C. Chorus

For by Thy trans - form-ing pow - er, Thou hast made me whole.
Com - pass-eth me round with bless-ings: Thine is love in - deed!
Keep me ev - er trust-ing, rest - ing, Fill me with Thy grace.

263 Ye Must Be Born Again

W. T. SLEEPER

GEO. C. STEBBINS

1 A ru-ler once came to Je-sus by night, To ask Him the way of sal-
2. Ye children of men, at-tend to the word So sol-emn-ly ut-tered by
3. Oh, ye who would en-ter that glo-ri-ous rest, And sing with the ransomed the
4. A dear one in heaven thy heart yearns to see, At the beautiful gate may be

va - tion and light; The Mas - ter made an-swer in words true and plain,
Je - sus the Lord; And let not this mes-sage to you be in vain,
song of the blest; The life ev - er - last-ing if ye would ob - tain,
watching for thee; Then list to the note of this sol-emn re-frain,

CHORUS

"Ye must be born a - gain." . . "Ye must be born a-
a - gain.

gain, . . Ye must be born a - gain; . . I ver - i - ly,
a - gain, a - gain;

ver - i - ly say un - to thee, Ye must be born a - gain." . . .
a - gain.

264   I Know Whom I Have Believed

EL NATHAN

JAMES McGRANAHAN

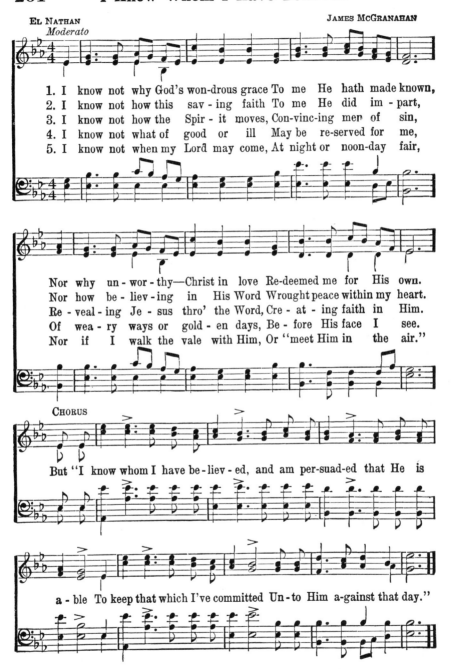

1. I know not why God's won-drous grace To me He hath made known,
2. I know not how this sav - ing faith To me He did im - part,
3. I know not how the Spir - it moves, Con-vinc-ing men of sin,
4. I know not what of good or ill May be re-served for me,
5. I know not when my Lord may come, At night or noon-day fair,

Nor why un - wor - thy—Christ in love Re-deemed me for His own.
Nor how be - liev-ing in His Word Wrought peace within my heart.
Re - veal-ing Je - sus thro' the Word, Cre - at - ing faith in Him.
Of wea - ry ways or gold - en days, Be - fore His face I see.
Nor if I walk the vale with Him, Or "meet Him in the air."

CHORUS

But "I know whom I have be - liev - ed, and am per-suad-ed that He is

a - ble To keep that which I've committed Un - to Him a-gainst that day."

265 I Need Jesus

GEORGE O. WEBSTER

CHAS. H. GABRIEL

1. I need Je-sus, my need I now con-fess; No friend like Him in times of
2. I need Je-sus, I need a friend like Him, A friend to guide when paths of
3. I need Je-sus, I need Him to the end; No one like Him, He is the

deep dis-tress; I need Je-sus, the need I glad-ly own; Tho' some may bear their
life are dim; I need Je-sus, when foes my soul assail; A - lone I know I
sin-ner's Friend; I need Je-sus, no oth-er friend will do; So constant, kind, so

CHORUS

load a-lone, Yet I need Je-sus. I need Je-sus, I need Je-sus,
can but fail, So I need Je-sus.
strong and true, Yes, I need Je-sus. I need Je-sus with me, I need Je-sus always,

I need Je-sus ev-'ry day; . . . Need Him in the sunshine hour,
ev-'ry day;

Need Him when the storm-clouds low'r; Ev'ry day a-long my way, Yes, I need Je-sus.

I Walk With the King

JAMES ROWE

B. D. ACKLEY

1. In sor-row I wan-dered, my spir-it op-prest, But now I am
hap-py—se-cure-ly I rest; From morn-ing till eve-ning glad
car-ols I sing, And this is the rea-son—I walk with the King.

2. For years in the fet-ters of sin I was bound, The world could not
help me—no com-fort I found; But now like the birds and the
sunbeams of spring, I'm free and re-joic-ing—I walk with the King.

3. O soul near de-spair in the low-lands of strife, Look up and let
Je-sus come in-to your life; The joy of sal-va-tion to
you He would bring—Come in-to the sun-light and walk with the King.

CHORUS

I walk with the King, hal-le-lu-jah! I walk with the King, praise His name!
No lon-ger I roam, my soul fa-ces home, I walk and I talk with the King.

267   I Was a Wandering Sheep

Horatius Bonar

J. Zundel

1. I was a wan-d'ring sheep, I did not love the fold,
2. The Shep-herd sought His sheep, The Fa-ther sought His child;
3. Je-sus my Shep-herd is; 'Twas He that loved my soul,
4. No more a wan-d'ring sheep, I love to be con-trolled,

I did not love my Shepherd's voice, I would not be con-trolled:
He fol-lowed me o'er vale and hill, O'er des-erts waste and wild:
'Twas He that washed me in His blood, 'Twas He that made me whole:
I love my ten-der Shepherd's voice, I love the peace-ful fold;

I was a way-ward child, I did not love my home,
He found me nigh to death, Fam-ished, and faint, and lone;
'Twas He that sought the lost, That found the wan-d'ring sheep;
No more a way-ward child, I seek no more to roam;

I did not love my Fa-ther's voice, I loved a-far to roam.
He bound me with the bands of love, He saved the wan-d'ring one.
'Twas He that bro't me to the fold, 'Tis He that still doth keep.
I love my heav'n-ly Fa-ther's voice, I love, I love His home!

In The Garden

268

C. A. M.

C. Austin Miles

1. I come to the gar-den a-lone, While the dew is still on the ros-es, And the voice I hear, Fall-ing on my ear, The Son of God dis-clos-es.
2. He speaks, and the sound of His voice Is so sweet the birds hush their sing-ing, And the mel-o-dy That He gave to me, With-in my heart is ring-ing.
3. I'd stay in the gar-den with Him Tho' the night a-round me be fall-ing, But He bids me go; Thro' the voice of woe His voice to me is call-ing.

Chorus

And He walks with me, and He talks with me, And He tells me I am His own; And the joy we share as we tar-ry there, None oth-er has ev-er known.

269 I've Found a Friend

J. G. SMALL

GEO. C. STEBBINS

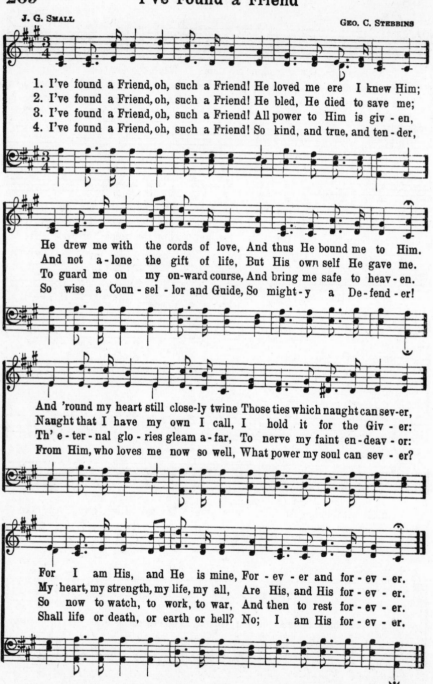

1. I've found a Friend, oh, such a Friend! He loved me ere I knew Him;
2. I've found a Friend, oh, such a Friend! He bled, He died to save me;
3. I've found a Friend, oh, such a Friend! All power to Him is giv - en,
4. I've found a Friend, oh, such a Friend! So kind, and true, and ten - der,

He drew me with the cords of love, And thus He bound me to Him.
And not a - lone the gift of life, But His own self He gave me.
To guard me on my on-ward course, And bring me safe to heav - en.
So wise a Coun - sel - lor and Guide, So might-y a De - fend - er!

And 'round my heart still close-ly twine Those ties which naught can sev-er,
Naught that I have my own I call, I hold it for the Giv - er:
Th' e - ter - nal glo - ries gleam a - far, To nerve my faint en - deav - or:
From Him, who loves me now so well, What power my soul can sev - er?

For I am His, and He is mine, For - ev - er and for - ev - er.
My heart, my strength, my life, my all, Are His, and His for - ev - er.
So now to watch, to work, to war, And then to rest for - ev - er.
Shall life or death, or earth or hell? No; I am His for - ev - er.

It is Mine

ELISHA A. HOFFMAN   WM. EDIE MARKS

1. God's a - bid - ing peace is in my soul to - day, Yes, I feel it
2. He has wrought in me a sweet and per-fect rest, In my rap-tured
3. He has giv - en me a nev - er - fail-ing joy, Oh, I have it
4. Oh, the love of God is com-fort-ing my soul, For His love is

now, yes, I feel it now; He has tak - en all my doubts and fears a-
heart I can feel it now; He each pass-ing mo-ment keeps me saved and
now! oh, I have it now! To His praise I will my ransomed pow'rs em-
mine, yes, His love is mine! Waves of joy and glad-ness o'er my spir - it

CHORUS

way, Tho' I can - not tell you how.
blest, Floods with light my heart and brow. It is mine, mine,
ploy, And re - new my grate-ful vow.
roll, Thrill-ing me with life di - vine. It is mine, this priceless treasure, ev-er

bless-ed be His name! He has giv - en peace, per-fect peace to me; It is

mine, mine, bless-ed be His name! Mine for all e - ter - ni - ty!
mine, this priceless treasure, ev-er

271   It Is Well with My Soul

H. G. SPAFFORD

P. P. BLISS

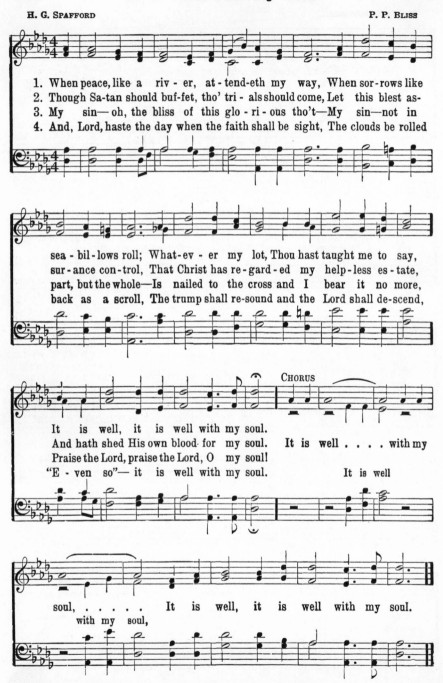

1. When peace, like a riv-er, at-tend-eth my way, When sor-rows like
2. Though Sa-tan should buf-fet, tho' tri-als should come, Let this blest as-
3. My sin—oh, the bliss of this glo-ri-ous tho't—My sin—not in
4. And, Lord, haste the day when the faith shall be sight, The clouds be rolled

sea-bil-lows roll; What-ev-er my lot, Thou hast taught me to say,
sur-ance con-trol, That Christ has re-gard-ed my help-less es-tate,
part, but the whole—Is nailed to the cross and I bear it no more,
back as a scroll, The trump shall re-sound and the Lord shall de-scend,

CHORUS

It is well, it is well with my soul.
And hath shed His own blood for my soul.   It is well .... with my
Praise the Lord, praise the Lord, O my soul!
"E-ven so"— it is well with my soul.   It is well

soul, ... It is well, it is well with my soul.
with my soul,

272 Jesus! Wonderful Name!

AVIS B. CHRISTIANSEN

C. L. DORRIS

1. Oh, won - der - ful name, how my heart thrills to hear it— The
2. When lost in my sin, 'twas the name of my Sav - ior That
3. I think of the cross where He suf - fered to save me, And

name of my ris - en Re - deem - er and King! It falls like the mu - sic of
ban - ished my fear and bro't peace to my soul; I'll sing it in glo - ry for-
oh, how my heart thrills with glo - ry di - vine To know it is life ev - er-

heav'n on my spir - it, And fills me with rap - ture di - vine while I sing.
ev - er and ev - er With joy while the years of e - ter - ni - ty roll.
last - ing He gave me, When, sin - less, He died for a soul such as mine.

CHORUS

Je - sus! won - der - ful name! Sweet - er than all the world to me;

Je - sus! ev - er the same—Now and thro' all e - ter - ni - ty.

273 **My Lord and I**

MRS. L. SHOREY

JOSEPH D. LITTLE

1. I have a Friend so pre - cious, So ver - y dear to me,
2. Some-times I'm faint and wea - ry, He knows that I am weak;
3. He knows how much I love Him, He knows I love Him well;
4. I tell Him all my sor - rows, I tell Him all my joys,
5. He knows how I am long - ing Some wea-ry soul to win,

He loves me with a ten-der love, He loves me faith-ful - ly;
And as He bids me lean on Him, His help I'll glad - ly seek;
But with what love He lov - eth me, My tongue can nev - er tell;
I tell Him all that pleas - es me, I tell Him what an - noys;
And so He bids me go and speak A lov - ing word for Him;

I could not live a - part from Him, I love to feel Him nigh;
He leads me in the path of light, Be-neath a sun - ny sky;
It is an ev - er - last-ing love In ev - er rich sup - ply;
He tells me what I ought to do, He tells me what to try;
He bids me tell His won-drous love, And why He came to die;

rit.

And so we dwell to - geth - er, My Lord and I.
And so we walk to - geth - er, My Lord and I.
And so we love to - geth - er, My Lord and I.
And so we talk to - geth - er, My Lord and I.
And so we work to - geth - er, My Lord and I.

274 I Belong to the King

IDA. L. REED

MAURICE A. CLIFTON

1. I be-long to the King, I'm a child of His love, I shall dwell in His
2. I be-long to the King, and He loves me I know, For His mer-cy and
3. I be-long to the King, and His prom-ise is sure, That we all shall be

pal-ace so fair; For He tells of its bliss in yon heav-en a-bove, And His
kindness, so free, Are un-ceas-ing-ly mine, where-so-ev-er I go, And my
gathered at last In His king-dom a-bove, by life's wa-ters so pure, When this

CHORUS

chil-dren in splen-dor shall share.
ref-uge un-fail-ing is He. I be-long to the King, I'm a
life with its tri-als is past.

child of His love, And He nev-er for-sak-eth His own; He will call me some

day to His pal-ace a-bove, I shall dwell by His glo-ri-fied throne.

275 Nothing Between

Words and Music by C. A. TINDLEY

Arr. by F. A. CLARK

1. Noth-ing be-tween my soul and the Sav-ior, Naught of this world's de-
2. Noth-ing be-tween, like world-ly pleas-ure, Hab-its of life though
3. Noth-ing be-tween, like pride or sta-tion, Self or friends shall
4. Noth-ing be-tween, e'en man-y hard tri-als, Tho' the whole world a-

lu-sive dream; I have re-nounced all sin-ful pleas-ure,
harm-less they seem, Must not my heart from Him e'er sev-er,
not in-ter-vene, Tho' it may cost me much trib-u-la-tion,
gainst me con-vene; Watching with prayer and much self-de-ni-al, I'll

Je-sus is mine; there's noth-ing be-tween.
He is my all; there's noth-ing be-tween.
I am re-solved; there's noth-ing be-tween.
tri-umph at last, with noth-ing be-tween.

CHORUS

Noth-ing be-tween my soul and the Sav-ior, So that His bless-ed face may be seen; Noth-ing pre-vent-ing the least of His fa-vor, Keep the way clear! Let nothing between.

276 Redeemed

FANNY J. CROSBY

WM. J. KIRKPATRICK

1. Redeemed—how I love to pro-claim it! Redeemed by the blood of the Lamb;
2. Redeemed and so happy in Je-sus, No language my rap-ture can tell;
3. I think of my bless-ed Re-deem-er, I think of Him all the day long;
4. I know I shall see in His beau-ty The King in whose law I de-light;

Redeemed thro' His in-fi-nite mer-cy, His child, and for-ev-er, I am.
I know that the light of His presence With me doth con-tin-ual-ly dwell.
I sing, for I can-not be si-lent; His love is the theme of my song.
Who lov-ing-ly guardeth my footsteps, And giv-eth me songs in the night.

CHORUS

Re-deemed, .. re-deemed, .. Redeemed by the blood of the Lamb;
re-deemed, re-deemed,

Re-deemed, .. re-deemed, .. His child, and for-ev-er, I am.
re-deemed, re-deemed,

277 Saved, Saved!

J. P. S.   J. P. SCHOLFIELD

1. I've found a friend who is all to me, His
2. He saves me from ev-ery sin and harm, Se-
3. When poor and need-y and all a-lone, In

love is ev-er true; . . . . . I love to tell how He
cures my soul each day; . . . . . I'm lean-ing strong on His
love He said to me, ... "Come un-to Me and I'll

lift-ed me And what His grace can do for you. . . .
might-y arm; I know He'll guide me all the way. . . .
lead you home, To live with Me e-ter-nal-ly." . . .

CHORUS

Saved . . . . by His power di-vine, Saved . . . . to new life sub-lime!
Saved by His power,   Saved to new life,

cres.   rit.

Life now is sweet and my joy is com-plete, For I'm saved, saved, saved!

Saved to the Uttermost

W. J. K.

WM. J. KIRKPATRICK

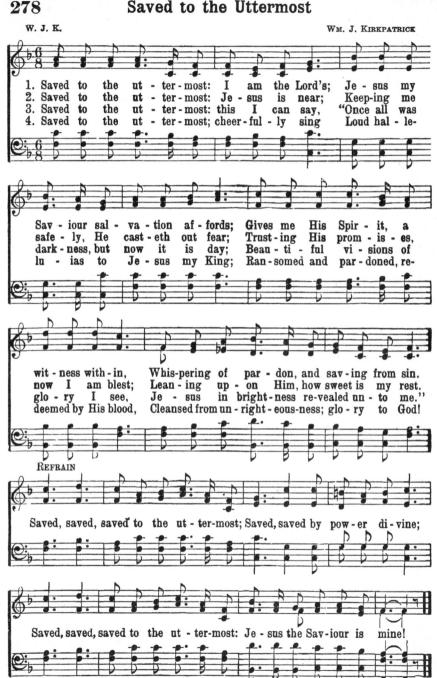

1. Saved to the ut-ter-most: I am the Lord's; Je-sus my
2. Saved to the ut-ter-most: Je-sus is near; Keep-ing me
3. Saved to the ut-ter-most: this I can say, "Once all was
4. Saved to the ut-ter-most; cheer-ful-ly sing Loud hal-le-

Sav-iour sal-va-tion af-fords; Gives me His Spir-it, a
safe-ly, He cast-eth out fear; Trust-ing His prom-is-es,
dark-ness, but now it is day; Beau-ti-ful vi-sions of
lu-ias to Je-sus my King; Ran-somed and par-doned, re-

wit-ness with-in, Whis-pering of par-don, and sav-ing from sin.
now I am blest; Lean-ing up-on Him, how sweet is my rest.
glo-ry I see, Je-sus in bright-ness re-vealed un-to me."
deemed by His blood, Cleansed from un-right-eous-ness; glo-ry to God!

REFRAIN

Saved, saved, saved to the ut-ter-most; Saved, saved by pow-er di-vine;

Saved, saved, saved to the ut-ter-most: Je-sus the Sav-iour is mine!

Since I Have Been Redeemed

E. O. E.

E. O. Excell

1. I have a song I love to sing, Since I have been re-deemed,
2. I have a Christ that sat-is-fies, Since I have been re-deemed,
3. I have a wit-ness bright and clear, Since I have been re-deemed,
4. I have a home pre-pared for me, Since I have been re-deemed,

Of my Re-deem-er, Sav-ior, King, Since I have been re-deemed.
To do His will my high-est prize, Since I have been re-deemed.
Dis-pel-ling ev-'ry doubt and fear, Since I have been re-deemed.
Where I shall dwell e-ter-nal-ly, Since I have been re-deemed.

Chorus.

Since I . . . . have been re-deemed, Since I have been re-
Since I have been redeemed, Since I have been redeemed,

deemed, I will glo-ry in His name; Since I . . . . . have been re-
Since I have been redeemed, Since

deemed, I will glo-ry in my Sav-ior's name.
I have been re-deemed,

280 Since Jesus Came Into My Heart

R. H. McDaniel

Chas. H. Gabriel

1. What a won-der-ful change in my life has been wrought Since Je-sus came
2. I have ceased from my wand'ring and go-ing a-stray, Since Je-sus came
3. I'm pos-sessed of a hope that is stead-fast and sure. Since Je-sus came
4. There's a light in the val-ley of death now for me, Since Je-sus came
5. I shall go there to dwell in that Cit-y, I know, Since Je-sus came

in-to my heart! I have light in my soul for which long I had sought,
in-to my heart! And my sins, which were man-y, are all washed a-way,
in-to my heart! And no dark clouds of doubt now my path-way ob-scure,
in-to my heart! And the gates of the Cit-y be-yond I can see,
in-to my heart! And I'm hap-py, so hap-py, as on-ward I go,

Chorus

Since Je-sus came in-to my heart!
Since Je-sus came in, came

Since Je-sus came in-to my
Since Je-sus came in-to my heart,

heart,
in-to my heart, Since Je-sus came in, came

Floods of joy o'er my
in-to my heart,

soul like the sea bil-lows roll, Since Je-sus came in-to my heart.

Still Sweeter Every Day

W. C. MARTIN

C. AUSTIN MILES

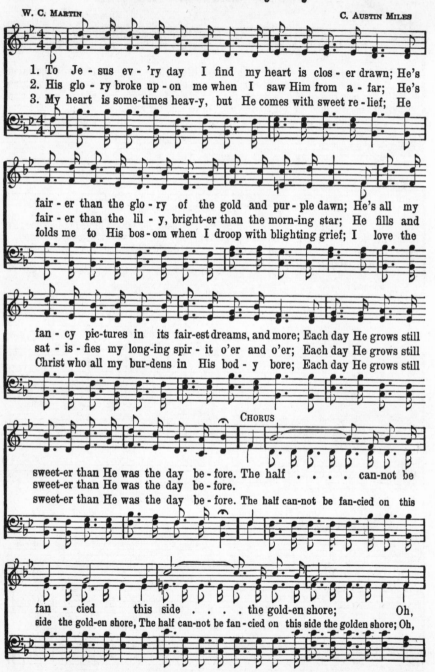

1. To Je-sus ev-'ry day I find my heart is clos-er drawn; He's
2. His glo-ry broke up-on me when I saw Him from a-far; He's
3. My heart is some-times heav-y, but He comes with sweet re-lief; He

fair-er than the glo-ry of the gold and pur-ple dawn; He's all my
fair-er than the lil-y, bright-er than the morn-ing star; He fills and
folds me to His bos-om when I droop with blighting grief; I love the

fan-cy pic-tures in its fair-est dreams, and more; Each day He grows still
sat-is-fies my long-ing spir-it o'er and o'er; Each day He grows still
Christ who all my bur-dens in His bod-y bore; Each day He grows still

CHORUS

sweet-er than He was the day be-fore. The half . . . . can-not be
sweet-er than He was the day be-fore.
sweet-er than He was the day be-fore. The half can-not be fan-cied on this

fan-cied this side . . . . the gold-en shore; Oh,
side the gold-en shore, The half can-not be fan-cied on this side the golden shore; Oh,

Still Sweeter Every Day

there . . . . He'll be still sweet-er than He ev-er was be-fore.
there He'll be still sweeter than He ev-er was be-fore, than He ev-er was be-fore.

282 Old-Time Power

P. R.

PAUL RADER

1. We are gath-ered for Thy bless-ing, We will wait up-on our God;
2. We will glo-ry in Thy pow-er, We will sing of won-drous grace;
3. Bring us low in prayer be-fore Thee, And with faith our souls in-spire,

We will trust in Him who loved us, And who bought us with His blood.
In our midst, as Thou hast prom-ised, Come, O come, and take Thy place.
Till we claim, by faith, the prom-ise Of the Ho-ly Ghost and fire.

CHORUS

Spir-it, now melt and move All of our hearts with love,

Breathe on us from a-bove With old-time pow'r.

283 Sweet Peace, the Gift of God's Love

P. P. B.

P. P. BILHORN

1. There comes to my heart one sweet strain, (sweet strain,) A glad and a joy-ous re-frain; (re-frain;) I sing it a-gain and a-gain, Sweet peace, the gift of God's love.

2. Thro' Christ on the cross peace was made, (was made.) My debt by His death was all paid; (all paid;) No oth-er foun-da-tion is laid For peace, the gift of God's love.

3. When Je-sus as Lord I had crowned, (had crowned,) My heart with this peace did a-bound; (a-bound;) In Him the rich bless-ing I found, Sweet peace, the gift of God's love.

4. In Je-sus for peace I a-bide, (a-bide,) And as I keep close to His side, (His side,) There's noth-ing but peace doth be-tide, Sweet peace, the gift of God's love.

CHORUS

Peace, peace, sweet peace! Won-der-ful gift from a-bove! (a-bove!)

cres.

Oh, won-der-ful, won-der-ful peace! Sweet peace, the gift of God's love!

284 The Haven of Rest

H. L. Gilmour

Geo. D. Moore

1. My soul in sad exile was out on life's sea, So
2. I yielded myself to His tender embrace, And
3. The song of my soul, since the Lord made me whole, Has
4. How precious the thought that we all may recline, Like
5. O come to the Savior, He patiently waits To

burdened with sin and distrest, Till I heard a sweet voice saying,
faith taking hold of the Word, My fetters fell off, and I
been the old story so blest, Of Jesus, who'll save whosoever
John the beloved and blest, On Jesus' strong arm, where no
save by His power divine; Come, anchor your soul in the

D. S.—The tempest may sweep o'er the

FINE.

"Make me your choice;" And I entered the "Haven of Rest!"
anchored my soul; The "Haven of Rest" is my Lord.
ever will have A home in the "Haven of Rest!"
tempest can harm,— Secure in the "Haven of Rest!"
"Haven of Rest," And say, "My Beloved is mine."

wild, stormy deep, In Jesus I'm safe evermore.

CHORUS

D. S.

I've anchored my soul in the "Haven of Rest," I'll sail the wide seas no more;

The Lily of the Valley

English Melody

1. I have found a friend in Je-sus, He's ev-'ry-thing to me, He's the
2. He all my griefs has tak-en, and all my sor-rows borne; In temp-
3. He will nev-er, nev-er leave me, nor yet for-sake me here, While I

fair-est of ten thou-sand to my soul; The Lil-y of the Val-ley,
ta-tion He's my strong and mighty tow'r; I have all for Him for-sak-en,
live by faith and do His bless-ed will; A wall of fire a-bout me,

D. S.—*Lil - y of the Val - ley,*
FINE.

in Him a-lone I see All I need to cleanse and make me ful-ly whole.
and all my i-dols torn From my heart, and now He keeps me by His pow'r.
I've noth-ing now to fear, With His man-na He my hun-gry soul shall fill.

the Bright and Morning Star, He's the fair-est of ten thou-sand to my soul.

In sor-row He's my com-fort, in troub-le He's my stay,
Though all the world for-sake me, and Sa-tan tempt me sore,
Then sweep-ing up to glo-ry to see His bless-ed face,

D. S.

He tells me ev-'ry care on Him to roll. He's the
Through Je-sus I shall safe-ly reach the goal. He's the
Where riv-ers of de-light shall ev-er roll. He's the

This is My Father's World

MALTBIE D. BABCOCK, 1901

Traditional English Melody
Arranged by S. F. L., 1915

1. This is my Fa-ther's world, And to my lis-t'ning ears, All
2. This is my Fa-ther's world, The birds their car-ols raise, The
3. This is my Fa-ther's world, O let me ne'er for-get That

na-ture sings, and round me rings The mu-sic of the spheres.
morn-ing light, the lil-y white, De-clare their Ma-ker's praise.
though the wrong seems oft so strong, God is the Rul-er yet.

This is my Fa-ther's world, I rest me in the thought Of
This is my Fa-ther's world, He shines in all that's fair; In the
This is my Fa-ther's world, The bat-tle is not done, Je- -

rocks and trees, of . . skies and seas—His hand the won-ders wrought.
rus-tling grass I . . hear Him pass, He speaks to me ev-'ry-where.
sus who died shall be sat-is-fied, And earth and heav'n be one. A-MEN.

Wonderful Peace

W. D. CORNELL. Alt.

W. G. COOPER

1. Far a-way in the depths of my spir-it to-night Rolls a
2. What a treas-ure I have in this won-der-ful peace, Bur-ied
3. I am rest-ing to-night in this won-der-ful peace, Rest-ing
4. And me-thinks when I rise to that Cit-y of peace, Where the
5. Ah! soul, are you here with-out com-fort or rest, March-ing

mel-o-dy sweet-er than psalm; In ce-les-tial-like strains it un-
deep in the heart of my soul; So se-cure that no pow-er can
sweet-ly in Je-sus' con-trol; For I'm kept from all dan-ger by
Au-thor of peace I shall see, That one strain of the song which the
down the rough pathway of time? Make Je-sus your friend ere the

ceas-ing-ly falls O'er my soul like an in-fi-nite calm.
mine it a-way, While the years of e-ter-ni-ty roll.
night and by day, And His glo-ry is flood-ing my soul.
ran-somed will sing, In that heav-en-ly king-dom shall be:
shad-ows grow dark; Oh, ac-cept this sweet peace so sub-lime.

CHORUS

Peace! peace! won-der-ful peace, Com-ing down from the Fa-ther a-bove; Sweep

o-ver my spir-it for-ev-er, I pray, In fath-om-less bil-lows of love.

Wonderful Peace

H. L.

HALDOR LILLENAS

1. Com - ing to Je - sus, my Sav - ior, I found Won - der - ful peace,
2. Peace like a riv - er, so deep and so broad, Won - der - ful peace,
3. Peace like a ho - ly and in - fi - nite calm, Won - der - ful peace,
4. Gone is the bat - tle that once raged with - in, Won - der - ful peace,

won - der - ful peace; Storms in their fu - ry may rage all a -
won - der - ful peace; Rest - ing my soul on the bos - om of
won - der - ful peace; Like to the strains of an e - ven - ing
won - der - ful peace; Je - sus has saved me and cleansed me from

REFRAIN

round, I have peace, sweet peace.
God, I have peace, sweet peace. Peace, peace, won - der - ful peace,
psalm, I have peace, sweet peace.
sin, I have peace, sweet peace.

Peace, peace, glo - ri - ous peace; Since my Re - deem - er has

ran - somed my soul, I have peace, sweet peace.......
won - der - ful peace.

289 Carry Your Cross With a Smile

INA DULEY OGDON

CHAS. H. GABRIEL

1. Tho' your heart may be heav-y with sor-row and care, You may
2. Let the well by the way-side that flows un-to all Strength im-do,
3. For the work that you faith-ful-ly, will-ing-ly do, You shall

oth-ers to glad-ness be-guile, If a face like the light of the
part for each step of the mile; Let your faith the great prom-is-es
reap a re-ward aft-er while; On-ly grace in your serv-ice can

CHORUS

morning you wear, And car-ry your cross with a smile! Car-ry your cross with a
oft-en re-call, And car-ry your cross with a smile!
glo-ri-fy you, So car-ry your cross with a smile! Car-ry your cross

smile,.... Car-ry your cross with a smile;... You may oth-ers from
with a smile, Car-ry your cross with a smile;

sad-ness to glad-ness be-guile, If you car-ry your cross with a smile!

290 Get God's Sunshine

R. H.

ROBERT HARKNESS

1. Trust - ing Je - sus, won - der - ful Guide, In His keep - ing
2. Won - drous prom - ise He will ful - fill, Glad - ly do - ing
3. Friend of sin - ners, ev - er the same, Will - ing Sav - ior,

safe - ly a - bide; Joys e - ter - nal He will im - part,
His ho - ly will; Peace un - end - ing He will im - part,
praise His dear name, Full for - give-ness He will im - part,

CHORUS

Get God's sun-shine in - to your heart.
Get God's sun-shine in - to your heart. Get God's sunshine in - to your heart,
Get God's sun-shine in - to your heart.

Get God's sun-shine in - to your heart; It will cheer you all the day, Drive the

gloom of life a - way, If you get God's sun-shine in - to your heart.

291 Heavenly Sunlight

Rev. H. J. Zelley

G. H. Cook

1. Walk-ing in sun-light, all of my jour-ney; O - ver the moun-tains,
2. Shad-ows a - round me, shad-ows a - bove me, Nev-er con - ceal my
3. In the bright sun-light, ev - er re - joic-ing, Press-ing my way to

thro' the deep vale; Je - sus has said "I'll nev - er for - sake thee,"
Sav - iour and Guide; He is the light, in Him is no dark-ness;
man-sions a - bove; Sing-ing His prais - es glad - ly I'm walk-ing,

Prom-ise di - vine that nev - er can fail.
Ev - er I'm walk-ing close to His side.
Walk-ing in sun - light, sun-light of love.

CHORUS

Heav-en - ly sun - light, heav-en - ly sun-light, Flood-ing my soul with glo - ry di - vine: Hal-le-lu - jah, I am re-joic-ing, Sing-ing His prais-es, Je - sus is mine.

292 I'm Happy In Jesus Today

C. HOUSTON GREENE

C. WESLEY HICKS

1. I have a friend whose life is sweet to me, I'm hap-py in
2. He bore my bur-dens all up-on the tree, I'm hap-py in
3. His grace to me grows sweet-er ev-'ry day, I'm hap-py in

Je-sus to-day, (to-day); His blood doth keep me clean and make me free,
Je-sus to-day, (to-day); His pre-cious life He gave to par-don me,
Je-sus to-day, (to-day); It helps to keep me from the e-vil way,

I'm hap-py in Je-sus to-day.

CHORUS

I'm hap-py in Je-sus to-
so

day, I'm hap-py in Je-sus to-day; For Je-sus goes
hap-py to-day, so hap-py to-day;

with me all the way, I'm hap-py in Je-sus to-day.

293 In the Service of the King

A. H. ACKLEY

BENTLEY D. ACKLEY

1. I am hap-py in the serv-ice of the King, I am
2. I am hap-py in the serv-ice of the King, I am
3. I am hap-py in the serv-ice of the King, I am
4. I am hap-py in the serv-ice of the King, I am

hap-py, oh, so hap-py; I have peace and joy that
hap-py, oh, so hap-py; Thro' the sun-shine and the
hap-py, oh, so hap-py; To His guid-ing hand for-
hap-py, oh, so hap-py; All that I pos-sess to

noth-ing else can bring, In the serv-ice of the King.
shad-ow I can sing, In the serv-ice of the King.
ev-er I will cling, In the serv-ice of the King.
Him I glad-ly bring, In the serv-ice of the King.

CHORUS

In the serv-ice of the King, Ev-'ry tal-ent I will bring;

I have peace and joy and bless-ing In the serv-ice of the King.

Joy in Serving Jesus

Rev. Oswald J. Smith

B. D. Ackley

1. There is joy in serv-ing Je-sus, As I jour-ney on my way,
2. There is joy in serv-ing Je-sus, Joy that tri-umphs o-ver pain;
3. There is joy in serv-ing Je-sus, As I walk a-lone with God;
4. There is joy in serv-ing Je-sus, Joy a-mid the dark-est night,

Joy that fills the heart with prais-es, Ev-'ry hour and ev-'ry day.
Fills my soul with heav-en's mu-sic, Till I join the glad re-frain.
'Tis the joy of Christ, my Sav-iour, Who the path of suf-f'ring trod.
For I've learned the wondrous se-cret, And I'm walk-ing in the light.

CHORUS

There is joy, joy, Joy in serv-ing Je-sus, Joy that throbs with-

in my heart; Ev-'ry mo-ment, ev-'ry hour, As I draw up-

on His pow'r, There is joy, joy, Joy that nev-er shall de-part.

295 Jesus Is the Joy of Living

A. H. A.

Rev. A. H. Ackley

1. I have found a won-drous Sav - iour, Je - sus Christ, The Soul's De-light;
2. Life is grow-ing rich with beau - ty, Toil has lost its wea - ry strain,
3. Heav'nly wis-dom He pro - vides me, Grace to keep my spir - it free;
4. O what splen-dor, O what glo - ry, O what match-less pow'r di - vine,

Ev - 'ry bless-ing of His fa - vor Fills my heart with hope so bright.
Now a ha - lo crowns each du - ty, And I sing a glad re - frain.
In His own sweet way He guides me When the path I can - not see.
Is the Christ of Gos - pel sto - ry, Christ, the Sav-iour, who is mine.

CHORUS

Je - sus is the Joy of Liv - ing, He's the King of Life to me; .....
of Life to me;

Un - to Him my all I'm giv - ing, His for - ev - er-more to be (to be).

I will do what He com-mands me, An - y-where He leads I'll go (I'll go);

Jesus Is the Joy of Living

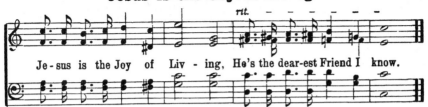

Je-sus is the Joy of Liv - ing, He's the dear-est Friend I know.

296 When We All Get to Heaven

E. E. HEWITT

Mrs. J. G. WILSON

1. Sing the won-drous love of Je-sus, Sing His mer-cy and His grace;
2. While we walk the pil-grim pathway, Clouds will o - ver-spread the sky;
3. Let us then be true and faith-ful, Trust-ing, serv-ing ev - 'ry day;
4. On - ward to the prize be-fore us! Soon His beau-ty we'll be - hold;

In the man-sions bright and blessed, He'll pre-pare for us a place.
But when trav'ling days are o - ver, Not a shad-ow, not a sigh.
Just one glimpse of Him in glo-ry Will the toils of life re - pay.
Soon the pearl - y gates will o - pen, We shall tread the streets of gold.

for us a place.

CHORUS

When we all get to heaven, What a day of re-joicing that will be!
When we all What a day of re-joicing that will be!

When we all see Je-sus, We'll sing and shout the vic-to-ry..........
When we all and shout the vic-to-ry.

297 Joy Unspeakable

B. E. W.
Lively

B. E. WARREN

1. I have found His grace is all com-plete, He sup-pli-eth ev-'ry need;
2. I have found the pleas-ure I once craved, It is joy and peace with-in;
3. I have found that hope so bright and clear, Liv-ing in the realm of grace;
4. I have found the joy no tongue can tell, How its waves of glo-ry roll!

While I sit and learn at Je-sus' feet, I am free, yes, free in-deed.
What a won-drous bless-ing! I am saved From the aw-ful gulf of sin.
Oh, the Sav-ior's pres-ence is so near, I can see His smil-ing face.
It is like a great o'er-flow-ing well, Springing up with-in my soul.

CHORUS

It is joy un-speak-a-ble and full of glo-ry, Full of glo-ry, full of glo-ry; It is joy un-speak-a-ble and full of glo-ry, Oh, the half has nev-er yet been told.

Let the Joy Overflow

E. E. HEWITT

S. B. JACKSON

1. There's a clear fountain flowing From the bright throne above, And its waters are
2. Man - y hearts need the story—Are a-thirst for His grace; Go to them with His
3. Be our lives free-ly yield-ed To the Sav-ior's command; By His care ev-er

glow-ing With the sunshine of love; Take the blest con-so - la - tion, Which the
glo - ry Shin-ing out from your face; Tell of Je - sus your Sav - ior! If His
shield-ed And up-held by His hand; In the path-ways of sad-ness, Sweet-est

Lord will be - stow, Take the cup of sal - va-tion—Let the joy o - ver-flow.
mer-cies you know, Show the light of His fa-vor—Let the joy o - ver-flow.
lil - ies may grow; Let us sow seeds of gladness—Let the joy o - ver-flow.

CHORUS

O the joy! . . . . With this wondrous salvation Be our hearts all a-glow;
O the joy!

O the joy! . . . . Let the bless-ing run o-ver, And joy o - ver - flow.
O the joy!

299 My Burdens Rolled Away

M. A. S.

Mrs. Minnie A. Steele

1. I re-mem-ber when my bur-dens rolled a-way, I had car-ried them for
2. I re-mem-ber when my bur-dens rolled a-way, That I feared would nev-er
3. I re-mem-ber when my bur-dens rolled a-way, That had hin-dered me for
4. I am sing-ing since my bur-dens rolled a-way, There's a song with-in my

years, night and day; When I sought the bless-ed Lord, and I took Him at His
leave night or day; Je-sus showed to me the loss, so I left them at the
years, night and day; As I sought the throne of grace, just a glimpse of Je-sus'
heart night and day; I am liv-ing for my King, and with joy I shout and

CHORUS

word, Then at once all my bur-dens rolled a-way. Rolled a-way, rolled a-
cross; I was glad when my bur-dens rolled a-way.
face, And I knew that my bur-dens could not stay.
sing Hal-le-lu-jah! all my bur-dens rolled a-way.

Rolled a-way,

way, Rolled a-way, I am hap-py since my bur-dens rolled a-way; Rolled a-
since my burdens rolled away;

way, rolled a-way, I am hap-py since my burdens rolled a-way.
Rolled a-way, rolled a-way,

Ring the Bells of Heaven

W. O. CUSHING

G. F. ROOT

Joyfully

1. Ring the bells of heav - en! there is joy to - day, For a soul, re-
2. Ring the bells of heav - en! there is joy to - day, For the wan-derer
3. Ring the bells of heav - en! spread the feast to - day! An - gels, swell the

turn - ing from the wild! See! the Fa-ther meets him out up - on the way,
now is rec - on - ciled; Yes, a soul is res - cued from his sin - ful way,
glad tri - um-phant strain! Tell the joy - ful ti dings, bear it far a - way!

CHORUS

Wel - com-ing His wea - ry, wandering child.
And is born a - new a ran-somed child.   Glo - ry! glo - ry! how the
For a pre-cious soul is born a - gain.

an-gels sing; Glo - ry! glo - ry! How the loud harps ring! 'Tis the ran-somed

ar - my, like a might-y sea, Peal-ing forth the an-them of the free.

301 Rejoice, Ye Pure in Heart

EDWARD H. PLUMPTRE

ARTHUR H. MESSITER

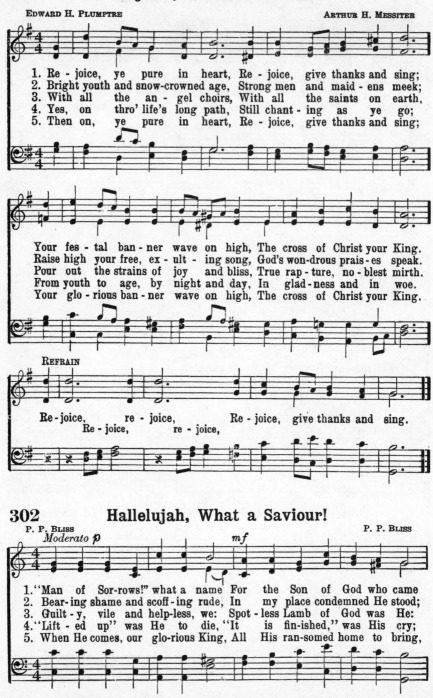

1. Re - joice, ye pure in heart, Re - joice, give thanks and sing;
2. Bright youth and snow-crowned age, Strong men and maid - ens meek;
3. With all the an - gel choirs, With all the saints on earth,
4. Yes, on thro' life's long path, Still chant - ing as ye go;
5. Then on, ye pure in heart, Re - joice, give thanks and sing;

Your fes - tal ban - ner wave on high, The cross of Christ your King.
Raise high your free, ex - ult - ing song, God's won-drous prais - es speak.
Pour out the strains of joy and bliss, True rap - ture, no - blest mirth.
From youth to age, by night and day, In glad - ness and in woe.
Your glo - rious ban - ner wave on high, The cross of Christ your King.

REFRAIN

Re - joice, re - joice, Re - joice, give thanks and sing.
Re - joice, re - joice,

302 Hallelujah, What a Saviour!

P. P. BLISS

P. P. BLISS

Moderato **p**   *mf*

1. "Man of Sor-rows!" what a name For the Son of God who came
2. Bear-ing shame and scoff-ing rude, In my place condemned He stood;
3. Guilt - y, vile and help-less, we: Spot - less Lamb of God was He:
4. "Lift - ed up" was He to die, "It is fin-ished," was His cry;
5. When He comes, our glo-rious King, All His ran-somed home to bring,

Hallelujah, What a Savior!

Ru - ined sin - ners to re-claim! Hal - le - lu - jah! what a Sav - ior!
Sealed my par - don with His blood; Hal - le - lu - jah! what a Sav - ior!
"Full a - tone-ment!" can it be? Hal - le - lu - jah! what a Sav - ior!
Now in heav'n ex - alt - ed high; Hal - le - lu - jah! what a Sav - ior!
Then a - new this song we'll sing: Hal - le - lu - jah! what a Sav - ior!

303 O Thou, In Whose Presence

JOSEPH SWAIN

FREEMAN LEWIS

1. O Thou, in whose pres - ence my soul takes de - light, On
2. Where dost Thou, dear Shep - herd, re - sort with thy sheep, To
3. Oh, why should I wan - der, an al - ien from Thee, Or
4. He looks! and the thou - sands of an - gels re - joice, And
5. Dear Shep - herd! I hear, and will fol - low Thy call; I

whom in af - flic - tion I call, My com - fort by day and my
feed them in pas - tures of love; Say, why in the val - ley of
cry in the des - ert for bread? Thy foes will re - joice when my
myr - i - ads wait for His word; He speaks! and e - ter - ni - ty
know the sweet sound of Thy voice; Re - store and de - fend me, for

song in the night, My hope, my sal - va - tion, my all!
death should I weep, Or a - lone in this wil - der-ness rove?
sor - rows they see, And smile at the tears I have shed.
filled with His voice, Re - ech - oes the praise of the Lord.
Thou art my all, And in Thee I will ev - er re - joice;

Singing Glory!

will I now o-bey, And all the time I'm sing-ing glo-ry!

305　I Would Be True

Howard Arnold Walter
Author of 3d stanza unknown

Joseph Yates Peek

1. I would be true, for there are those who trust me; I would be
2. I would be friend of all—the foe, the friend-less; I would be
3. I would be prayer-ful thru each bus-y mo-ment; I would be

pure, for there are those who care; I would be strong, for
giv-ing, and for-get the gift; I would be hum-ble,
con-stant-ly in touch with God; I would be tuned to

there is much to suf-fer; I would be brave, for there is
for I know my weak-ness; I would look up, and laugh, and
hear His slight-est whis-per; I would have faith to keep the

much to dare; I would be brave, for there is much to dare.
love, and lift; I would look up, and laugh, and love, and lift.
path Christ trod; I would have faith to keep the path Christ trod.

Stepping In the Light

E. E. HEWITT

WM. J. KIRKPATRICK

1. Try-ing to walk in the steps of the Sav-ior, Try-ing to fol-low our
2. Press-ing more close-ly to Him who is lead-ing, When we are tempted to
3. Walk-ing in foot-steps of gen-tle for-bear-ance, Foot-steps of faith-ful-ness,
4. Try-ing to walk in the steps of the Sav-ior, Up-ward, still upward we'll

Sav-ior and King; Shap-ing our lives by His bless-ed ex-am-ple,
turn from the way; Trust-ing the arm that is strong to de-fend us,
mer-cy and love, Look-ing to Him for the grace free-ly prom-ised,
fol-low our Guide; When we shall see Him, "the King in His beau-ty,"

CHORUS

Hap-py, how hap-py, the songs that we bring.
Hap-py, how hap-py, our prais-es each day. How beau-ti-ful to walk in the
Hap-py, how hap-py, our jour-ney a-bove.
Hap-py, how hap-py, our place at His side.

steps of the Sav-ior, Stepping in the light, Step-ping in the light; How

beau-ti-ful to walk in the steps of the Sav-ior, Led in paths of light.

307 Sunlight

J. W. Van DeVenter

W. S. Weeden

1. I wan-dered in the shades of night, Till Je - sus came to me,
2. Tho' clouds may gath - er in the sky, And bil - lows round me roll,
3. While walk-ing in the light of God, I sweet com-mun-ion find;
4. I cross the wide - ex - tend - ed fields, I jour - ney o'er the plain,
5. Soon I shall see Him as He is, The light that came to me,

And with the sun - light of His love Bid all my dark - ness flee.
How - ev - er dark the world may be, I've sun - light in my soul.
I press with ho - ly vig - or on, And leave the world be - hind.
And in the sun - light of His love I reap the gold - en grain.
Be - hold the bright - ness of His face, Thro'-out e - ter - ni - ty.

CHORUS

Sun-light, sun - light in my soul to - day, Sun-light, sun-light
to - day, yes,

all a - long the way; Since the Sav - iour found me,
nar - row way;

Took a-way my sin, I have had the sun-light of His love with - in.
load of sin;

Sunshine In the Soul

E. E. HEWITT

JNO. R. SWENEY

1. There's sun-shine in my soul to-day, More glo - ri - ous and bright
2. There's mu - sic in my soul to-day, A car - ol to my King,
3. There's springtime in my soul to-day, For, when the Lord is near,
4. There's glad-ness in my soul to-day, And hope and praise and love,

Than glows in an - y earth-ly sky, For Je - sus is my light.
And Je - sus, lis - ten-ing, can hear The songs I can-not sing.
The dove of peace sings in my heart, The flow'rs of grace ap - pear.
For bless-ings which He gives me now, For joys "laid up" a - bove.

REFRAIN

O there's sun - - - shine, bless-ed sun - - - shine,
O there's sun-shine in the soul, bless - ed sun-shine in the soul,

When the peace-ful, hap - py mo-ments roll; When
hap - py mo-ments roll;

Je - sus shows His smil - ing face, There is sun-shine in the soul.

309 He Keeps Me Singing

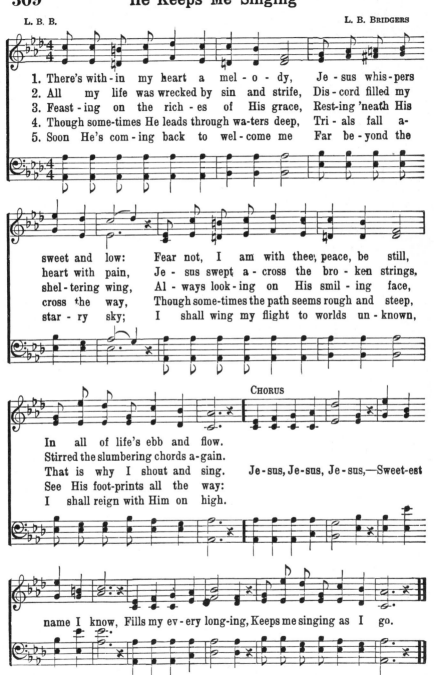

L. B. B.

L. B. BRIDGERS

1. There's with-in my heart a mel-o-dy, Je-sus whis-pers
2. All my life was wrecked by sin and strife, Dis-cord filled my
3. Feast-ing on the rich-es of His grace, Rest-ing 'neath His
4. Though some-times He leads through wa-ters deep, Tri-als fall a-
5. Soon He's com-ing back to wel-come me Far be-yond the

sweet and low: Fear not, I am with thee, peace, be still,
heart with pain, Je-sus swept a-cross the bro-ken strings,
shel-tering wing, Al-ways look-ing on His smil-ing face,
cross the way, Though some-times the path seems rough and steep,
star-ry sky; I shall wing my flight to worlds un-known,

Chorus

In all of life's ebb and flow.
Stirred the slumbering chords a-gain.
That is why I shout and sing. Je-sus, Je-sus, Je-sus,—Sweet-est
See His foot-prints all the way:
I shall reign with Him on high.

name I know, Fills my ev-ery long-ing, Keeps me singing as I go.

310 Beulah Land

EDGAR PAGE

JNO. R. SWENEY

1. I've reached the land of corn and wine, And all its rich-es free-ly mine;
2. My Sav-ior comes and walks with me, And sweet com-mun-ion here have we;
3. A sweet per-fume up-on the breeze Is borne from ev-er-ver-nal trees,
4. The zeph-yrs seem to float to me, Sweet sounds of Heaven's mel-o-dy,

Here shines undimmed one bliss-ful day, For all my night has passed a-way.
He gen-tly leads me by His hand, For this is Heav-en's bor-der-land.
And flow'rs, that nev-er-fad-ing grow, Where streams of life for-ev-er flow.
As an-gels with the white-robed throng Join in the sweet Re-demp-tion song.

CHORUS

O Beu-lah Land, sweet Beu-lah Land, As on thy high-est mount I stand,

I look a-way a-cross the sea, Where mansions are pre-pared for me, And

view the shin-ing glo-ry-shore,—My Heav'n, my home for-ev-er-more!

Blessed Assurance

FANNY J. CROSBY

Mrs. J. F. KNAPP

1. Bless-ed as-sur-ance, Je-sus is mine! Oh, what a fore-taste of
2. Per-fect sub-mis-sion, per-fect de-light, Vi-sions of rap-ture now
3. Per-fect sub-mis-sion, all is at rest, I in my Sav-iour am

glo-ry di-vine! Heir of sal-va-tion, pur-chase of God,
burst on my sight; An-gels de-scend-ing, bring from a-bove
hap-py and blest; Watch-ing and wait-ing, look-ing a-bove,

CHORUS

Born of His Spir-it, washed in His blood.
Ech-oes of mer-cy, whis-pers of love. This is my sto-ry,
Filled with His good-ness, lost in His love.

this is my song, Prais-ing my Sav-iour all the day long; This is my

sto-ry, this is my song, Prais-ing my Sav-iour all the day long.

312 **Security**

LINA SANDELL. (Swedish)
Tr. Composite

Swedish

1. More se - cure is no one ev - er Than the
2. God His own doth tend and nour - ish, In His
3. Nei - ther life nor death can ev - er From the
4. Lit - tle flock, to joy then yield thee! Ja - cob's
5. What He takes or what He gives us Shows the

loved ones of the Sav - ior; Not yon star on high a -
ho - ly courts they flour - ish; Like a fa - ther kind He
Lord His chil - dren sev - er; For His love and deep com -
God will ev - er shield thee; Rest se - cure with this De -
Fa - ther's love so pre - cious; We may trust His pur - pose

bid - ing, Nor the bird in home - nest hid - ing.
spares them, In His lov - ing arms He bears them.
pas - sion Com - forts them in trib - u - la - tion.
fend - er, At His will all foes sur - ren - der.
whol - ly— 'Tis His chil - dren's wel - fare sole - ly.

313 **Dear Lord and Father of Mankind**

JOHN G. WHITTIER

FREDERICK C. MAKER

1. Dear Lord and Fa - ther of man - kind, For - give our fe - v'rish
2. In sim - ple trust like theirs who heard, Be - side the Syr - ian
3. O Sab - bath rest by Gal - i - lee! O calm of hills a -
4. Drop thy still dews of qui - et - ness, Till all our striv - ings
5. Breathe thro' the heats of our de - sire Thy cool - ness and thy

Dear Lord and Father of Mankind

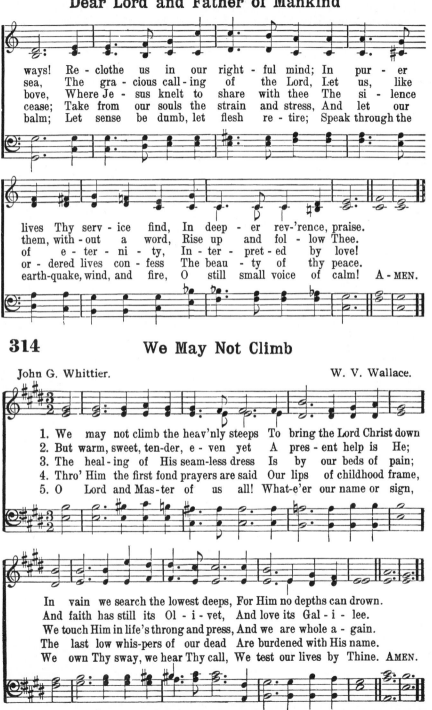

ways! Re - clothe us in our right - ful mind; In pur - er
sea, The gra - cious call - ing of the Lord, Let us, like
bove, Where Je - sus knelt to share with thee The si - lence
cease; Take from our souls the strain and stress, And let our
balm; Let sense be dumb, let flesh re - tire; Speak through the

lives Thy serv - ice find, In deep - er rev-'rence, praise.
them, with - out a word, Rise up and fol - low Thee.
of e - ter - ni - ty, In - ter - pret - ed by love!
or - dered lives con - fess The beau - ty of thy peace.
earth-quake, wind, and fire, O still small voice of calm! A - MEN.

314   We May Not Climb

John G. Whittier.   W. V. Wallace.

1. We may not climb the heav'nly steeps To bring the Lord Christ down
2. But warm, sweet, ten-der, e - ven yet A pres - ent help is He;
3. The heal - ing of His seam-less dress Is by our beds of pain;
4. Thro' Him the first fond prayers are said Our lips of childhood frame,
5. O Lord and Mas - ter of us all! What-e'er our name or sign,

In vain we search the lowest deeps, For Him no depths can drown.
And faith has still its Ol - i - vet, And love its Gal - i - lee.
We touch Him in life's throng and press, And we are whole a - gain.
The last low whis-pers of our dead Are burdened with His name.
We own Thy sway, we hear Thy call, We test our lives by Thine. AMEN.

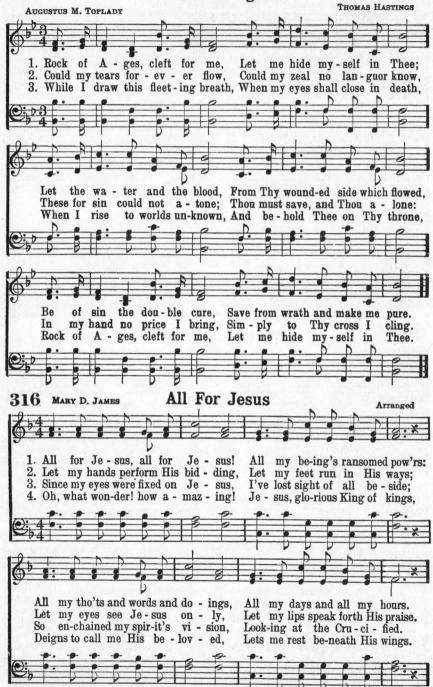

315 Rock of Ages

AUGUSTUS M. TOPLADY

THOMAS HASTINGS

1. Rock of A - ges, cleft for me, Let me hide my - self in Thee;
2. Could my tears for - ev - er flow, Could my zeal no lan - guor know,
3. While I draw this fleet - ing breath, When my eyes shall close in death,

Let the wa - ter and the blood, From Thy wound-ed side which flowed,
These for sin could not a - tone; Thou must save, and Thou a - lone:
When I rise to worlds un-known, And be - hold Thee on Thy throne,

Be of sin the dou - ble cure, Save from wrath and make me pure.
In my hand no price I bring, Sim - ply to Thy cross I cling.
Rock of A - ges, cleft for me, Let me hide my - self in Thee.

316 All For Jesus

MARY D. JAMES

Arranged

1. All for Je - sus, all for Je - sus! All my be-ing's ransomed pow'rs:
2. Let my hands perform His bid - ding, Let my feet run in His ways;
3. Since my eyes were fixed on Je - sus, I've lost sight of all be - side;
4. Oh, what won-der! how a - maz - ing! Je - sus, glo-rious King of kings,

All my tho'ts and words and do - ings, All my days and all my hours.
Let my eyes see Je - sus on - ly, Let my lips speak forth His praise.
So en-chained my spir-it's vi - sion, Look-ing at the Cru - ci - fied.
Deigns to call me His be - lov - ed, Lets me rest be-neath His wings.

All For Jesus

All for Je-sus! all for Je - sus! All my days and all my hours; hours.
All for Je-sus! all for Je - sus! Let my lips speak forth His praise; praise.
All for Je-sus! all for Je - sus! Look-ing at the Cru - ci - fied; fied.
All for Je-sus! all for Je - sus! Rest-ing now beneath His wings; wings.

317 'Tis So Sweet to Trust in Jesus

LOUISA M. R. STEAD

WM. J. KIRKPATRICK

1. 'Tis so sweet to trust in Je - sus, Just to take Him at His Word;
2. O how sweet to trust in Je - sus, Just to trust His cleans-ing blood;
3. Yes, 'tis sweet to trust in Je - sus, Just from sin and self to cease;
4. I'm so glad I learned to trust Thee, Pre-cious Je - sus, Sav - ior, Friend;

Just to rest up - on His prom-ise; Just to know, "Thus saith the Lord."
Just in sim - ple faith to plunge me 'Neath the heal - ing, cleans-ing flood!
Just from Je - sus sim - ply tak - ing Life and rest, and joy and peace.
And I know that Thou art with me, Wilt be with me to the end.

CHORUS

Je - sus, Je - sus, how I trust Him! How I've proved Him o'er and o'er!

Je - sus, Je - sus, pre-cious Je - sus! O for grace to trust Him more!

Blessed Quietness

MANIE PAYNE FERGUSON

W. S. MARSHALL
Adapted by JAMES M. KIRK

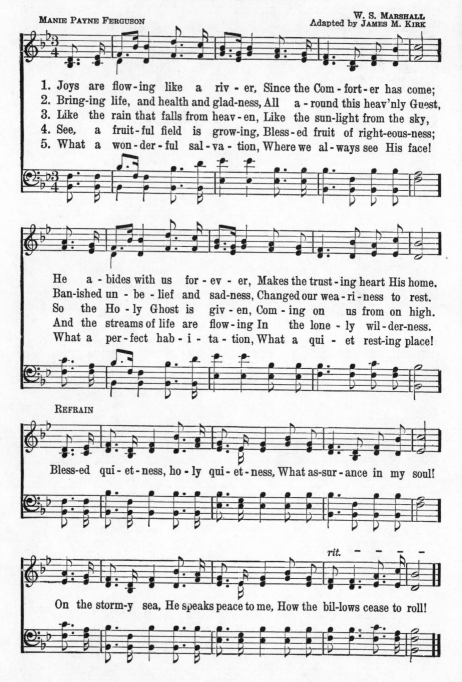

1. Joys are flow-ing like a riv-er, Since the Com-fort-er has come;
2. Bring-ing life, and health and glad-ness, All a-round this heav'nly Guest,
3. Like the rain that falls from heav-en, Like the sun-light from the sky,
4. See, a fruit-ful field is grow-ing, Bless-ed fruit of right-eous-ness;
5. What a won-der-ful sal-va-tion, Where we al-ways see His face!

He a-bides with us for-ev-er, Makes the trust-ing heart His home.
Ban-ished un-be-lief and sad-ness, Changed our wea-ri-ness to rest.
So the Ho-ly Ghost is giv-en, Com-ing on us from on high.
And the streams of life are flow-ing In the lone-ly wil-der-ness.
What a per-fect hab-i-ta-tion, What a qui-et rest-ing place!

REFRAIN

Bless-ed qui-et-ness, ho-ly qui-et-ness, What as-sur-ance in my soul!

rit.

On the storm-y sea, He speaks peace to me, How the bil-lows cease to roll!

319 Builded on the Rock

Mrs. C. R.

Mrs. C. RICE

1. I build-ed on the Rock, on the Rock of God, Build - ed on the
2. Why should I fear when the winds sweep by? Build - ed on the
3. Hush, rag - ing bil - lows at His com - mand, Build - ed on the
4. Praise God for our foun - da - tion sure! Build - ed on the

Rock, Christ Je - sus; I dug down deep and build-ed on the Rock,
Rock, Christ Je - sus; Or shak - en be when the waves roll high?
Rock, Christ Je - sus; Oh, peace be still 'neath His lov - ing hand!
Rock, Christ Je - sus; No storms can harm our house se - cure,

CHORUS

Build - ed on the Rock of God. I hold not the Rock, but the

Rock holds me, The Rock holds me, the Rock holds me; I rest on the

Rock, and the Rock holds me, Rest - ing on the Rock of God.

320 Dwelling in Beulah Land

C. A. M.

C. Austin Miles

1. Far a-way the noise of strife up-on my ear is fall-ing, Then I know the
2. Far be-low the storm of doubt up-on the world is beat-ing, Sons of men in
3. Let the storm-y breez-es blow, their cry can-not a-larm me; I am safe-ly
4. Viewing here the works of God, I sink in con-tem-pla-tion, Hearing now His

sins of earth be-set on ev-'ry hand: Doubt and fear and things of earth in
bat-tle long the en-e-my with-stand: Safe am I with-in the cas-tle
sheltered here, pro-tect-ed by God's hand: Here the sun is al-ways shin-ing,
bless-ed voice, I see the way He planned: Dwell-ing in the Spir-it, here I

vain to me are call-ing, None of these shall move me from Beu-lah Land.
of God's word re-treat-ing, Nothing then can reach me—'tis Beu-lah Land.
here there's naught can harm me, I am safe for-ev-er in Beu-lah Land.
learn of full sal-va-tion, Glad-ly will I tar-ry in Beu-lah Land.

CHORUS

I'm liv-ing on the moun-tain, un-der-neath a cloud-less sky, I'm

Praise God!

drink-ing at the foun-tain that never shall run dry; O yes! I'm feasting on the

Dwelling in Beulah Land

man-na from a boun-ti-ful sup-ply, For I am dwell-ing in Beu-lah Land.

321 Does Jesus Care?

FRANK E. GRAEFF

J. LINCOLN HALL

1. Does Je-sus care when my heart is pained Too deep-ly for mirth and song;
2. Does Je-sus care when my way is dark With a name-less dread and fear?
3. Does Je-sus care when I've tried and failed To re-sist some temp-ta-tion strong;
4. Does Je-sus care when I've said "good-by" To the dear-est on earth to me,

As the burdens press, and the cares distress, And the way grows wea-ry and long?
As the daylight fades into deep night shades, Does He care e-nough to be near?
When for my deep grief I find no re-lief, Tho' my tears flow all the night long?
And my sad heart aches till it nearly breaks—Is it aught to Him? Does He see?

CHORUS

O yes, He cares; I know He cares, His heart is touched with my grief;

ad lib. *rit.*

When the days are wea-ry, the long nights dreary, I know my Sav-ior cares.

He cares.

322　He Ransomed Me

JULIA H. JOHNSTON

J. W. HENDERSON

1. There's a sweet and bless-ed sto - ry Of the Christ who came from glo - ry,
2. From the depth of sin and sad - ness To the heights of joy and glad-ness
3. From the throne of heav'n-ly glo - ry—Oh, the sweet and bless-ed sto - ry!
4. By and by with joy in-creas-ing, And with grat - i - tude un-ceas-ing,

Just to res-cue me from sin and mis - er - y; He in loving kindness sought me,
Je - sus lift - ed me, in mer - cy full and free; With His precious blood He bo't me,
Je - sus came to lift the lost in sin and woe In - to lib - er - ty all - glo-rious,
Lift-ed up with Christ for-ev-er-more to be; I will join the hosts there sing-ing,

ad lib.

And from sin and shame Lath bro't me, Hal - le - lu - jah! Je - sus ran-somed me.
When I knew Him not, He sought me, And in love di - vine He ran-somed me.
Tro- phies of His grace vic - to - rious, Ev - er-more re - joic-ing here be - low.
In the an-them ev - er ring-ing, To the King of Love who ran-somed me.

CHORUS

Hal - le - lu - jah, what a Sav - ior! Who can take a poor lost sin - ner, Lift him

from the mi - ry clay and set him free; (Hal-le-lu-jah!) I will ev - er tell the sto-ry,

He Ransomed Me

ad lib.

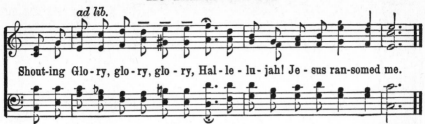

Shout-ing Glo - ry, glo - ry, glo - ry, Hal - le - lu - jah! Je - sus ran-somed me.

323   Leaning On the Everlasting Arms

Rev. E. A. Hoffman   A. J. Showalter

1. What a fel-low-ship, what a joy di-vine, Lean-ing on the ev-er-last-ing arms;
2. Oh, how sweet to walk in this pilgrim way, Lean-ing on the ev-er-last-ing arms;
3. What have I to dread, what have I to fear, Lean-ing on the ev-er-last-ing arms;

What a bless-ed-ness, what a peace is mine, Leaning on the ev-er-last-ing arms.
Oh, how bright the path grows from day to day, Leaning on the ev-er-last-ing arms.
I have bless-ed peace with my Lord so near, Leaning on the ev-er-last-ing arms.

Refrain

Lean - ing, lean - ing, Safe and se-cure from all a-larms;
Lean-ing on Je - sus, lean-ing on Je - sus,

Lean - ing, lean - ing, Lean-ing on the ev-er-last-ing arms.
Lean-ing on Je - sus, lean-ing on Je - sus,

324   Faith of Our Fathers

Frederick W. Faber.

H. F. Hemy.

1. Faith of our fa - thers! liv - ing still In spite of dun-geon, fire, and sword:
2. Our fa-thers, chained in pris-ons dark, Were still in heart and conscience free:
3. Faith of our fa - thers! we will love Both friend and foe in all our strife:

O how our hearts beat high with joy When-e'er we hear that glo-rious word!
How sweet would be their children's fate, If they, like them, could die for thee!
And preach thee, too, as love knows how, By kind-ly words and vir-tuous life:

Faith of our fa - thers! ho - ly faith! We will be true to thee till death!
Faith of our fa - thers! ho - ly faith! We will be true to thee till death!
Faith of our fa - thers! ho - ly faith! We will be true to thee till death! A - MEN.

325   How Firm a Foundation

George Keith.

Anne Steele.

1. How firm a foun - da - tion, ye saints of the Lord, Is laid for your
2. "Fear not, I am with thee, O be not dis-mayed, For I am thy
3. "When thro' the deep wa-ters I call thee to go, The riv - ers of
4. "When thro' fier-y tri - als thy path-way shall lie, My grace, all - suf-

How Firm a Foundation

faith in His ex - cel - lent Word! What more can He say than to
God, I will still give thee aid; I'll strength-en thee, help thee, and
sor - row shall not o - ver - flow; For I will be with thee thy
fi - cient, shall be thy sup - ply; The flames shall not hurt thee, I

you He hath said, To you, who for ref - uge to Je-sus have fled?
cause thee to stand, Up-held by My gra-cious, om-nip-o-tent hand.
tri - als to bless, And sanc-ti-fy to thee thy deep-est dis-tress.
on - ly de - sign Thy dross to con-sume, and thy gold to re-fine." A-MEN.

326 [Second Tune.] Unknown.

1. How firm a foun-da-tion, ye saints of the Lord, Is laid for your faith in His

ex - cel-lent Word! What more can He say than to you He hath said, To you, who for

ref-uge to Je - sus have fled? To you, who for ref-uge to Je-sus have fled? A-MEN.

327 Only Believe

P. R.

PAUL RADER

1. Fear not, lit-tle flock, from the cross to the throne, From death in-to
2. Fear not, lit-tle flock, He go-eth a-head, Your Shep-herd se-
3. Fear not, lit-tle flock, what-ev-er your lot, He en-ters all

life He went for His own; All pow-er in earth, all pow-er a-bove,
lect-eth the path you must tread; The wa-ters of Ma-rah He'll sweeten for thee,
rooms, "the doors be-ing shut;" He nev-er for-sakes, He nev-er is gone,

CHORUS

Is giv-en to Him for the flock of His love.
He drank all the bit-ter in Geth-sem-a-ne. On-ly be-lieve,
So count on His pres-ence in dark-ness and dawn.

on-ly be-lieve; All things are pos-si-ble, on-ly be-lieve;

On-ly be-lieve, on-ly be-lieve; All things are pos-si-ble, on-ly be-lieve.

Standing On the Promises

R. K. C.

R. KELSO CARTER

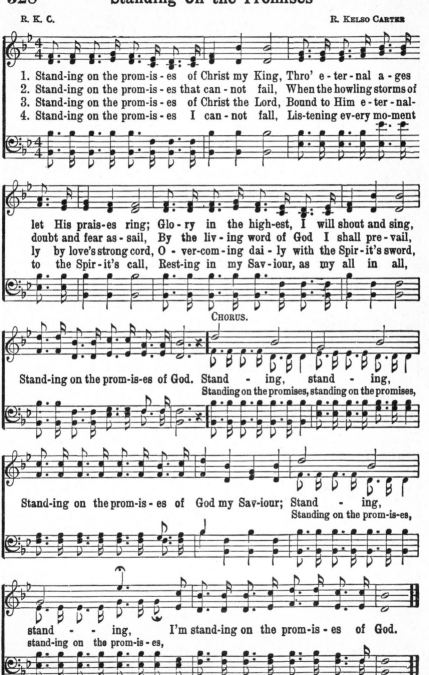

1. Stand-ing on the prom-is - es of Christ my King, Thro' e - ter - nal a - ges
2. Stand-ing on the prom-is - es that can - not fail, When the howling storms of
3. Stand-ing on the prom-is - es of Christ the Lord, Bound to Him e - ter - nal-
4. Stand-ing on the prom-is - es I can - not fall, Lis-tening ev-ery mo-ment

let His prais-es ring; Glo - ry in the high-est, I will shout and sing,
doubt and fear as - sail, By the liv-ing word of God I shall pre - vail,
ly by love's strong cord, O - ver-com-ing dai - ly with the Spir-it's sword,
to the Spir-it's call, Rest-ing in my Sav-iour, as my all in all,

CHORUS.

Stand-ing on the prom-is-es of God. Stand - ing, stand - ing,
Standing on the promises, standing on the promises,

Stand-ing on the prom-is- es of God my Sav-iour; Stand - ing,
Standing on the prom-is-es,

stand - - ing, I'm stand-ing on the prom-is - es of God.
stand-ing on the prom-is-es,

329 The Solid Rock

EDWARD MOTE

WILLIAM B. BRADBURY

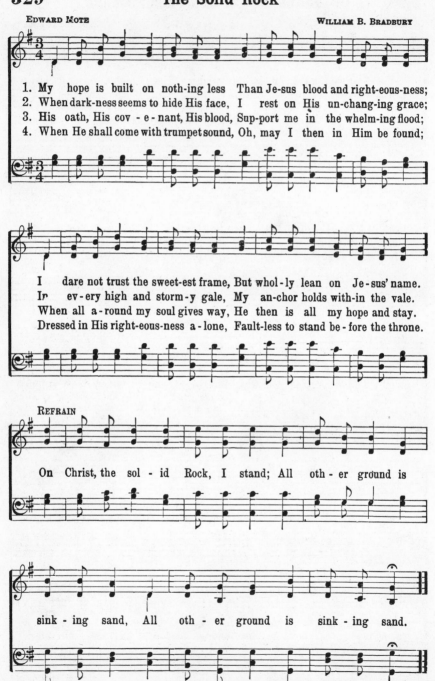

1. My hope is built on noth-ing less Than Je-sus blood and right-eous-ness;
2. When dark-ness seems to hide His face, I rest on His un-chang-ing grace;
3. His oath, His cov - e - nant, His blood, Sup-port me in the whelm-ing flood;
4. When He shall come with trumpet sound, Oh, may I then in Him be found;

I dare not trust the sweet-est frame, But whol-ly lean on Je-sus' name.
In ev-ery high and storm-y gale, My an-chor holds with-in the vale.
When all a-round my soul gives way, He then is all my hope and stay.
Dressed in His right-eous-ness a-lone, Fault-less to stand be-fore the throne.

REFRAIN

On Christ, the sol - id Rock, I stand; All oth - er ground is

sink - ing sand, All oth - er ground is sink - ing sand.

330 Go to the Deeps of God's Promise

Mrs. Frank A. Breck

Chas. H. Gabriel

1. Go to the deeps of God's prom - ise; Ask free - ly of
2. Go to the deeps of God's prom - ise, And know of His
3. Go to the deeps of God's prom - ise; The bless - ing is
4. Go to the deeps of God's prom - ise, And claim what - so-

Him, and re - ceive; All good may be had for the ask - ing,
won - der - ful might; What-ev - er would be a true bless - ing,
nev - er de - nied; He loves, and re - mem-bers His chil - dren,
ev - er ye will; The bless - ing of God will not fail thee,

CHORUS

If, seek - ing, ye tru - ly be - lieve.
For Je - sus' sake, comes as thy right.   Go to the deeps of God's
And ev - 'ry good thing is sup - plied.
His word He will sure - ly ful - fill.

prom - ise; There's wideness of mean-ing un - told In the prom - is - es

giv - en His peo - ple, And the treasures they ev - er un - fold.

331 Trust in the Lord

T. O. CHISHOLM

WENDELL P. LOVELESS

1. "Trust in the Lord with all thine heart," This is God's gra-cious com-mand;
2. "Trust in the Lord" who rul-eth all, See-eth all things as they are,
3. "Trust in the Lord" and peace-ful be, Fret not thy spir-it in vain,
4. "Trust in the Lord"—His eye will guide All thro' the path-way a-head,

"In all thy ways ac-know-ledge Him, So shalt thou dwell in the land."
Be it a bird-ling in its nest, Or yon-der ut-ter-most star.
What tho' the an-swer tar-ries long, Still shalt thou praise Him a-gain.
He hath re-deemed and He will keep, Trust Him and be not a-fraid.

REFRAIN

"Trust in the Lord," O trou-bled soul, Rest in the arms of His care; . What-
care, of His care;

ev-er thy lot, It mat-ter-eth not, For noth-ing can trou-ble thee there;

"Trust in the Lord," O trou-bled soul, Noth-ing can trou-ble thee there.

We Have An Anchor

Priscilla J. Owens

Wm. J. Kirkpatrick

1. Will your an - chor hold in the storms of life, When the
2. It is safe - ly moored, 'twill the storm with - stand, For 'tis
3. When our eyes be - hold through the gath - ering night The

clouds un - fold their wings of strife? When the strong tides lift, and the
well se - cured by the Sav-iour's hand; Though the tem-pest rage and the
cit - y of gold, our har - bor bright, We shall an - chor fast by the

ca - bles strain, Will your an - chor drift, or firm re - main?
wild winds blow, Not an an - gry wave shall our bark o'er - flow.
heaven-ly shore, With the storms all past for - ev - er - more.

REFRAIN

We have an an-chor that keeps the soul Steadfast and sure while the bil-lows roll,

Fastened to the Rock which cannot move, Grounded firm and deep in the Saviour's love.

333 **Trusting Jesus**

E. PAGE

IRA D. SANKEY

1. Sim - ply trust - ing ev - ery day, Trust - ing through a storm - y way;
2. Bright-ly doth His Spir - it shine In - to this poor heart of mine;
3. Sing - ing if my way is clear: Pray - ing if the path be drear;
4. Trust - ing Him while life shall last, Trust - ing Him till earth be past;

E - ven when my faith is small, Trust - ing Je - sus, that is all.
While He leads I can - not fall; Trust - ing Je - sus, that is all.
If in dan - ger, for Him call; Trust - ing Je - sus, that is all.
Till with - in the jas - per wall: Trust - ing Je - sus, that is all.

CHORUS

Trust - ing as the mo - ments fly, Trust - ing as the days go by;

Trust - ing Him what-e'er be - fall, Trust - ing Je - sus, that is all.

334 **Fall Fresh On Me**

D. I.

DANIEL IVERSON

Spir - it of the liv - ing God, Fall fresh on me, Spir - it of the

D. S.—*Spir - it of the*

Copyright, 1935, by Daniel Iverson. Used by permission

Fall Fresh On Me

FINE.

D. S.

liv-ing God, Fall fresh on me. Break me, melt me, mould me, fill me.

liv - ing God, Fall fresh on me.

335 The Light of the World Is Jesus

P. P. B.

P. P. BLISS

1. The whole world was lost in the darkness of sin, The Light of the world is Je - sus;
2. No darkness have we who in Je-sus a-bide, The Light of the world is Je - sus;
3. Ye dwell-ers in darkness with sin-blinded eyes, The Light of the world is Je - sus;
4. No need of the sun-light in heaven we're told, The Light of that world is Je - sus;

Like sunshine at noon-day His glo-ry shone in, The Light of the world is Je - sus.
We walk in the Light when we follow our Guide, The Light of the world is Je - sus.
Go, wash, at His bidding, and light will a-rise, The Light of the world is Je - sus.
The Lamb is the Light in the Cit - y of Gold, The Light of that world is Je - sus.

CHORUS.

Come to the Light,'tis shining for thee; Sweetly the Light has dawned upon me;

Once I was blind, but now I can see: The Light of the world is Je - sus.

336 Near to the Heart of God

CLELAND B. McAFEE

CLELAND B. McAFEE

1. There is a place of qui-et rest, Near to the heart of God,
2. There is a place of com-fort sweet, Near to the heart of God,
3. There is a place of full re-lease, Near to the heart of God,

A place where sin can-not mo-lest, Near to the heart of God.
A place where we our Sav-ior meet, Near to the heart of God.
A place where all is joy and peace, Near to the heart of God.

REFRAIN

O Je-sus, blest Re-deem-er, Sent from the heart of God,

Hold us, who wait be-fore Thee, Near to the heart of God.

337 Lord, Speak to Me, That I May Speak

FRANCES R. HAVERGAL

ROBERT SCHUMANN

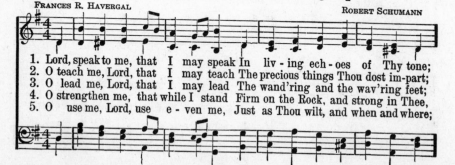

1. Lord, speak to me, that I may speak In liv-ing ech-oes of Thy tone;
2. O teach me, Lord, that I may teach The precious things Thou dost im-part;
3. O lead me, Lord, that I may lead The wand'ring and the wav'ring feet;
4. O strengthen me, that while I stand Firm on the Rock, and strong in Thee,
5. O use me, Lord, use e-ven me, Just as Thou wilt, and when and where;

Lord, Speak to Me, That I May Speak

As Thou hast sought, so let me seek Thy err-ing children lost and lone.
And wing my words,that they may reach The hid-den depths of man-y a heart.
O   feed me, Lord, that I may feed The hung'ring ones with manna sweet.
I   may stretch out a   lov-ing hand To wrestlers with the troubled sea.
Un - til Thy bless-ed face I see, Thy rest, Thy joy, Thy glo-ry share. A-MEN.

338   My Prayer

P. P. B.

P. P. BLISS

1. More ho - li - ness give me, More striv-ing with-in;   More pa-tience in
2. More grat - i - tude give me, More trust in the Lord;   More pride in His
3. More pu - ri - ty give me, More strength to o'ercome;   More freedom from

suf - f'ring, More sor - row for sin; More faith in my Sav - ior,
glo - ry, More hope in His word; More tears for His sor - rows,
earth-stains, More long-ings for home; More fit for the king-dom,

rit.

More sense of His care; More joy in His serv-ice, More pur-pose in prayer.
More pain at His grief; More meekness in tri - al, More praise for re - lief.
More used would I be; More bless-ed and ho - ly, More, Sav-ior, like Thee.

339 My Soul, Be On Thy Guard

GEORGE HEATH

LOWELL MASON

1. My soul, be on thy guard; Ten thou-sand foes a - rise; The
2. O watch, and fight, and pray; The bat - tle ne'er give o'er; Re-
3. Ne'er think the vic - t'ry won, Nor lay thine ar - mor down; The
4. Fight on, my soul, till death Shall bring thee to thy God; He'll

hosts of sin are press - ing hard To draw thee from the skies.
new it bold - ly ev - 'ry day, And help di - vine im - plore.
work of faith will not be done, Till thou ob - tain the crown.
take thee, at thy part - ing breath, To His di - vine a - bode.

340 Close to Thee

FANNY J. CROSBY

SILAS J. VAIL

1. Thou, my ev - er - last - ing por - tion, More than friend or life to me;
2. Not for ease or world - ly pleas - ure, Nor for fame my prayer shall be;
3. Lead me thro' the vale of shad - ows, Bear me o'er life's fit - ful sea;

FINE

D.S.—All a - long my pil - grim jour - ney, Sav - ior, let me walk with Thee.
D.S.—Glad - ly will I toil and suf - fer, On - ly let me walk with Thee.
D.S.—Then the gate of life e - ter - nal May I en - ter, Lord, with Thee.

Close to Thee

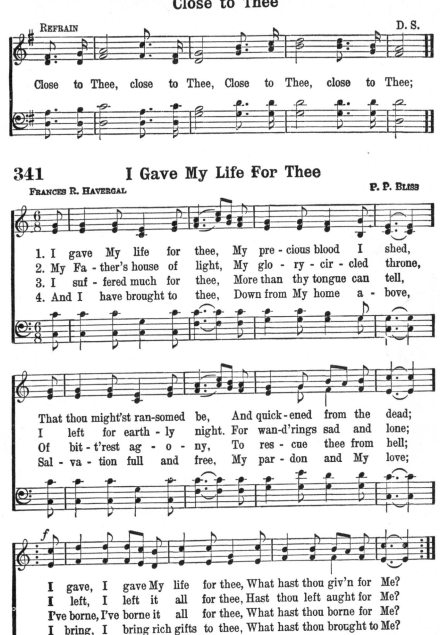

REFRAIN   D. S.

Close to Thee, close to Thee, Close to Thee, close to Thee;

341   I Gave My Life For Thee

FRANCES R. HAVERGAL   P. P. BLISS

1. I gave My life for thee, My pre-cious blood I shed,
2. My Fa-ther's house of light, My glo-ry-cir-cled throne,
3. I suf-fered much for thee, More than thy tongue can tell,
4. And I have brought to thee, Down from My home a-bove,

That thou might'st ran-somed be, And quick-ened from the dead;
I left for earth-ly night. For wan-d'rings sad and lone;
Of bit-t'rest ag-o-ny, To res-cue thee from hell;
Sal-va-tion full and free, My par-don and My love;

f

I gave, I gave My life for thee, What hast thou giv'n for Me?
I left, I left it all for thee, Hast thou left aught for Me?
I've borne, I've borne it all for thee, What hast thou borne for Me?
I bring, I bring rich gifts to thee, What hast thou brought to Me?

342   A Passion for Souls

HERBERT G. TOVEY   FOSS L. FELLERS

1. Give me a pas - sion for souls, dear Lord, A pas - sion to save the lost;
2. Though there are dan-gers un-told and stern Con-front-ing me in the way,
3. How shall this pas - sion for souls be mine? Lord, make Thou the an-swer clear;

O that Thy love were by all a-dored, And wel-comed at an - y cost.
Will-ing - ly still would I go, nor turn, But trust Thee for grace each day.
Help me to throw out the old Life-Line To those who are strug-gling near.

CHORUS.

Je - sus, I long, I long to be win - ning Men who are

lost, and con - stant - ly sin - ning; O may this hour be

one of be - gin-ning The sto - ry of par - don to tell.

343   Follow On

W. O. CUSHING

ROBERT LOWRY

1. Down in the val-ley with my Sav-iour I would go,   Where the flowers are
2. Down in the val-ley with my Sav-iour I would go,   Where the storms are
3. Down in the val-ley, or up-on the moun-tain steep, Close be-side my

bloom-ing and the sweet wa-ters flow;   Ev-ery-where He leads me   I would
sweep-ing and the dark wa-ters flow;   With His hand to lead me   I will
Sav-iour would my soul ev-er keep;   He will lead me safe-ly   in the

fol-low, fol-low on,   Walk-ing in His foot-steps till the crown be won.
nev-er, nev-er fear,   Dan-ger can-not fright me if   my Lord is near.
path that He has trod,   Up to where they gath-er on   the hills of God.

REFRAIN

Fol-low! fol-low! I would follow Je-sus! Anywhere, everywhere, I would follow on!

Fol-low! fol-low! I would follow Jesus! Everywhere He leads me I would follow on!

344 Give Me Jesus

FANNY J. CROSBY

JNO. R. SWENEY

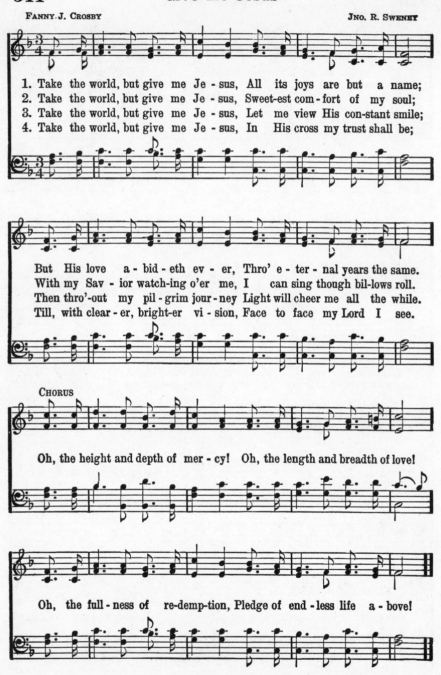

1. Take the world, but give me Je - sus, All its joys are but a name;
2. Take the world, but give me Je - sus, Sweet-est com - fort of my soul;
3. Take the world, but give me Je - sus, Let me view His con-stant smile;
4. Take the world, but give me Je - sus, In His cross my trust shall be;

But His love a - bid - eth ev - er, Thro' e - ter - nal years the same.
With my Sav - ior watch-ing o'er me, I can sing though bil-lows roll.
Then thro'-out my pil - grim jour - ney Light will cheer me all the while.
Till, with clear - er, bright-er vi - sion, Face to face my Lord I see.

CHORUS

Oh, the height and depth of mer - cy! Oh, the length and breadth of love!

Oh, the full - ness of re-demp-tion, Pledge of end - less life a - bove!

345 Higher Ground

JOHNSON OATMAN, JR.

CHAS. H. GABRIEL

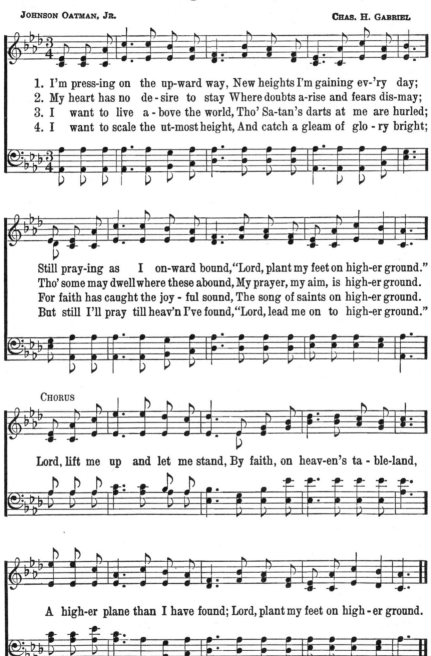

1. I'm press-ing on the up-ward way, New heights I'm gaining ev-'ry day;
2. My heart has no de-sire to stay Where doubts a-rise and fears dis-may;
3. I want to live a-bove the world, Tho' Sa-tan's darts at me are hurled;
4. I want to scale the ut-most height, And catch a gleam of glo-ry bright;

Still pray-ing as I on-ward bound, "Lord, plant my feet on high-er ground."
Tho' some may dwell where these abound, My prayer, my aim, is high-er ground.
For faith has caught the joy-ful sound, The song of saints on high-er ground.
But still I'll pray till heav'n I've found, "Lord, lead me on to high-er ground."

CHORUS

Lord, lift me up and let me stand, By faith, on heav-en's ta-ble-land,

A high-er plane than I have found; Lord, plant my feet on high-er ground.

346 His Way with Thee

C. S. N.

Cyrus S. Nusbaum

1. Would you live for Je - sus, and be al-ways pure and good? Would you walk with
2. Would you have Him make you free, and fol-low at His call? Would you know the
3. Would you in His king-dom find a place of con-stant rest? Would you prove Him

Him with-in the nar-row road? Would you have Him bear your bur-den, car - ry
peace that comes by giv-ing all? Would you have Him save you, so that you can
true in prov - i - den-tial test? Would you in His serv - ice la - bor al-ways

CHORUS

all your load? Let Him have His way with thee.
nev - er fall? Let Him have His way with thee. His power can make you what you
at your best? Let Him have His way with thee.

ought to be; His blood can cleanse your heart and make you free; His love can

rit.

fill your soul, and you will see 'Twas best for Him to have His way with thee.

347 I Am Thine, O Lord

FANNY J. CROSBY

W. H. DOANE

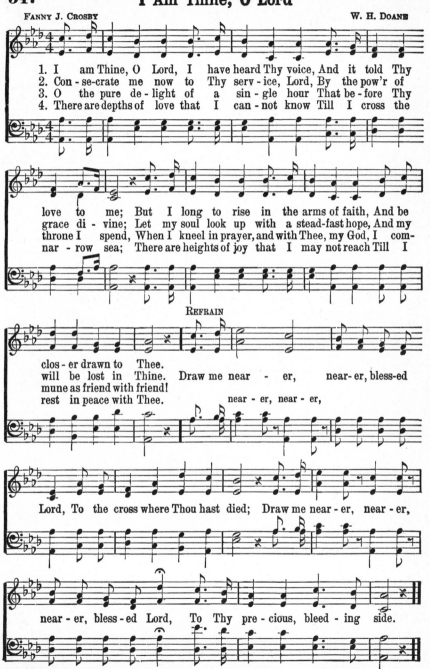

1. I am Thine, O Lord, I have heard Thy voice, And it told Thy love to me; But I long to rise in the arms of faith, And be clos-er drawn to Thee.

2. Con-se-crate me now to Thy serv-ice, Lord, By the pow'r of grace di-vine; Let my soul look up with a stead-fast hope, And my will be lost in Thine.

3. O the pure de-light of a sin-gle hour That be-fore Thy throne I spend, When I kneel in prayer, and with Thee, my God, I com-mune as friend with friend!

4. There are depths of love that I can-not know Till I cross the nar-row sea; There are heights of joy that I may not reach Till I rest in peace with Thee.

REFRAIN

Draw me near - er, near-er, bless-ed Lord, To the cross where Thou hast died; Draw me near-er, near-er, near-er, bless-ed Lord, To Thy pre-cious, bleed-ing side.

348

I Surrender All

J. W. Van DeVenter

W. S. Weeden

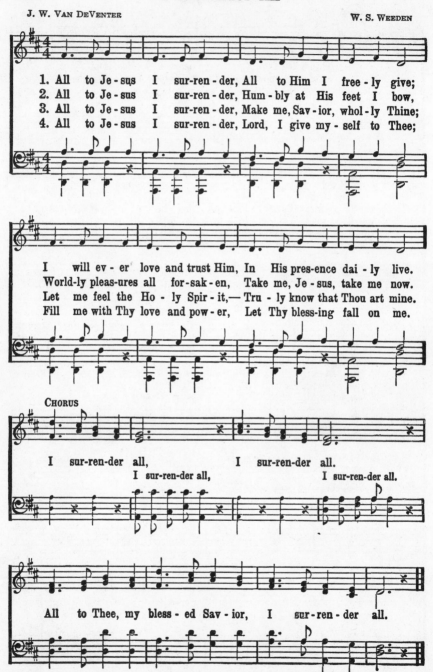

1. All to Je-sus I sur-ren-der, All to Him I free-ly give;
2. All to Je-sus I sur-ren-der, Hum-bly at His feet I bow,
3. All to Je-sus I sur-ren-der, Make me, Sav-ior, whol-ly Thine;
4. All to Je-sus I sur-ren-der, Lord, I give my-self to Thee;

I will ev-er love and trust Him, In His pres-ence dai-ly live.
World-ly pleas-ures all for-sak-en, Take me, Je-sus, take me now.
Let me feel the Ho-ly Spir-it,— Tru-ly know that Thou art mine.
Fill me with Thy love and pow-er, Let Thy bless-ing fall on me.

CHORUS

I sur-ren-der all, I sur-ren-der all.
I sur-ren-der all, I sur-ren-der all.

All to Thee, my bless-ed Sav-ior, I sur-ren-der all.

349 I Would Be Like Jesus

JAMES ROWE

B. D. ACKLEY

1. Earth-ly pleas-ures vain-ly call me; I would be like Je - sus;
2. He has bro-ken ev - 'ry fet - ter, I would be like Je - sus;
3. All the way from earth to Glo - ry, I would be like Je " sus;
4. That in Heav-en He may meet me, I would be like Je - sus;
 would be like Je - sus;

Noth-ing world-ly shall en-thrall me; I would be like Je - sus.
That my soul may serve Him bet - ter, I would be like Je - sus.
Tell - ing o'er and o'er the sto - ry, I would be like Je - sus.
That His words "Well done" may greet me, I would be like Je - sus.
 would be like Je - sus.

CHORUS.

Be like Je - sus, this my song, In the home and in the throng;

Be like Je - sus, all day long! I would be like Je - sus. A - MEN.

350 In the Secret of His Presence

ELLEN LAKSHMI GOREH

GEO. C. STEBBINS

1. In the se-cret of His pres-ence how my soul de-lights to hide! Oh, how
2. When my soul is faint and thirst-y, 'neath the shad-ow of His wing There is
3. On-ly this I know: I tell Him all my doubts, my griefs and fears; Oh, how
4. Would you like to know the sweet-ness of the se-cret of the Lord? Go and

pre-cious are the les-sons which I learn at Je-sus' side! Earth-ly cares can
cool and pleas-ant shel-ter, and a fresh and crys-tal spring; And my Sav-ior
pa-tient-ly He lis-tens! and my droop-ing soul He cheers: Do you think He
hide beneath His shad-ow: this shall then be your re-ward; And when-e'er you

nev-er vex me, nei-ther tri-als lay me low; For when Sa-tan comes to
rests be-side me, as we hold com-mun-ion sweet: If I tried, I could not
ne'er reproves me? What a false friend He would be, If He nev-er, nev-er
leave the si-lence of that hap-py meet-ing place, You must mind and bear the

rit.

tempt me, to the se-cret place I go, to the se-cret place I go.
ut-ter what He says when thus we meet, what He says when thus we meet.
told me of the sins which He must see, of the sins which He must see.
im-age of the Mas-ter in your face, of the Mas-ter in your face.

351

Is Your All on the Altar?

E. A. H.

ELISHA A. HOFFMAN

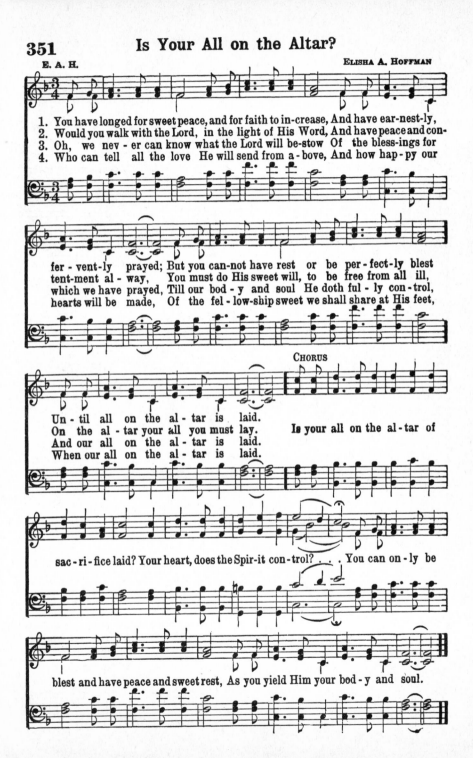

1. You have longed for sweet peace, and for faith to in-crease, And have ear-nest-ly,
2. Would you walk with the Lord, in the light of His Word, And have peace and con-
3. Oh, we nev - er can know what the Lord will be-stow Of the bless-ings for
4. Who can tell all the love He will send from a-bove, And how hap-py our

fer - vent-ly prayed; But you can-not have rest or be per-fect-ly blest
tent-ment al - way, You must do His sweet will, to be free from all ill,
which we have prayed, Till our bod - y and soul He doth ful - ly con-trol,
hearts will be made, Of the fel - low-ship sweet we shall share at His feet,

Un - til all on the al - tar is laid.
On the al - tar your all you must lay.
And our all on the al - tar is laid.
When our all on the al - tar is laid.

CHORUS

Is your all on the al - tar of
sac - ri - fice laid? Your heart, does the Spir-it con-trol?.... You can on - ly be
blest and have peace and sweet rest, As you yield Him your bod - y and soul.

352 Jesus, I My Cross Have Taken

HENRY F. LYTE

From MOZART

1. Je - sus, I my cross have tak - en, All to leave and fol - low Thee;
2. Let the world de - spise and leave me, They have left my Sav - iour, too;
3. Man may trou - ble and dis - tress me, 'Twill but drive me to Thy breast;
4. Haste thee on from grace to glo - ry, Armed by faith, and winged by prayer;

Des - ti - tute, de - spised, for - sak - en, Thou, from hence, my all shalt be:
Hu - man hearts and looks de - ceive me; Thou art not, like man, un - true;
Life with tri - als hard may press me, Heaven will bring me sweet - er rest.
Heaven's e - ter - nal day's be - fore thee, God's own hand shall guide thee there.

Per - ish ev - ery fond am - bi - tion, All I've sought, and hoped, and known;
And, while Thou shalt smile up - on me, God of wis - dom, love, and might,
O 'tis not in grief to harm me, While Thy love is left to me;
Soon shall close thy earth - ly mis - sion, Swift shall pass thy pil - grim days,

Yet how rich is my con - di - tion, God and heaven are still my own!
Foes may hate, and friends may shun me; Show Thy face, and all is bright.
O 'twere not in joy to charm me, Were that joy un - mixed with Thee.
Hope shall change to glad fru - i - tion, Faith to sight, and prayer to praise.

353 Moment By Moment

D. W. WHITTLE

MAY WHITTLE MOODY

1, Dy - ing with Je - sus, by death reckoned mine; Liv-ing with Je - sus, a
2. Nev - er a tri - al that He is not there, Nev-er a bur-den that
3. Nev - er a heart-ache, and nev - er a groan, Nev-er a tear-drop and
4. Nev - er a weak-ness that He doth not feel, Nev-er a sick-ness that

new life di-vine; Look-ing to Je - sus till glo - ry doth shine, Mo-ment by
He doth not bear, Nev - er a sor - row that He doth not share, Mo-ment by
nev - er a moan; Mo - ment by moment, in woe or in weal, Jesus, my
He can-not heal; Mo - ment by moment, in woe or in weal, Je - sus, my

CHORUS

mo - ment, O Lord, I am Thine.
mo - ment, I'm un - der His care; Moment by mo-ment I'm kept in His love;
mo - ment He thinks of His own.
Sav - ior, a-bides with me still.

Mo-ment by mo-ment I've life from a - bove; Look-ing to Je - sus till

glo - ry doth shine; Mo-ment by mo-ment, O Lord, I am Thine.

354 Living for Jesus

T. O. Chisholm

C. Harold Lowden

Not fast

1. Liv-ing for Je-sus a life that is true, Striv-ing to please Him in
2. Liv-ing for Je-sus who died in my place, Bear-ing on Cal-v'ry my
3. Liv-ing for Je-sus wher-ev-er I am, Do-ing each du-ty in
4. Liv-ing for Je-sus thro' earth's lit-tle while, My dear-est treas-ure, the

all that I do, Yield-ing al-le-giance, glad-heart-ed and free,
sin and dis-grace, Such love con-strains me to an-swer His call,
His ho-ly name, Will-ing to suf-fer af-flic-tion and loss,
light of His smile, Seek-ing the lost ones He died to re-deem,

* CHORUS Unison. Slower

This is the path-way of bless-ing for me.
Fol-low His lead-ing and give Him my all. O Je-sus, Lord and
Deem-ing each tri-al a part of my cross.
Bring-ing the wea-ry to find rest in Him.

Sav-ior, I give my-self to Thee, For Thou, in Thy a-tone-ment, Didst

give Thy-self for me; I own no oth-er Mas-ter, My heart shall be Thy

Living for Jesus

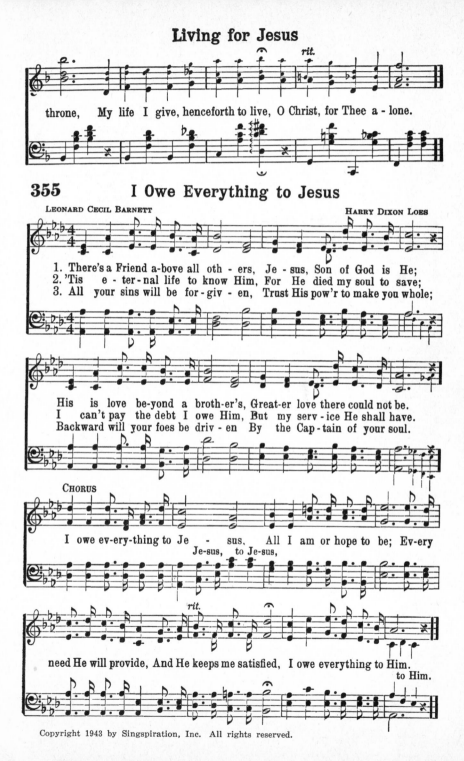

throne, My life I give, henceforth to live, O Christ, for Thee a-lone.

355 I Owe Everything to Jesus

LEONARD CECIL BARNETT

HARRY DIXON LOES

1. There's a Friend a-bove all oth - ers, Je - sus, Son of God is He;
2. 'Tis e - ter - nal life to know Him, For He died my soul to save;
3. All your sins will be for - giv - en, Trust His pow'r to make you whole;

His is love be-yond a broth-er's, Great-er love there could not be.
I can't pay the debt I owe Him, But my serv - ice He shall have.
Backward will your foes be driv - en By the Cap-tain of your soul.

CHORUS

I owe ev-ery-thing to Je - sus, All I am or hope to be; Ev-ery
Je-sus, to Je-sus,

rit.

need He will provide, And He keeps me satisfied, I owe everything to Him.
to Him.

More About Jesus

E. E. HEWITT
JNO. R. SWENEY

1. More a-bout Je-sus would I know, More of His grace to oth-ers show;
2. More a-bout Je-sus let me learn, More of His ho-ly will dis-cern;
3. More a-bout Je-sus; in His word, Holding com-mun-ion with my Lord;
4. More a-bout Je-sus on His throne, Rich-es in glo-ry all His own;

More of His sav-ing full-ness see, More of His love who died for me.
Spir-it of God, my teach-er be, Show-ing the things of Christ to me.
Hear-ing His voice in ev-'ry line, Mak-ing each faith-ful say-ing mine.
More of His kingdom's sure in-crease; More of His com-ing, Prince of Peace.

D.S.—*More of His sav-ing full-ness see, More of His love who died for me.*

REFRAIN

More, more a-bout Je-sus, More, more a-bout Je-sus;

He Cares for Me

Anonymous
J. R. Murray

1. How strong and sweet my Father's care, That round a-bout me, like the air,
2. The tho't great won-der with it brings, My cares are all such lit-tle things,
3. O keep me ev-er in Thy love, Dear Fa-ther, watching from a-bove,

He Cares for Me

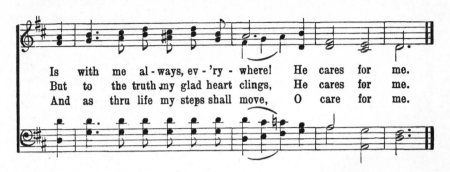

Is with me al-ways, ev-'ry-where! He cares for me.
But to the truth my glad heart clings, He cares for me.
And as thru life my steps shall move, O care for me.

358 Through the Love of God Our Savior

Mrs. MARY B. PETERS

Welsh Traditional

1. Thro' the love of God our Sav-ior, All will be well; Free and changeless is His
2. Tho' we pass thro' trib-u-la-tion, All will be well: Ours is such a full sal-
3. We ex-pect a bright to-mor-row; All will be well; Faith can sing thro' days of

fa-vor; All, all is well. Precious is the blood that healed us; Per-fect is the
va-tion; All, all is well. Hap-py still in God con-fid-ing, Fruit-ful, if in
sor-row, All, all is well. On our Father's love re-ly-ing, Je-sus ev-'ry

grace that sealed us; Strong the hand stretched out to shield us; All must be well.
Christ a-bid-ing, Ho-ly thro' the Spir-it's guiding, All must be well.
need sup-ply-ing, Or in liv-ing, or in dy-ing, All must be well.   A-MEN.

359 More Like the Master

C. H. G.

CHAS. H. GABRIEL

1. More like the Mas-ter I would ev-er be, More of His meek-ness,
2. More like the Mas-ter is my dai-ly prayer; More strength to car-ry
3. More like the Mas-ter I would live and grow; More of His love to

more hu-mil-i-ty; More zeal to la-bor, more cour-age to be true,
cross-es I must bear; More ear-nest ef-fort to bring His kingdom in;
oth-ers I would show; More self-de-ni-al, like His in Gal-i-lee,

rit.

CHORUS.

More con-se-cra-tion for work He bids me do. . . . . . Take Thou my
More of His Spir-it, the wan-der-er to win. . . . .
More like the Mas-ter I long to ev-er be. . . . . Take my heart, O

heart, . . I would be Thine a-lone; . . Take Thou my heart . . and
take my heart, I would be Thine a-lone; Take my heart, O take my heart and

make it all Thine own; . . Purge me from sin, . . . O Lord, I now im-
make it all Thine own; Purge Thou me from ev'ry sin, O Lord, I

More Like the Master

plore,.... Wash me and keep.... me Thine for-ev - er - more.
now im-plore, Wash and keep, O wash and keep me Thine for-ev - er - more.

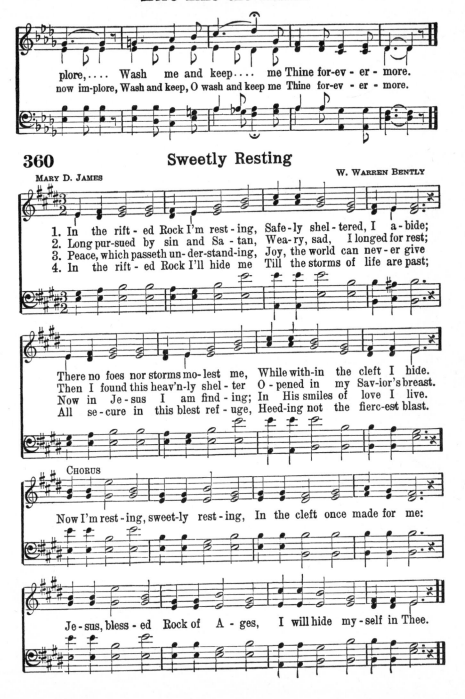

360 Sweetly Resting

MARY D. JAMES

W. WARREN BENTLY

1. In the rift - ed Rock I'm rest - ing, Safe-ly shel - tered, I a - bide;
2. Long pur-sued by sin and Sa - tan, Wea - ry, sad, I longed for rest;
3. Peace, which passeth un-der-stand-ing, Joy, the world can nev - er give
4. In the rift - ed Rock I'll hide me Till the storms of life are past;

There no foes nor storms mo-lest me, While with-in the cleft I hide.
Then I found this heav'n-ly shel - ter O - pened in my Sav-ior's breast.
Now in Je - sus I am find - ing; In His smiles of love I live.
All se - cure in this blest ref - uge, Heed-ing not the fierc-est blast.

CHORUS

Now I'm rest - ing, sweet-ly rest - ing, In the cleft once made for me:

Je - sus, bless - ed Rock of A - ges, I will hide my - self in Thee.

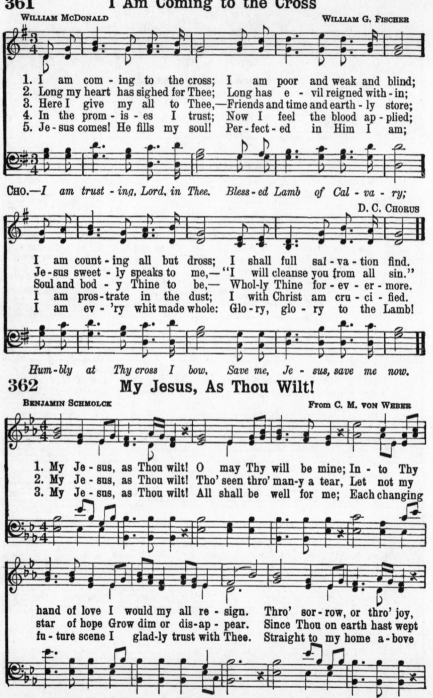

361 I Am Coming to the Cross

WILLIAM McDONALD

WILLIAM G. FISCHER

1. I am com-ing to the cross; I am poor and weak and blind;
2. Long my heart has sighed for Thee; Long has e-vil reigned with-in;
3. Here I give my all to Thee,—Friends and time and earth-ly store;
4. In the prom-is-es I trust; Now I feel the blood ap-plied;
5. Je-sus comes! He fills my soul! Per-fect-ed in Him I am;

CHO.—I am trust-ing, Lord, in Thee. Bless-ed Lamb of Cal-va-ry;

D. C. CHORUS

I am count-ing all but dross; I shall full sal-va-tion find.
Je-sus sweet-ly speaks to me,—"I will cleanse you from all sin."
Soul and bod-y Thine to be,— Whol-ly Thine for-ev-er-more.
I am pros-trate in the dust; I with Christ am cru-ci-fied.
I am ev-'ry whit made whole: Glo-ry, glo-ry to the Lamb!

Hum-bly at Thy cross I bow. Save me, Je-sus, save me now.

362 My Jesus, As Thou Wilt!

BENJAMIN SCHMOLCK

From C. M. VON WEBER

1. My Je-sus, as Thou wilt! O may Thy will be mine; In-to Thy
2. My Je-sus, as Thou wilt! Tho' seen thro' man-y a tear, Let not my
3. My Je-sus, as Thou wilt! All shall be well for me; Each changing

hand of love I would my all re-sign. Thro' sor-row, or thro' joy,
star of hope Grow dim or dis-ap-pear. Since Thou on earth hast wept
fu-ture scene I glad-ly trust with Thee. Straight to my home a-bove

My Jesus, As Thou Wilt!

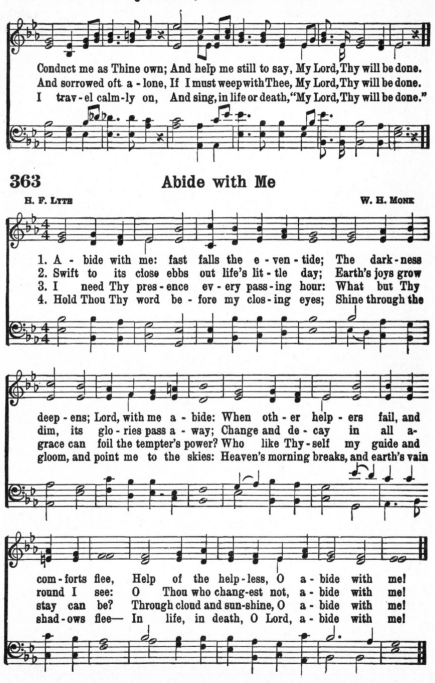

Conduct me as Thine own; And help me still to say, My Lord, Thy will be done.
And sorrowed oft a-lone, If I must weep with Thee, My Lord, Thy will be done.
I trav-el calm-ly on, And sing, in life or death, "My Lord, Thy will be done."

363 Abide with Me

H. F. LYTE

W. H. MONK

1. A - bide with me: fast falls the e - ven - tide; The dark - ness
2. Swift to its close ebbs out life's lit - tle day; Earth's joys grow
3. I need Thy pres - ence ev - ery pass - ing hour: What but Thy
4. Hold Thou Thy word be - fore my clos - ing eyes; Shine through the

deep - ens; Lord, with me a - bide: When oth - er help - ers fail, and
dim, its glo - ries pass a - way; Change and de - cay in all a-
grace can foil the tempter's power? Who like Thy - self my guide and
gloom, and point me to the skies: Heaven's morning breaks, and earth's vain

com - forts flee, Help of the help - less, O a - bide with me!
round I see: O Thou who chang - est not, a - bide with me!
stay can be? Through cloud and sun - shine, O a - bide with me!
shad - ows flee— In life, in death, O Lord, a - bide with me!

364 My Jesus, I Love Thee

WILLIAM R. FEATHERSTONE

A. J. GORDON

1. My Je - sus, I love Thee, I know Thou art mine, For Thee all the fol - lies of sin I re - sign; My gra - cious Re - deem - er, my Sav - ior art Thou; If ev - er I loved Thee, my Je - sus, 'tis now.

2. I love Thee, be - cause Thou hast first lov - ed me, And pur - chased my par - don on Cal - va - ry's tree; I love Thee for wear - ing the thorns on Thy brow: If ev - er I loved Thee, my Je - sus, 'tis now.

3. I'll love Thee in life, I will love Thee in death, And praise Thee as long as Thou lend - est me breath; And say when the death - dew lies cold on my brow, If ev - er I loved Thee, my Je - sus, 'tis now.

4. In man - sions of glo - ry and end - less de - light, I'll ev - er a - dore Thee in heav - en so bright; I'll sing with the glit - ter - ing crown on my brow, If ev - er I loved Thee, my Je - sus, 'tis now.

365 Must Jesus Bear the Cross Alone?

THOMAS SHEPHERD

GEORGE N. ALLEN

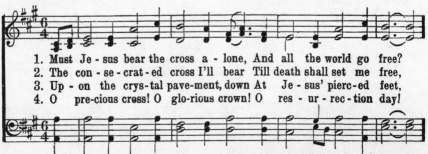

1. Must Je - sus bear the cross a - lone, And all the world go free?

2. The con - se - crat - ed cross I'll bear Till death shall set me free,

3. Up - on the crys - tal pave - ment, down At Je - sus' pierc - ed feet,

4. O pre - cious cross! O glo - rious crown! O res - ur - rec - tion day!

Must Jesus Bear the Cross Alone?

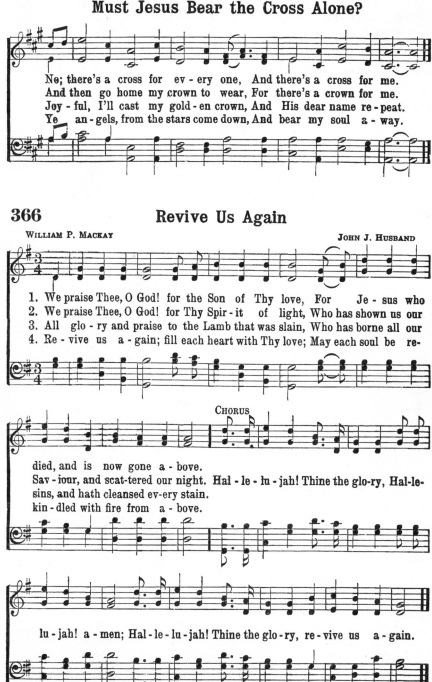

No; there's a cross for ev - ery one, And there's a cross for me.
And then go home my crown to wear, For there's a crown for me.
Joy - ful, I'll cast my gold - en crown, And His dear name re - peat.
Ye an - gels, from the stars come down, And bear my soul a - way.

366 Revive Us Again

WILLIAM P. MACKAY

JOHN J. HUSBAND

1. We praise Thee, O God! for the Son of Thy love, For Je - sus who
2. We praise Thee, O God! for Thy Spir - it of light, Who has shown us our
3. All glo - ry and praise to the Lamb that was slain, Who has borne all our
4. Re - vive us a - gain; fill each heart with Thy love; May each soul be re-

died, and is now gone a - bove.
Sav - iour, and scat-tered our night. Hal - le - lu - jah! Thine the glo-ry, Hal-le-
sins, and hath cleansed ev-ery stain.
kin - dled with fire from a - bove.

CHORUS

lu - jah! a - men; Hal - le - lu - jah! Thine the glo-ry, re - vive us a - gain.

Walk in the Light

BERNARD BARTON

FROM FRANCIS J. HAYDN

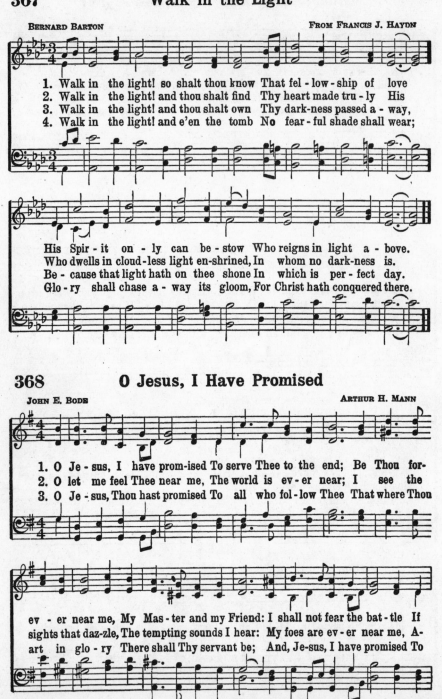

1. Walk in the light! so shalt thou know That fel-low-ship of love
2. Walk in the light! and thou shalt find Thy heart made tru-ly His
3. Walk in the light! and thou shalt own Thy dark-ness passed a-way,
4. Walk in the light! and e'en the tomb No fear-ful shade shall wear;

His Spir-it on-ly can be-stow Who reigns in light a-bove.
Who dwells in cloud-less light en-shrined, In whom no dark-ness is.
Be-cause that light hath on thee shone In which is per-fect day.
Glo-ry shall chase a-way its gloom, For Christ hath conquered there.

368

O Jesus, I Have Promised

JOHN E. BODE

ARTHUR H. MANN

1. O Je-sus, I have prom-ised To serve Thee to the end; Be Thou for-
2. O let me feel Thee near me, The world is ev-er near; I see the
3. O Je-sus, Thou hast promised To all who fol-low Thee That where Thou

ev-er near me, My Mas-ter and my Friend: I shall not fear the bat-tle If
sights that daz-zle, The tempting sounds I hear: My foes are ev-er near me, A-
art in glo-ry There shall Thy servant be; And, Je-sus, I have promised To

O Jesus, I Have Promised

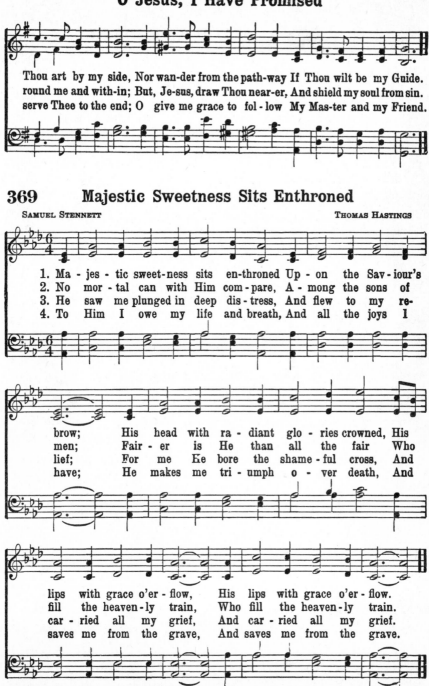

Thou art by my side, Nor wan-der from the path-way If Thou wilt be my Guide.
round me and with-in; But, Je-sus, draw Thou near-er, And shield my soul from sin.
serve Thee to the end; O give me grace to fol-low My Mas-ter and my Friend.

369 Majestic Sweetness Sits Enthroned

SAMUEL STENNETT

THOMAS HASTINGS

1. Ma - jes - tic sweet-ness sits en-throned Up - on the Sav - iour's
2. No mor - tal can with Him com - pare, A - mong the sons of
3. He saw me plunged in deep dis - tress, And flew to my re-
4. To Him I owe my life and breath, And all the joys I

brow; His head with ra - diant glo - ries crowned, His
men; Fair - er is He than all the fair Who
lief; For me He bore the shame - ful cross, And
have; He makes me tri - umph o - ver death, And

lips with grace o'er - flow, His lips with grace o'er - flow.
fill the heaven - ly train, Who fill the heaven - ly train.
car - ried all my grief, And car - ried all my grief.
saves me from the grave, And saves me from the grave.

370 Not I, But Christ

A. A. F.

A. B. Simpson

1. Not I but Christ, be hon-ored, loved, ex-alt-ed; Not I, but
2. Not I but Christ, to gen-tly soothe in sor-row; Not I, but
3. Not I but Christ, my ev-'ry need sup-ply-ing; Not I, but
4. Christ, on-ly Christ, ere long will fill my vis-ion; Glo-ry ex-

Christ, be seen, be known, be heard; Not I, but Christ, in ev-'ry
Christ to wipe the fall-ing tear: Not I, but Christ, to lift the
Christ, my strength and health to be; Christ, on-ly Christ, for bod-y,
cell-ing soon, full soon I'll see— Christ, on-ly Christ, my ev-'ry

look and ac-tion, Not I, but Christ, in ev-'ry tho't and word.
wea-ry bur-den; Not I, but Christ, to hush a-way all fear.
soul, and spir-it; Christ, on-ly Christ, live then Thy life in me.
wish ful-fill-ing— Christ, on-ly Christ, my all in all to be.

Chorus *Slower*

O to be saved from my-self, dear Lord, O to be lost in Thee,

O that it might be no more I, but Christ, that lives in me.

371

Open My Eyes That I May See

C. H. S.

CHAS. H. SCOTT

1. O - pen my eyes, that I may see Glimps-es of truth Thou hast for me;
2. O - pen my ears, that I may hear Voi - ces of truth Thou send-est clear;
3. O - pen my mouth, and let me bear Glad - ly the warm truth ev-'ry-where;

Place in my hands the won-der-ful key That shall un-clasp, and set me free.
And while the wave-notes fall on my ear, Ev - 'ry-thing false will dis - ap-pear.
O - pen my heart, and let me pre-pare Love with Thy chil-dren thus to share.

Si - lent - ly now I wait for Thee, Read-y, my God, Thy will to see;
Si - lent - ly now I wait for Thee, Read-y, my God, Thy will to see;
Si - lent - ly now I wait for Thee, Read-y, my God, Thy will to see;

O - pen my eyes, il - lu - mine me, Spir - it di - vine!
O - pen my ears, il - lu - mine me, Spir - it di - vine!
O - pen my heart, il - lu - mine me, Spir - it di - vine!

Sitting At the Feet of Jesus

Anon.

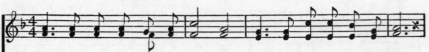

1. Sit - ting at the feet of Je - sus, O, what words I hear Him say!
2. Sit - ting at the feet of Je - sus, Where can mor-tal be more blest?
3. Bless me, O my Sav - ior, bless me, As I sit low at Thy feet;

Hap - py place! so near, so pre - cious! May it find me there each day!
There I lay my sins and sor - rows, And when wea - ry, find sweet rest;
O look down in love up - on me, Let me see Thy face so sweet;

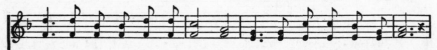

Sit - ting at the feet of Je - sus, I would look up - on the past;
Sit - ting at the feet of Je - sus, There I love to weep and pray,
Give me, Lord, the mind of Je - sus, Make me ho - ly as He is;

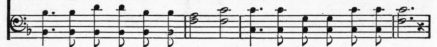

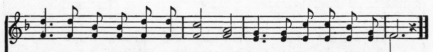

For His love has been so gra - cious, It has won my heart at last.
While I from His full - ness gath - er Grace and com-fort ev - 'ry day.
May I prove I've been with Je - sus, Who is all my right-eous-ness.

Speak to My Soul

L. L. P.

Adapted by L. L. PICKETT

1. Speak to my soul, dear Je - sus, Speak now in ten-d'rest tone; Whis-per in
2. Speak to Thy chil-dren ev - er, Lead in the ho - ly way; Fill them with
3. Speak now as in the old time Thou didst re - veal Thy will; Let me know

lov - ing kindness; "Thou art not left a - lone." O - pen my heart to hear Thee,
joy and gladness, Teach them to watch and pray. May they in con - se - cra - tion
all my du - ty, Let me Thy law ful - fill. Lead me to glo - ri - fy Thee,

Quick - ly to hear Thy voice, Fill Thou my soul with praises, Let me in Thee re-joice.
Yield their whole lives to Thee, Hasten Thy coming kingdom, Till our dear Lord we see.
Help me to show Thy praise, Glad-ly to do Thy bid-ding, Honor Thee all my days.

CHORUS

{ Speak Thou in soft - est whis - pers, Whis-pers of love to me;
{ Speak Thou to me each day, Lord, Al - ways in ten - d'rest tone,

1. 2.

"Thou shalt be al-ways con-qu'ror, Thou shalt be al-ways free." }
Let me now hear Thy whis-per, "Thou art not left (*Omit*) } a - lone."

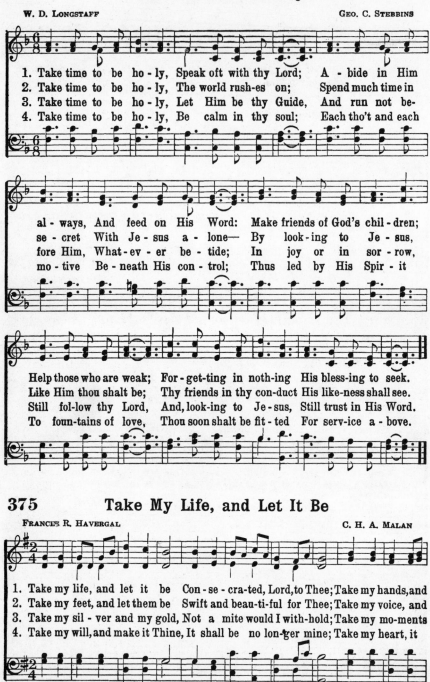

374 Take Time to Be Holy

W. D. LONGSTAFF

GEO. C. STEBBINS

1. Take time to be ho-ly, Speak oft with thy Lord; A - bide in Him
2. Take time to be ho-ly, The world rush-es on; Spend much time in
3. Take time to be ho-ly, Let Him be thy Guide, And run not be-
4. Take time to be ho-ly, Be calm in thy soul; Each tho't and each

al - ways, And feed on His Word: Make friends of God's chil - dren;
se - cret With Je - sus a - lone— By look - ing to Je - sus,
fore Him, What - ev - er be - tide; In joy or in sor - row,
mo - tive Be - neath His con - trol; Thus led by His Spir - it

Help those who are weak; For-get-ting in noth-ing His bless-ing to seek.
Like Him thou shalt be; Thy friends in thy con-duct His like-ness shall see.
Still fol-low thy Lord, And, look-ing to Je-sus, Still trust in His Word.
To foun-tains of love, Thou soon shalt be fit-ted For serv-ice a - bove.

375 Take My Life, and Let It Be

FRANCES R. HAVERGAL

C. H. A. MALAN

1. Take my life, and let it be Con - se - cra-ted, Lord, to Thee; Take my hands, and
2. Take my feet, and let them be Swift and beau-ti-ful for Thee; Take my voice, and
3. Take my sil - ver and my gold, Not a mite would I with-hold; Take my mo-ments
4. Take my will, and make it Thine, It shall be no lon-ger mine; Take my heart, it

Take My Life, and Let It Be

let them move At the im-pulse of Thy love, At the im-pulse of Thy love.
let me sing, Al-ways, on-ly, for my King, Al-ways, on-ly, for my King.
and my days, Let them flow in ceaseless praise, Let them flow in ceaseless praise.
is Thine own; It shall be Thy roy-al throne, It shall be Thy roy-al throne.

376   Glory to His Name

Rev. E. A. HOFFMAN   Rev. J. H. STOCKTON

1. Down at the cross where my Sav-iour died, Down where for cleansing from
2. I am so won-drous-ly saved from sin, Je - sus so sweet-ly a-
3. Oh, pre-cious foun-tain that saves from sin, I am so glad I have
4. Come to this foun-tain so rich and sweet; Cast thy poor soul at the

FINE

sin I cried, There to my heart was the blood ap-plied; Glo-ry to His name.
bides with-in, There at the cross where He took me in; Glo-ry to His name.
en-tered in; There Je-sus saves me and keeps me clean; Glo-ry to His name.
Sav-iour's feet; Plunge in to-day, and be made com-plete; Glo-ry to His name.

D. S.—*There to my heart was the blood ap-plied; Glo-ry to His name.*

CHORUS   D. S.

Glo-ry to His name, .. Glo-ry to His name; ..

377 Teach Me to Pray

A. S. R.

ALBERT SIMPSON REITZ

1. Teach me to pray, Lord, teach me to pray; This is my heart-cry,
2. Pow-er in prayer, Lord, pow-er in prayer, Here 'mid earth's sin and
3. My weakened will, Lord, Thou canst re-new; My sin-ful na-ture
4. Teach me to pray, Lord, teach me to pray; Thou art my Pat-tern,

day un-to day; I long to know Thy will and Thy way;
sor-row and care; Men lost and dy-ing, souls in de-spair:
Thou canst sub-due; Fill me just now with pow-er a-new:
day un-to day; Thou art my Sure-ty, now and for aye;

CHORUS

Teach me to pray, Lord, teach me to pray.
O give me pow-er, pow-er in prayer! Liv-ing in Thee, Lord,
Pow-er to pray and pow-er to do!
Teach me to pray, Lord, teach me to pray.

and Thou in me; Con-stant a-bid-ing, this is my plea; Grant me Thy

pow-er, boundless and free: Pow-er with men and pow-er with Thee.

378 The Beautiful Garden of Prayer

ELEANOR ALLEN SCHROLL

J. H. FILLMORE

1. There's a gar-den where Je-sus is wait-ing, There's a place that is
2. There's a gar-den where Je-sus is wait-ing, And I go with my
3. There's a gar-den where Je-sus is wait-ing, And He bids you to

won-drous-ly fair; For it glows with the light of His pres-ence, 'Tis the
bur-den and care, Just to learn from His lips words of com-fort, In the
come meet Him there, Just to walk and to talk with my Sav-iour, In the

REFRAIN

beau-ti-ful gar-den of prayer. O the beau-ti-ful gar-den, the

gar-den of prayer, O the beau-ti-ful gar-den of prayer; There my Sav-iour a-

poco rit. — — — — —

waits, and He o-pens the gates To the beau-ti-ful gar-den of prayer.

379 Turn Your Eyes upon Jesus

H. H. L.
HELEN HOWARTH LEMMEL

With expression

1. O soul, are you wea - ry and troub - led? No light in the
2. Thro' death in - to life ev - er - last - ing He passed, and we
3. His word shall not fail you—He prom - ised; Be - lieve Him, and

dark-ness you see? There's light for a look at the Sav - ior,
fol - low Him there; O - ver us sin no more hath do - min - ion—
all will be well: Then go to a world that is dy - ing,

REFRAIN

And life more a - bun-dant and free!
For more than con-qu'rors we are!
His per - fect sal - va - tion to tell!

Turn your eyes up-on Je-

sus, Look full in His won-der-ful face; .... And the things of

earth will grow strange-ly dim In the light of His glo - ry and grace.

380   There Shall Be Showers of Blessing

EL NATHAN   JAMES McGRANAHAN

1. "There shall be show-ers of bless-ing:" This is the prom-ise of love;
2. "There shall be show-ers of bless-ing"—Pre-cious re-viv-ing a-gain;
3. "There shall be show-ers of bless-ing:" Send them up-on us, O Lord;
4. "There shall be show-ers of bless-ing:" Oh, that to-day they might fall,

There shall be sea-sons re-fresh-ing, Sent from the Sav-iour a-bove.
O-ver the hills and the val-leys, Sound of a-bun-dance of rain.
Grant to us now a re-fresh-ing, Come, and now hon-or Thy Word.
Now as to God we're con-fess-ing, Now as on Je-sus we call!

CHORUS

Show - - ers of bless-ing, Show-ers of bless-ing we need:
Show - ers, show-ers of bless-ing,

Mer-cy-drops round us are fall-ing, But for the show-ers we plead.

381   'Tis the Blessed Hour of Prayer

FANNY J. CROSBY   WILLIAM H. DOANE

1. 'Tis the bless-ed hour of prayer, when our hearts low-ly bend,
2. 'Tis the bless-ed hour of prayer, when the Sav-iour draws near,
3. 'Tis the bless-ed hour of prayer, when the tempt-ed and tried
4. At the bless-ed hour of prayer, trust-ing Him we be-lieve

And we gath-er to Je-sus, our Sav-iour and Friend; If we
With a ten-der com-pas-sion His chil-dren to hear; When He
To the Sav-iour who loves them their sor-row con-fide; With a
That the bless-ings we're need-ing we'll sure-ly re-ceive; In the

come to Him in faith, His pro-tec-tion to share, What a balm for the
tells us we may cast at His feet ev-ery care, What a balm for the
sym-pa-thiz-ing heart He re-moves ev-ery care; What a balm for the
full-ness of this trust we shall lose ev-ery care; What a balm for the

CHORUS

wea-ry! O how sweet to be there! Bless-ed hour of prayer, Bless-ed

hour of prayer; What a balm for the wea-ry! O how sweet to be there!

382 Whiter Than Snow

JAMES NICHOLSON

WILLIAM G. FISCHER

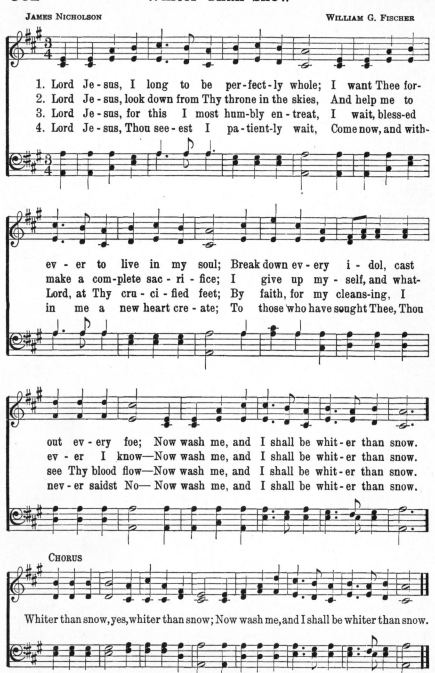

1. Lord Je - sus, I long to be per - fect - ly whole; I want Thee for-
2. Lord Je - sus, look down from Thy throne in the skies, And help me to
3. Lord Je - sus, for this I most hum - bly en - treat, I wait, bless - ed
4. Lord Je - sus, Thou see - est I pa - tient - ly wait, Come now, and with-

ev - er to live in my soul; Break down ev - er - y i - dol, cast
make a com - plete sac - ri - fice; I give up my - self, and what-
Lord, at Thy cru - ci - fied feet; By faith, for my cleans - ing, I
in me a new heart cre - ate; To those who have sought Thee, Thou

out ev - ery foe; Now wash me, and I shall be whit - er than snow.
ev - er I know—Now wash me, and I shall be whit - er than snow.
see Thy blood flow—Now wash me, and I shall be whit - er than snow.
nev - er saidst No— Now wash me, and I shall be whit - er than snow.

CHORUS

Whiter than snow, yes, whiter than snow; Now wash me, and I shall be whiter than snow.

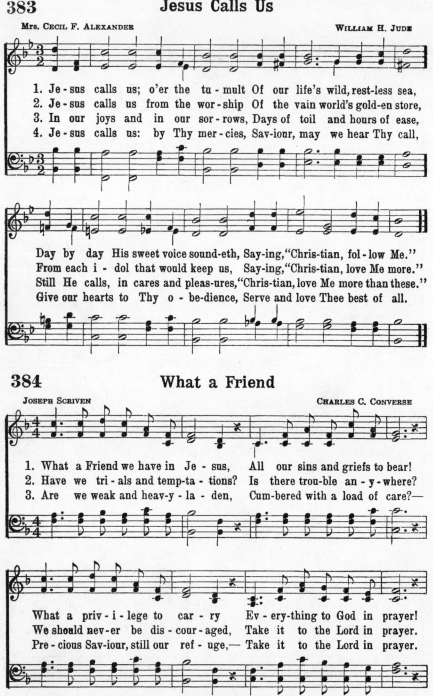

383 **Jesus Calls Us**

Mrs. Cecil F. Alexander

William H. Jude

1. Je-sus calls us; o'er the tu-mult Of our life's wild, rest-less sea,
2. Je-sus calls us from the wor-ship Of the vain world's gold-en store,
3. In our joys and in our sor-rows, Days of toil and hours of ease,
4. Je-sus calls us: by Thy mer-cies, Sav-iour, may we hear Thy call,

Day by day His sweet voice sound-eth, Say-ing, "Chris-tian, fol-low Me."
From each i-dol that would keep us, Say-ing, "Chris-tian, love Me more."
Still He calls, in cares and pleas-ures, "Chris-tian, love Me more than these."
Give our hearts to Thy o-be-dience, Serve and love Thee best of all.

384 **What a Friend**

Joseph Scriven

Charles C. Converse

1. What a Friend we have in Je-sus, All our sins and griefs to bear!
2. Have we tri-als and temp-ta-tions? Is there trou-ble an-y-where?
3. Are we weak and heav-y-la-den, Cum-bered with a load of care?—

What a priv-i-lege to car-ry Ev-ery-thing to God in prayer!
We should nev-er be dis-cour-aged, Take it to the Lord in prayer.
Pre-cious Sav-iour, still our ref-uge,— Take it to the Lord in prayer.

What a Friend

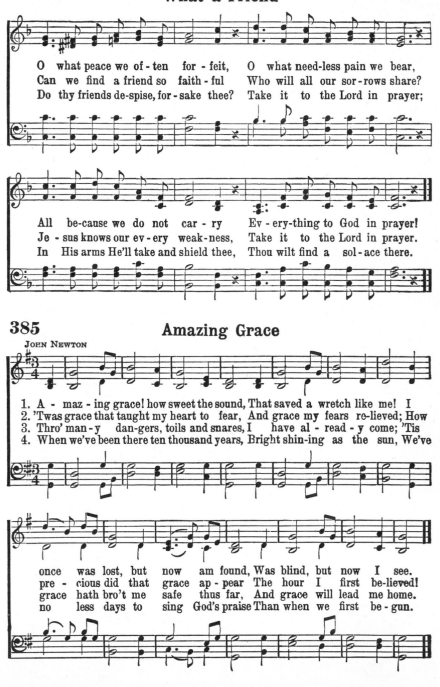

O what peace we of-ten for-feit, O what need-less pain we bear,
Can we find a friend so faith-ful Who will all our sor-rows share?
Do thy friends de-spise, for-sake thee? Take it to the Lord in prayer;

All be-cause we do not car-ry Ev-ery-thing to God in prayer!
Je-sus knows our ev-ery weak-ness, Take it to the Lord in prayer.
In His arms He'll take and shield thee, Thou wilt find a sol-ace there.

385   Amazing Grace

JOHN NEWTON

1. A-maz-ing grace! how sweet the sound, That saved a wretch like me! I
2. 'Twas grace that taught my heart to fear, And grace my fears re-lieved; How
3. Thro' man-y dan-gers, toils and snares, I have al-read-y come; 'Tis
4. When we've been there ten thousand years, Bright shin-ing as the sun, We've

once was lost, but now am found, Was blind, but now I see.
pre-cious did that grace ap-pear The hour I first be-lieved!
grace hath bro't me safe thus far, And grace will lead me home.
no less days to sing God's praise Than when we first be-gun.

Bringing In the Sheaves

KNOWLES SHAW

GEORGE A. MINOR

1. Sow-ing in the morn-ing, sow-ing seeds of kind-ness, Sow-ing in the
2. Sow-ing in the sun-shine, sow-ing in the shad-ows, Fear-ing nei-ther
3. Go-ing forth with weep-ing, sow-ing for the Mas-ter, Tho' the loss sus-

noon-tide and the dew-y eve; Wait-ing for the har-vest,
clouds nor win-ter's chill-ing breeze; By and by the har-vest,
tained our spir-it oft-en grieves; When our weep-ing's o-ver,

and the time of reap-ing, We shall come re-joic-ing, bring-ing in the sheaves.
and the la-bor end-ed, We shall come re-joic-ing, bring-ing in the sheaves.
He will bid us wel-come, We shall come re-joic-ing, bring-ing in the sheaves.

CHORUS

{ Bring-ing in the sheaves, bring-ing in the sheaves, We shall come re-joic-
{ Bring-ing in the sheaves, bring-ing in the sheaves, We shall come re-joic-

1. ing, bring-ing in the sheaves; 2. ing, bring-ing in the sheaves.

387   Channels Only

MARY E. MAXWELL   ADA ROSE GIBBS

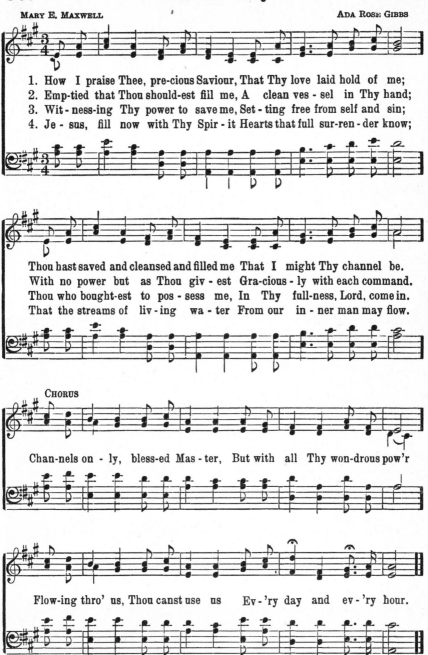

1. How I praise Thee, pre-cious Saviour, That Thy love laid hold of me;
2. Emp-tied that Thou should-est fill me, A clean ves - sel in Thy hand;
3. Wit - ness-ing Thy power to save me, Set - ting free from self and sin;
4. Je - sus, fill now with Thy Spir - it Hearts that full sur-ren - der know;

Thou hast saved and cleansed and filled me That I might Thy channel be.
With no power but as Thou giv - est Gra-cious - ly with each command.
Thou who bought-est to pos - sess me, In Thy full-ness, Lord, come in.
That the streams of liv - ing wa - ter From our in - ner man may flow.

CHORUS

Chan-nels on - ly, bless-ed Mas - ter, But with all Thy won-drous pow'r

Flow-ing thro' us, Thou canst use us Ev - 'ry day and ev - 'ry hour.

388 Proclaim It Wherever You Go

C. H. L.

C. HAROLD LOWDEN

1. If you know Christ Je-sus died and saved you from your sin, Pro-claim it wher-
2. If you find that Je-sus is suf-fi-cient for your need, Pro-claim it wher-
3. If you know His pres-ence gives you hap-pi-ness and peace, Pro-claim it wher-
4. If His word you've tested and have found each promise true, Pro-claim it wher-

ev-er you go! If you feel God's Ho-ly Spir-it prompting you with-in,
ev-er you go! If you know that dai-ly He your hun-gry soul doth feed,
ev-er you go! That in cares and tri-als He will grant a sweet re-lease,
ev-er you go! If a home you're building In that Land be-yond the blue,

CHORUS

Pro-claim it wher-ev-er you go!
Pro-claim it wher-ev-er you go!
Pro-claim it wher-ev-er you go!   Proclaim it wher-ev-er you go!
Pro-claim it wher-ev-er you go!   you go!

Pro-claim it wher-ev-er you go (you go)! Souls are wait-ing, yearning for the

bless-ings that you know, Pro-claim it wher-ev-er you go (you go)!

389 Count Me

W. C. POOLE

HALDOR LILLENAS

1. When you count the ones who love the Lord, Count me, count me;
2. When you count up those who're saved by grace, Count me, count me;
3. When you count up those who do the right, Count me, count me;
4. When you count up those who for-ward press, Count me, count me;
Count me, count me;

When you count up those who trust His Word, Count me, count me.
Who have found in Christ a hid-ing place, Count me, count me.
Who are walk-ing in the Gos-pel light, Count me, count me.
Who shall gain the crown of right-eous-ness, Count me, count me.
Count me, count me.

CHORUS

Count me with the chil-dren of the heav'n-ly King; Count me with the serv-ants who would serv-ice bring; Count me with the ran-somed who His prais-es sing; Count me, . . . count me. . . .
Count me, count me.

390 Help Somebody Today

Mrs. Frank M. Breck

Chas. H. Gabriel

1. Look all a-round you, find some one in need, Help some-bod-y to - day!
2. Man - y are wait-ing a kind, lov-ing word, Help some-bod-y to - day!
3. Man - y have bur-dens too heav-y to bear, Help some-bod-y to - day!
4. Some are dis-cour-aged and wea-ry in heart, Help some-bod-y to - day!

Tho' it be lit - tle—a neigh-bor-ly deed— Help some-bod-y to - day!
Thou hast a mes-sage, O let it be heard, Help some-bod-y to - day!
Grief is the por-tion of some ev - 'ry-where, Help some-bod-y to - day!
Some one the jour-ney to heav-en should start, Help some-bod-y to - day!

CHORUS

Help some-bod - y to - day, ... Some-bod - y a-long life's way; ... Let
to-day,   home-ward way;

sor-row be end-ed, The friendless befriended, Oh, help some-bod-y to - day!

391
Here Am I

JULIA A. JOHNSTON

J. B. TROWBRIDGE

1. Je - sus, Mas - ter, hast Thou mes - sag - es to send? Here am I,
2. Sav - iour, is there not some low - ly task to do? O send me,
3. Dost Thou need a hand to bear a shin - ing light? Use my hand,
4. Work-ing, wait - ing, what-so - e'er Thy ho - ly will, Here am I,

Here am I! Wait - ing, lis - t'ning at Thy feet I low - ly bend,
O send me Gird me now for serv - ice, make me strong and true,
Use my hand! Dost Thou need a pa - tient watch-er in the night?
Here am I! Mas - ter, let me Thy de - sire a - lone ful - fill,

CHORUS

Here am I— O do not pass me by!
Send me on some er-rand, Lord, for Thee.
Let me serve Thee, Lord, at Thy com - mand.
Keep me to Thy heart for - ev - er nigh.

Read - y for Thy serv - ice,

Mas - ter, here am I! Hush my heart to hear Thee call - ing from on high.

Choose Thou for me, let me still re - ply—O Mas - ter, here am I!

392 Labor On

Dr. C. R. BLACKALL

W. H. DOANE

Spirited

1. In the har-vest field there is work to do, For the
2. Crowd the gar-ner well with its sheaves all bright, Let the
3. In the glean-er's path may be rich re-ward, Tho' the
4. Lo! the Har-vest Home in the realms a-bove Shall be

grain is ripe, and the reap-ers few; And the Mas-ter's voice
song be glad, and the heart be light, Fill the pre-cious hours,
time seems long, and the la-bor hard; For the Mas-ter's joy,
gained by each who has toiled and strove, When the Mas-ter's voice,

bids the work-ers true Heed the call that He gives to-day.
ere the shades of night Take the place of the gold-en day.
with His cho-sen shared, Drives the gloom from the dark-est day.
in His words of love, Calls a-way to e-ter-nal day.

CHORUS

La-bor on, la-bor on, Keep the bright re-ward in view, For the
La-bor on, la-bor on,

Mas-ter has said He will strength re-new; La-bor on till the close of day.

393 Our Best

S. C. Kirk

Grant Colfax Tullar

1. Hear ye the Mas-ter's call, "Give Me thy best!" For, be it great or small,
2. Wait not for men to laud, Heed not their slight; Win-ning the smile of God
3. Night soon comes on a-pace, Day has-tens by; Workman and work must face

That is His test. Do then the best you can, Not for re - ward, Not for the
Brings its de-light! Aid-ing the good and true Ne'er goes unblest, All that we
Test-ing on high. Oh, may we in that day Find rest, sweet rest, Which God has

Chorus

praise of man, But for the Lord.
think or do, Be it the best. Ev - ery work for Je-sus will be blest,
prom-ised those Who do their best.

But He asks from ev-ery - one His best. Our tal - ents may be few,

These may be small, But un - to Him is due Our best, our all.

394 Make Me a Blessing

Ira B. Wilson

George S. Schuler

Slowly

1. Out in the highways and byways of life, Man-y are weary and sad; . . . .
   are wea-ry and sad;
2. Tell the sweet story of Christ and His love, Tell of His power to forgive; . . .
   His power to for-give;
3. Give as 'twas giv-en to you in your need, Love as the Master loved you; . . .
   the Mas-ter loved you;

Car - ry the sunshine where darkness is rife, Making the sor-row-ing glad. . . .
Oth - ers will trust Him if on - ly you prove True, every moment you live. . . .
Be to the help-less a help-er in - deed, Un - to your mis-sion be true. . . .

CHORUS *Men or Unison* *Women*

Make me a bless - ing, Make me a bless - ing, Out of my

life . . . . may Je - sus shine; . . Make me a bless - ing,

Men Out of my life

Women Parts ad lib.

O Sav - iour, I pray, . . . Make me a bless-ing to some-one to-day.
I pray Thee, my Sav-iour,

Tenors

Make Me a Channel of Blessing

H. G. S.

H. G. SMYTH

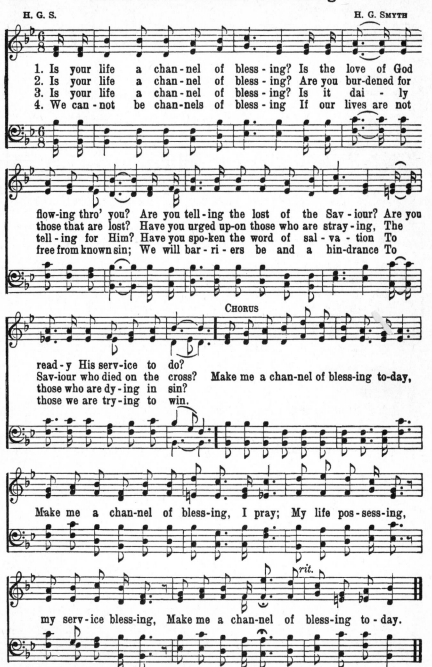

1. Is your life a chan-nel of bless-ing? Is the love of God
2. Is your life a chan-nel of bless-ing? Are you bur-dened for
3. Is your life a chan-nel of bless-ing? Is it dai - ly
4. We can-not be chan-nels of bless-ing If our lives are not

flow-ing thro' you? Are you tell-ing the lost of the Sav - iour? Are you
those that are lost? Have you urged up-on those who are stray-ing, The
tell-ing for Him? Have you spo-ken the word of sal - va - tion To
free from known sin; We will bar - ri - ers be and a hin-drance To

read - y His serv-ice to do?
Sav-iour who died on the cross?
those who are dy-ing in sin?
those we are try-ing to win.

CHORUS

Make me a chan-nel of bless-ing to-day,

Make me a chan-nel of bless-ing, I pray; My life pos-sess-ing,

rit.

my serv-ice bless-ing, Make me a chan-nel of bless-ing to - day.

396 Lead Me to Calvary

JENNIE EVELYN HUSSEY   WM. J. KIRKPATRICK

1. King of my life, I crown Thee now, Thine shall the glo - ry be;
2. Show me the tomb where Thou wast laid, Ten-der-ly mourned and wept;
3. Let me like Ma - ry, thro' the gloom, Come with a gift to Thee;
4. May I be will - ing, Lord, to bear Dai - ly my cross for Thee;

Lest I for-get Thy thorn-crowned brow, Lead me to Cal - va - ry.
An - gels in robes of light ar - rayed Guarded Thee whilst Thou slept.
Show to me now the emp - ty tomb, Lead me to Cal - va - ry.
E - ven Thy cup of grief to share, Thou hast borne all for me.

CHORUS

Lest I for - get Geth-sem - a - ne; Lest I for - get Thine ag - o - ny;

Lest I for - get Thy love for me, Lead me to Cal - va - ry.

397 Rescue the Perishing

FANNY J. CROSBY

WILLIAM H. DOANE

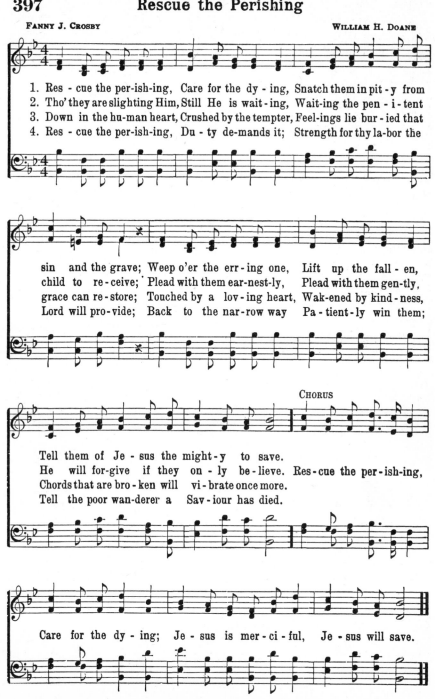

1. Res - cue the per-ish-ing, Care for the dy - ing, Snatch them in pit - y from
2. Tho' they are slighting Him, Still He is wait-ing, Wait-ing the pen - i - tent
3. Down in the hu-man heart, Crushed by the tempter, Feel-ings lie bur - ied that
4. Res - cue the per-ish-ing, Du - ty de-mands it; Strength for thy la-bor the

sin and the grave; Weep o'er the err - ing one, Lift up the fall - en,
child to re - ceive; Plead with them ear-nest-ly, Plead with them gen-tly,
grace can re - store; Touched by a lov - ing heart, Wak-ened by kind - ness,
Lord will pro - vide; Back to the nar-row way Pa - tient-ly win them;

CHORUS

Tell them of Je - sus the might-y to save.
He will for-give if they on - ly be - lieve. Res-cue the per-ish-ing,
Chords that are bro - ken will vi - brate once more.
Tell the poor wan-derer a Sav - iour has died.

Care for the dy - ing; Je - sus is mer-ci-ful, Je - sus will save.

Scattering Precious Seed

W. A. OGDEN

GEO. C. HUGG

1. Scat-ter-ing precious seed by the way-side, Scat-ter-ing precious seed by the
2. Scat-ter-ing precious seed for the grow-ing, Scat-ter-ing precious seed, free-ly
3. Scat-ter-ing precious seed, doubting never, Scat-ter-ing precious seed, trusting

hill - side; Scat-ter-ing precious seed o'er the field, wide, Scat-ter-ing precious
sow - ing, Scat-ter-ing precious seed, trusting, knowing, Sure-ly the Lord will
ev - er; Sow-ing the word with prayer and en-deav-or, Trusting the Lord for

CHORUS

seed by the way. Sow - ing in the morn - ing,
send it the rain.
growth and for yield. Sow-ing the precious seed, Sow-ing the precious seed,

Sow ing at the noon - tide; Sow - ing in the
Sowing the seed at noontide, Sowing the precious seed; Sowing the precious seed,

pp

eve ning, Sow-ing the pre-cious seed by the way. . . . .
Sowing the precious seed, by the way

399 Seeking the Lost

W. A. O.

W. A. ODGEN

1. Seek-ing the lost, yes, kind-ly en-treat-ing Wan-der-ers
2. Seek-ing the lost, and point-ing to Je-sus, Souls that are
3. Thus I would go on mis-sions of mer-cy, Fol-low-ing

on the moun-tain a-stray; "Come un-to Me," His mes-sage re-
weak and hearts that are sore; Lead-ing them forth in ways of sal-
Christ from day un-to day; Cheer-ing the faint, and rais-ing the

peat-ing, Words of the Mas-ter speak-ing to-day.
va-tion, Show-ing the path to life ev-er-more.
fall-en; Point-ing the lost to Je-sus, the Way.

CHORUS

{ Go-ing a-far
{ In-to the fold
up-on the moun-tain,
of my Re-deem-er,

{ Go-ing a-far . . . . . up-on the moun-tain, . . . Bring-ing the
{ In-to the fold . . . . . of my Re-deem-er, ... Je-sus, the

1.
2.

Bring-ing the wan-d'rer back a-gain,
Je-sus, the Lamb for sin-ners (*Omit.*) . . . . } slain, for sinners slain.

wan - - - - - d'rer back a-gain, ... }
Lamb . . . . for sin-ners (*Omit.*) . . . . } slain. . . . . . .

400 Throw Out the Life-Line

EDWARD S. UFFORD

E. S. UFFORD
Arr. by GEORGE C. STEBBINS

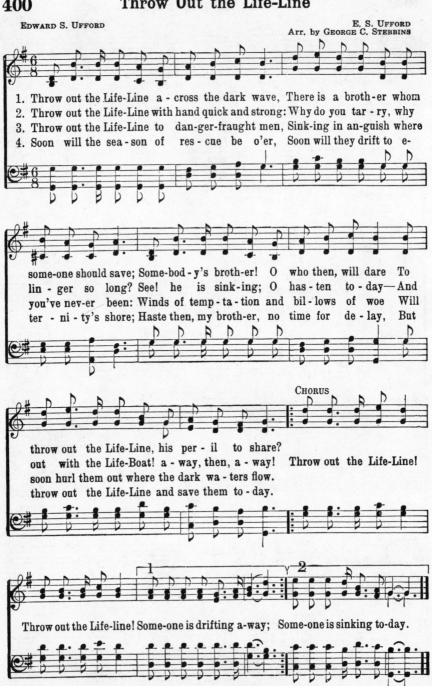

1. Throw out the Life-Line a - cross the dark wave, There is a broth - er whom some-one should save; Some-bod - y's broth-er! O who then, will dare To throw out the Life-Line, his per - il to share?

2. Throw out the Life-Line with hand quick and strong: Why do you tar - ry, why lin - ger so long? See! he is sink-ing; O has - ten to - day— And out with the Life-Boat! a - way, then, a - way!

3. Throw out the Life-Line to dan-ger-fraught men, Sink-ing in an-guish where you've nev-er been: Winds of temp - ta - tion and bil - lows of woe Will soon hurl them out where the dark wa - ters flow.

4. Soon will the sea - son of res - cue be o'er, Soon will they drift to e - ter - ni - ty's shore; Haste then, my broth - er, no time for de - lay, But throw out the Life-Line and save them to - day.

CHORUS

Throw out the Life-Line! Throw out the Life-line! Some-one is drifting a - way; Some-one is sinking to-day.

401 To the Work

FANNY J. CROSBY

W. H. DOANE

1. To the work! to the work! we are serv-ants of God, Let us fol-low the
2. To the work! to the work! let the hun-gry be fed; To the foun-tain of
3. To the work! to the work! there is la-bor for all; For the king-dom of
4. To the work! to the work! in the strength of the Lord, And a robe and a

path that our Mas-ter has trod; With the balm of His coun-sel our
life let the wea-ry be led; In the cross and its ban-ner our
dark-ness and er-ror shall fall; And the name of Je-ho-vah ex-
crown shall our la-bor re-ward, When the home of the faith-ful our

strength to re-new, Let us do with our might what our hands find to do.
glo-ry shall be, While we her-ald the ti-dings, "Sal-va-tion is free!"
alt-ed shall be, In the loud swell-ing cho-rus, "Sal-va-tion is free!"
dwell-ing shall be, And we shout with the ransomed, "Sal-va-tion is free!"

CHORUS

Toil-ing on, toil-ing on, Toil-ing on, toil-ing on;
Toil-ing on, toil-ing on, Toil-ing on, toil-ing on;

Let us hope, let us watch, And la-bor till the Mas-ter comes.
and trust, and pray,

Trust and Obey

J. H. SAMMIS

D. B. TOWNER

1. When we walk with the Lord In the Light of His Word What a glo-ry He
2. Not a shad-ow can rise, Not a cloud in the skies, But His smile quickly
3. Not a bur-den we bear, Not a sor-row we share, But our toil He doth
4. But we nev-er can prove The de-lights of His love Un-til all on the
5. Then in fel-low-ship sweet We will sit at His feet, Or we'll walk by His

sheds on our way! While we do His good-will, He a-bides with us still,
drives it a-way; Not a doubt or a fear, Not a sigh nor a tear,
rich-ly re-pay; Not a grief nor a loss, Not a frown or a cross,
al-tar we lay; For the fa-vor He shows, And the joy He be-stows,
side in the way; What He says we will do, Where He sends we will go,—

CHORUS.

And with all who will trust and o-bey.
Can a-bide while we trust and o-bey.
But is blest if we trust and o-bey. Trust and o-bey, for there's no oth-er
Are for them who will trust and o-bey.
Nev-er fear, on-ly trust and o-bey.

way To be hap-py in Je-sus, But to trust and o-bey.

403 Great is Thy Faithfulness

T. O. CHISHOLM   WILLIAM M. RUNYAN

1. "Great is Thy faith-ful-ness," O God my Fa-ther, There is no shad-ow of
2. Sum-mer and win-ter, and spring-time and harvest, Sun, moon and stars in their
3. Par-don for sin and a peace that en-dur-eth, Thy own dear presence to

turn-ing with Thee; Thou chang-est not, Thy com-pas-sions, they fail not;
cours-es a-bove, Join with all na-ture in man-i-fold wit-ness,
cheer and to guide; Strength for to-day and bright hope for to-mor-row,

CHORUS

As Thou hast been Thou for-ev-er wilt be.
To Thy great faith-ful-ness, mer-cy and love. "Great is Thy faith-ful-ness!
Blessings all mine, with ten thou-sand be-side!

Great is Thy faithfulness!" Morning by morning new mercies I see; All I have

rall.

need-ed Thy hand hath provided—"Great is Thy faithfulness," Lord, un-to me!

404 From Every Stormy Wind

HUGH STOWELL

THOMAS HASTINGS

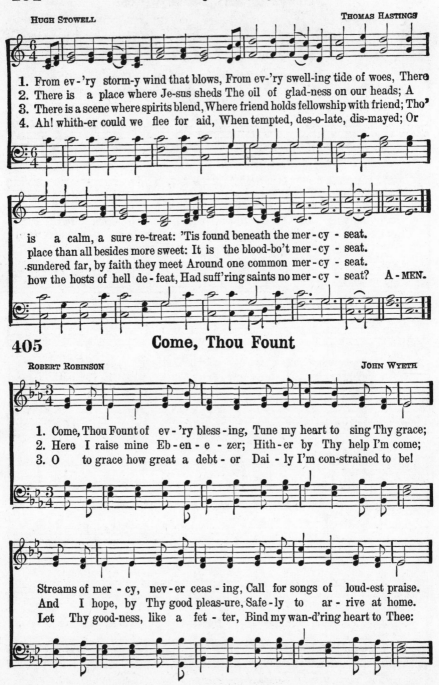

1. From ev-'ry storm-y wind that blows, From ev-'ry swell-ing tide of woes, There
2. There is a place where Je-sus sheds The oil of glad-ness on our heads; A
3. There is a scene where spirits blend, Where friend holds fellowship with friend; Tho'
4. Ah! whith-er could we flee for aid, When tempted, des-o-late, dis-mayed; Or

is a calm, a sure re-treat: 'Tis found beneath the mer-cy - seat.
place than all besides more sweet: It is the blood-bo't mer-cy - seat.
sundered far, by faith they meet Around one common mer-cy - seat.
how the hosts of hell de-feat, Had suff'ring saints no mer-cy - seat? A - MEN.

405 Come, Thou Fount

ROBERT ROBINSON

JOHN WYETH

1. Come, Thou Fount of ev-'ry bless-ing, Tune my heart to sing Thy grace;
2. Here I raise mine Eb-en-e-zer; Hith-er by Thy help I'm come;
3. O to grace how great a debt-or Dai-ly I'm con-strained to be!

Streams of mer-cy, nev-er ceas-ing, Call for songs of loud-est praise.
And I hope, by Thy good pleas-ure, Safe-ly to ar-rive at home.
Let Thy good-ness, like a fet-ter, Bind my wan-d'ring heart to Thee:

Come, Thou Fount

Teach me some me - lo - dious son - net, Sung by flam-ing tongues a - bove;
Je - sus sought me when a stran-ger, Wandering from the fold of God;
Prone to wan - der, Lord, I feel it, Prone to leave the God I love;

Praise the mount—I'm fixed up-on it— Mount of Thy re - deem-ing love.
He, to res - cue me from dan - ger, In - ter-posed His pre-cious blood.
Here's my heart, O take and seal it; Seal it for Thy courts a - bove.

406   ## Depth of Mercy

CHARLES WESLEY   WILLIAM B. BRADBURY

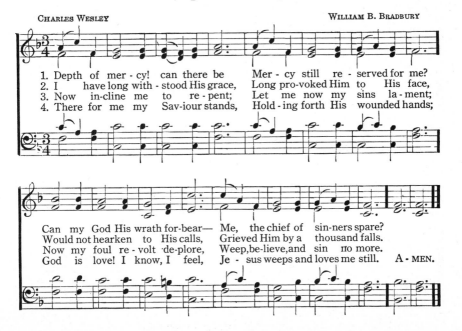

1. Depth of mer - cy! can there be   Mer - cy still re - served for me?
2. I have long with - stood His grace,   Long pro-voked Him to His face,
3. Now in-cline me to re - pent;   Let me now my sins la - ment;
4. There for me my Sav-iour stands,   Hold-ing forth His wounded hands;

Can my God His wrath for-bear— Me, the chief of sin-ners spare?
Would not hearken to His calls, Grieved Him by a thousand falls.
Now my foul re - volt de-plore, Weep, be-lieve, and sin no more.
God is love! I know, I feel, Je - sus weeps and loves me still. A - MEN.

O Worship the King

ROBERT GRANT

FRANCIS JOSEPH HAYDN

1. O wor-ship the King, all - glo-rious a - bove, And grate-ful-ly
2. O tell of His might, O sing of His grace, Whose robe is the
3. Thy boun - ti - ful care what tongue can re - cite? It breathes in the
4. Frail chil-dren of dust, and fee - ble as frail, In Thee do we

sing His pow'r and His love; Our Shield and De - fen - der, the An-cient of
light, whose can - o - py space; His char - iots of wrath the deep thunder-clouds
air, it shines in the light, It streams from the hills, it de-scends to the
trust, nor find Thee to fail; Thy mer - cies how ten - der, how firm to the

Days, Pa - vil - ioned in splen-dor, and gird - ed with praise.
form, And dark is His path on the wings of the storm.
plain, And sweet-ly dis - tills in the dew and the rain.
end! Our Mak - er, De - fend - er, Re - deem - er and Friend. A - MEN.

408   O for a Closer Walk with God

WILLIAM COWPER

Arr. from W. GARDINER

1. O for a clos - er walk with God, A calm and heav'n-ly frame,
2. Where is the bless - ed - ness I knew When first I saw the Lord?
3. The dear-est i - dol I have known, What-e'er that i - dol be,
4. So shall my walk be close with God, Calm and se - rene my frame;

O for a Closer Walk with God

409 My Faith Looks Up to Thee

410 Work, for the Night Is Coming

ANNIE L. COGHILL

LOWELL MASON

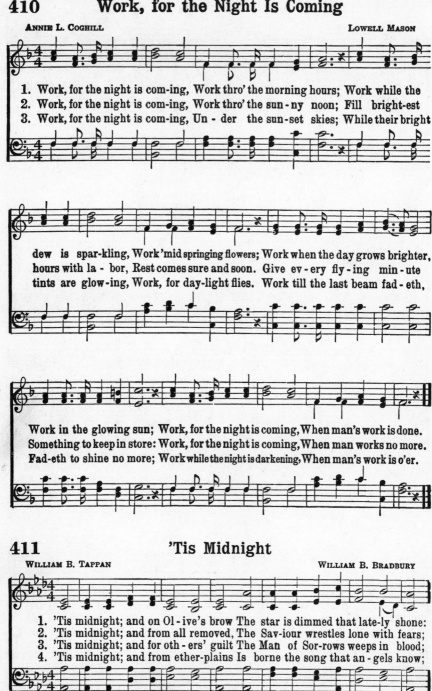

1. Work, for the night is com-ing, Work thro' the morning hours; Work while the
2. Work, for the night is com-ing, Work thro' the sun-ny noon; Fill bright-est
3. Work, for the night is com-ing, Un-der the sun-set skies; While their bright

dew is spar-kling, Work 'mid springing flowers; Work when the day grows brighter,
hours with la-bor, Rest comes sure and soon. Give ev-ery fly-ing min-ute
tints are glow-ing, Work, for day-light flies. Work till the last beam fad-eth,

Work in the glowing sun; Work, for the night is coming, When man's work is done.
Something to keep in store: Work, for the night is coming, When man works no more.
Fad-eth to shine no more; Work while the night is darkening, When man's work is o'er.

411 'Tis Midnight

WILLIAM B. TAPPAN

WILLIAM B. BRADBURY

1. 'Tis midnight; and on Ol-ive's brow The star is dimmed that late-ly shone:
2. 'Tis midnight; and from all removed, The Sav-iour wrestles lone with fears;
3. 'Tis midnight; and for oth-ers' guilt The Man of Sor-rows weeps in blood;
4. 'Tis midnight; and from ether-plains Is borne the song that an-gels know;

'Tis Midnight

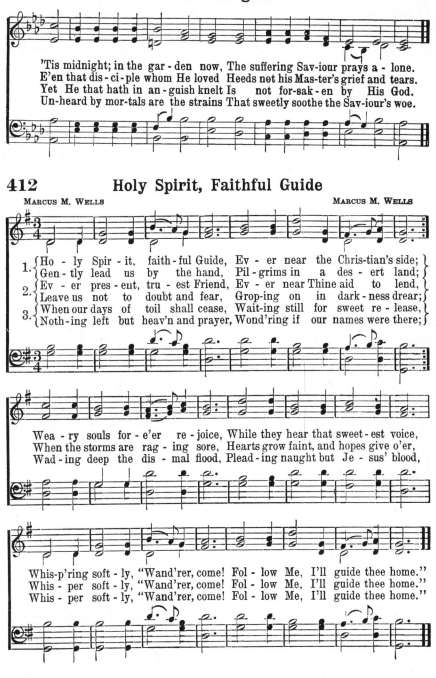

'Tis midnight; in the gar-den now, The suffering Sav-iour prays a-lone.
E'en that dis-ci-ple whom He loved Heeds not his Mas-ter's grief and tears.
Yet He that hath in an-guish knelt Is not for-sak-en by His God.
Un-heard by mor-tals are the strains That sweetly soothe the Sav-iour's woe.

412 Holy Spirit, Faithful Guide

MARCUS M. WELLS   MARCUS M. WELLS

1. {Ho - ly Spir - it, faith-ful Guide, Ev - er near the Chris-tian's side;}
   {Gen - tly lead us by the hand, Pil-grims in a des - ert land;}

2. {Ev - er pres - ent, tru - est Friend, Ev - er near Thine aid to lend,}
   {Leave us not to doubt and fear, Grop-ing on in dark-ness drear;}

3. {When our days of toil shall cease, Wait-ing still for sweet re - lease,}
   {Noth-ing left but heav'n and prayer, Wond'ring if our names were there;}

Wea - ry souls for - e'er re - joice, While they hear that sweet-est voice,
When the storms are rag - ing sore, Hearts grow faint, and hopes give o'er,
Wad-ing deep the dis - mal flood, Plead-ing naught but Je - sus' blood,

Whis-p'ring soft - ly, "Wand'rer, come! Fol - low Me, I'll guide thee home."
Whis - per soft - ly, "Wand'rer, come! Fol - low Me, I'll guide thee home."
Whis - per soft - ly, "Wand'rer, come! Fol - low Me, I'll guide thee home."

A Shelter in the Time of Storm

Words arranged

IRA D. SANKEY

1. The Lord's our Rock, in Him we hide, A shel-ter in the time of storm;
2. A shade by day, de-fense by night, A shel-ter in the time of storm;
3. The rag - ing storms may round us beat, A shel-ter in the time of storm;
4. O Rock di - vine, O Ref - uge dear, A shel-ter in the time of storm;

Se - cure what - ev - er ill be - tide, A shel-ter in the time of storm.
No fears a - larm, no foes af - fright, A shel-ter in the time of storm.
We'll nev-er leave our safe re - treat, A shel-ter in the time of storm.
Be Thou our help - er ev - er near, A shel-ter in the time of storm.

CHORUS

Oh, Je-sus is a Rock in a wea-ry land, A wea-ry land, a wea-ry land;

Oh, Je-sus is a Rock in a wea-ry land, A shel-ter in the time of storm.

414 Day is Dying in the West

MARY A. LATHBURY

WILLIAM F. SHERWIN

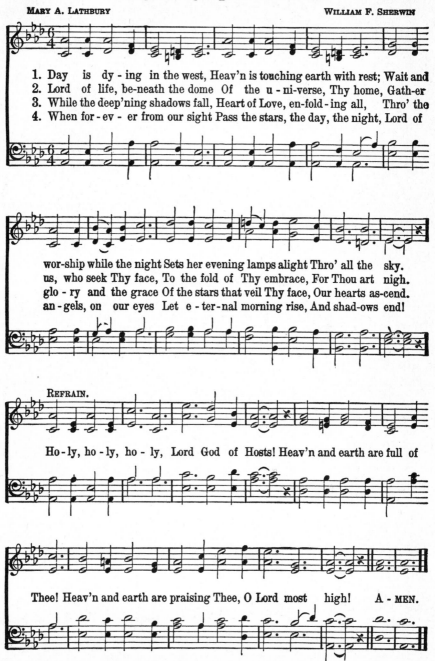

1. Day is dy-ing in the west, Heav'n is touching earth with rest; Wait and
2. Lord of life, be-neath the dome Of the u-ni-verse, Thy home, Gath-er
3. While the deep'ning shadows fall, Heart of Love, en-fold-ing all, Thro' the
4. When for-ev-er from our sight Pass the stars, the day, the night, Lord of

wor-ship while the night Sets her evening lamps alight Thro' all the sky.
us, who seek Thy face, To the fold of Thy embrace, For Thou art nigh.
glo-ry and the grace Of the stars that veil Thy face, Our hearts as-cend.
an-gels, on our eyes Let e-ter-nal morning rise, And shad-ows end!

REFRAIN.

Ho-ly, ho-ly, ho-ly, Lord God of Hosts! Heav'n and earth are full of

Thee! Heav'n and earth are praising Thee, O Lord most high! A-MEN.

415 Be Still, My Soul

KATHARINA VON SCHLEGEL
Tr. by JANE L. BORTHWICK

JEAN SIBELIUS

1. Be still, my soul: the Lord is on thy side;   Bear pa-tient-ly the
2. Be still, my soul: thy God doth un - der - take   To guide the fu - ture
3. Be still, my soul: the hour is has-tening on   When we shall be for-

cross of grief or pain; Leave to thy God to or - der and pro - vide;
as He has the past. Thy hope, thy con - fi-dence let noth-ing shake;
ev - er with the Lord, When dis-ap-point-ment, grief, and fear are gone,

In ev - ery change He faith-ful will re - main.   Be still, my soul: thy
All now mys - te - rious shall be bright at last.   Be still, my soul: the
Sor-row for-got, love's pur - est joys re - stored.   Be still, my soul: when

best, thy heaven-ly Friend Thro' thorny ways leads to a joy - ful end.
waves and winds still know His voice who ruled them while He dwelt below.
change and tears are past, All safe and bless - ed we shall meet at last.   A-MEN.

416   Grace Greater Than Our Sins

JULIA H. JOHNSTON

D. B. TOWNER

1. Mar - vel-ous grace of our lov - ing Lord, Grace that ex - ceeds our
2. Sin and de - spair like the sea waves cold, Threat-en the soul with
3. Dark is the stain that we can - not hide, What can a - vail to
4. Mar - vel-ous, in - fi - nite, match-less grace, Free - ly be - stowed on

sin and our guilt, Yon - der on Cal - va - ry's mount out - poured,
in - fi - nite loss; Grace that is great - er, yes, grace un - told,
wash it a - way? Look! there is flow - ing a crim - son tide;
all who be - lieve; You that are long - ing to see His face,

CHORUS

There where the blood of the Lamb was spilt.
Points to the Ref - uge, the Might - y Cross. Grace, grace,
Whit - er than snow you may be to - day.
Will you this mo - ment His grace re - ceive? Mar - vel - ous grace,

God's grace, Grace that will par-don and cleanse with-in; Grace,
In - fi - nite grace,   Mar - vel-ous

grace, God's grace, Grace that is great-er than all our sin.
grace, In - fi - nite grace,

417 Day by Day

Lina Sandell. (Swedish)
Tr. A. L. S.

Oscar Ahnfelt

1. Day by day, and with each pass - ing mo - ment, Strength I
2. Ev - 'ry day the Lord Him - self is near me, With a
3. Help me then, in ev - 'ry trib - u - la - tion, So to

find to meet my tri - als here; Trust-ing in my Fa - ther's
spe - cial mer - cy for each hour; All my cares He fain would
trust Thy prom - is - es, O Lord, That I lose not faith's sweet

wise be - stow - ment, I've no cause for wor - ry or for
bear and cheer me, He whose name is Coun - sel - lor and
con - so - la - tion, Of - fered me with - in Thy ho - ly

fear. He, whose heart is kind be - yond all meas - ure,
Pow'r. The pro - tec - tion of His child and treas - ure
word. Help me, Lord, when toil and troub - le meet - ing,

Gives un - to each day what He deems best, Lov - ing-
Is a charge that on Him - self He laid; "As thy
E'er to take, as from a fa - ther's hand, One by

ly   its part of pain and pleas-ure, Min-gling toil with peace and rest.
days, thy strength shall be in meas-ure,"–This the pledge to me He made.
one, the days, the moments fleet-ing, Till I reach the prom-ised land.

418   **Something for Jesus**

S. D. PHELPS

ROBERT LOWRY

1. Sav - ior, Thy dy - ing love Thou gav-est me,   Nor should I
2. At   the blest mer - cy-seat, Plead-ing for me,   My fee - ble
3. Give me a faith-ful heart,—Like-ness to Thee,— That each de-
4. All that I am and have,—Thy gifts so free,—   In joy, in

aught with-hold, Dear Lord, from Thee: In love my soul would bow, My heart ful-
faith looks up, Je - sus, to Thee: Help me the cross to bear, Thy wondrous
part - ing day Hence-forth may see Some work of love be - gun, Some deed of
grief, thro' life, Dear Lord, for Thee! And when Thy face I see, My ran-somed

fill its vow, Some of-f'ring bring Thee now, Something for Thee.
love de-clare, Some song to raise, or prayer, Something for Thee.
kindness done, Some wand'rer sought and won, Something for Thee.
soul shall be, Thro' all e - ter - ni - ty, Something for Thee. A - MEN.

He's the One

J. B. M.

J. B. MACKAY

1. Is there an-y-one can help us—one who understands our hearts, When the
2. Is there an-y-one can help us when the load is hard to bear, And we
3. Is there an-y-one can help us who can give the sin-ner peace, When his
4. Is there an-y-one can help us when the end is draw-ing near, Who will

thorns of life have pierced them till they bleed; One who sym-pa-thiz-es with us,
faint and fall be-neath it in a-larm; Who in ten-der-ness will lift us,
heart is bur-dened down with pain and woe; Who can speak the word of par-don,
go thro' death's dark wa-ters by our side; Who will light the way be-fore us,

who in wondrous love imparts Just the ver-y, ver-y bless-ing that we need?
and the heav-y bur-den share, And sup-port us with an ev-er-last-ing arm?
that af-fords a sweet release, And whose blood can wash and make us white as snow?
and dis-pel all doubt and fear, And will bear our spir-its safe-ly o'er the tide?

CHORUS

Yes, there's One! on-ly One! The bless-ed, bless-ed
Yes, there's One, on-ly One!

Je-sus, He's the One! When af-flic-tions press the soul, When

He's the One

waves of troub-le roll, And you need a Friend to help you, He's the One!

420

Have You Any Room For Jesus?

Arr. by W. W. D. from L. W. M.

C. C. WILLIAMS

1. Have you an-y room for Je - sus, He who bore your load of sin?
2. Room for pleas-ure, room for busi-ness, But for Christ the Cru-ci-fied,
3. Have you an-y room for Je - sus, As in grace He calls a-gain?
4. Room and time now give to Je - sus, Soon will pass God's day of grace;

As He knocks and asks ad-mis-sion, Sin - ner, will you let Him in?
Not a place that He can en - ter, In the heart for which He died?
O to - day is time ac-cept - ed, To-mor-row you may call in vain.
Soon thy heart left cold and si - lent, And thy Sav-ior's pleading cease.

CHORUS

Room for Je-sus, King of glo - ry! Has-ten now His word o-bey;

Swing the heart's door wide-ly o - pen, Bid Him en-ter while you may.

Hiding In Thee

Rev. WILLIAM O. CUSHING

IRA D. SANKEY

1. O safe to the Rock that is high-er than I,
2. In the calm of the noon-tide, in sor-row's lone hour,
3. How oft in the con-flict, when pressed by the foe,

My soul in its con-flicts and sor-rows would fly; So
In times when temp-ta-tion casts o'er me its power; In the
I have fled to my Ref-uge and breathed out my woe; How

sin-ful, so wea-ry, Thine, Thine would I be; Thou
tem-pests of life, on its wide, heav-ing sea, Thou
oft-en, when tri-als like sea-bil-lows roll, Have I

REFRAIN

blest "Rock of A-ges," I'm hid-ing in Thee.
blest "Rock of A-ges," I'm hid-ing in Thee. Hid-ing in Thee,
hid-den in Thee, O Thou Rock of my soul.

Hid-ing in Thee, Thou blest "Rock of A-ges," I'm hid-ing in Thee.

423

When I Survey the Wondrous Cross

From a Gregorian chant
Arr. by LOWELL MASON

ISAAC WATTS

1. When I sur-vey the won-drous cross, On which the Prince of Glo-ry died,
2. For-bid it, Lord, that I should boast, Save in the death of Christ, my God;
3. See, from His head, His hands, His feet, Sor-row and love flow min-gled down;
4. Were the whole realm of na-ture mine, That were a pres-ent far too small;

My rich-est gain I count but loss, And pour con-tempt on all my pride.
All the vain things that charm me most, I sac-ri-fice them to His blood.
Did e'er such love and sor-row meet, Or thorns compose so rich a crown.
Love so a-maz-ing, so di-vine, De-mands my soul, my life, my all. A-MEN.

424

The King of Love

Psalm 23
HENRY W. BAKER

JOHN B. DYKES

1. The King of love my Shep-herd is, Whose good-ness fail-eth nev-er;
2. Where streams of liv-ing wa-ter flow, My ran-somed soul He lead-eth,
3. Per-verse and fool-ish oft I strayed, But yet in love He sought me,
4. In death's dark vale I feel no ill With Thee, dear Lord, be-side me;
5. And so through all the length of days, Thy good-ness fail-eth nev-er;

I noth-ing lack if I am His, And He is mine for-ev-er.
And, where the ver-dant pas-tures grow, With food ce-les-tial feed-eth.
And on His shoul-der gent-ly laid, And home, re-joic-ing, bro't me.
Thy rod and staff they com-fort still, Thy cross be-fore to guide me.
Good Shepherd, may I sing Thy praise With-in Thy house for-ev-er. A-MEN.

425 There is Power in the Blood

L. E. J.   L. E. JONES

1. Would you be free from the bur - den of sin? There's pow'r in the blood,
2. Would you be free from your pas-sion and pride? There's pow'r in the blood,
3. Would you be whit - er, much whiter than snow? There's pow'r in the blood,
4. Would you do serv - ice for Je-sus your King? There's pow'r in the blood,

pow'r in the blood; Would you o'er e - vil a vic - to - ry win? There's
pow'r in the blood; Come for a cleans-ing to Cal - va - ry's tide; There's
pow'r in the blood; Sin-stains are lost in its life - giv - ing flow; There's
pow'r in the blood; Would you live dai - ly His prais - es to sing? There's

CHORUS.

won - der-ful pow'r in the blood. There is pow'r, pow'r, Wonder-working pow'r
there is

In the blood of the Lamb; There is pow'r, pow'r,
In the blood of the Lamb; there is

Won - der-work-ing pow'r In the pre - cious blood of the Lamb. A - MEN.

426   I'll Stand By Until the Morning

W. W. D.

James McGranahan

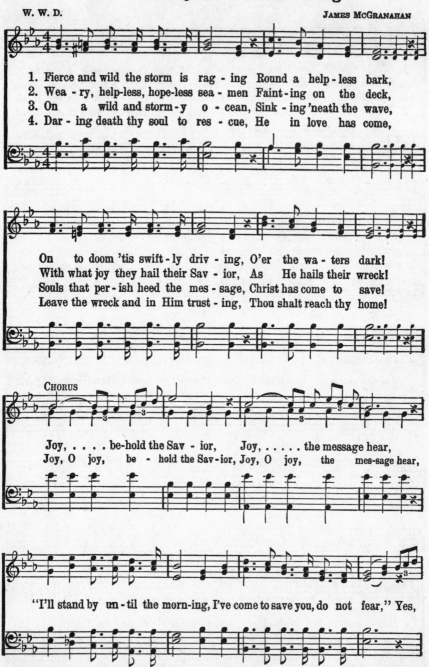

1. Fierce and wild the storm is rag-ing Round a help-less bark,
2. Wea-ry, help-less, hope-less sea-men Faint-ing on the deck,
3. On a wild and storm-y o-cean, Sink-ing 'neath the wave,
4. Dar-ing death thy soul to res-cue, He in love has come,

On to doom 'tis swift-ly driv-ing, O'er the wa-ters dark!
With what joy they hail their Sav-ior, As He hails their wreck!
Souls that per-ish heed the mes-sage, Christ has come to save!
Leave the wreck and in Him trust-ing, Thou shalt reach thy home!

Chorus

Joy, ... be-hold the Sav-ior, Joy, ... the message hear,
Joy, O joy, be-hold the Sav-ior, Joy, O joy, the mes-sage hear,

"I'll stand by un-til the morn-ing, I've come to save you, do not fear," Yes,

I'll Stand By Until the Morning

I'll stand by un-til the morn-ing, I've come to save you, do not fear (do not fear).

427   Shall We Gather At the River?

R. L.   ROBERT LOWRY

1. Shall we gath-er at the riv-er, Where bright an-gel feet have trod;
2. On the bos-om of the riv-er, Where the Sav-ior-King we own,
3. Ere we reach the shin-ing riv-er, Lay we ev-'ry bur-den down;
4. Soon we'll reach the shining riv-er, Soon our pil-grim-age will cease;

With its crys-tal tide for-ev-er Flow-ing by the throne of God?
We shall meet, and sor-row nev-er, 'Neath the glo-ry of the throne.
Grace our spir-its will de-liv-er, And pro-vide a robe and crown.
Soon our hap-py hearts will qui-ver With the mel-o-dy of peace.

CHORUS

Yes, we'll gather at the riv-er, The beau-ti-ful, the beau-ti-ful riv-er,

Gath-er with the saints at the riv-er That flows by the throne of God.

428 God Will Take Care of You

C. D. Martin

W. S. Martin

1. Be not dis-mayed what-e'er be-tide, God will take care of you;
2. Thru days of toil when heart doth fail, God will take care of you;
3. All you may need He will pro-vide, God will take care of you;
4. No mat-ter what may be the test, God will take care of you;

Be-neath His wings of love a-bide, God will take care of you.
When dan-gers fierce your path as-sail, God will take care of you.
Noth-ing you ask will be de-nied, God will take care of you.
Lean, wea-ry one, up-on His breast, God will take care of you.

CHORUS

God will take care of you, Thru ev-'ry day, O'er all the way;

He will take care of you, God will take care of you. . . . . .
take care of you.

429 Jesus, Blessed Jesus

COPYRIGHT 1906. RENEWAL 1934
THE RODEHEAVER CO., OWNER

Chas. H. Gabriel

Chas. H. Gabriel

Very effective as a Duet.

1. There's One who can com-fort when all else fails, Je - sus, bless-ed Je - sus;
2. He hear-eth the cry of the soul dis-tressed, Je - sus, bless-ed Je - sus;
3. He nev - er for-sakes in the dark-est hour, Je - sus, bless-ed Je - sus;
4. What joy it will be when we see His face, Je - sus, bless-ed Je - sus;

A Sav - ior who saves tho' the foe as - sails, Je - sus, bless-ed Je - sus:
He heal-eth the wound-ed, He giv - eth rest, Je - sus, bless-ed Je - sus:
His arm is a - round us with keep-ing pow'r, Je - sus, bless-ed Je - sus:
For-ev - er to sing of His love and grace, Je - sus, bless-ed Je - sus:

Once He trav - eled the way we go, Felt the pangs of de - ceit and woe;
When from loved ones we're called to part, When the tears in our an-guish start,
When we en - ter the Shad-ow - land, When at Jor - dan we trem-bling stand,
There at home on that shin-ing shore, With the loved ones gone on be - fore,

Who more per - fect-ly then can know Than Je - sus, bless-ed Je - sus?
None can com - fort the break-ing heart Like Je - sus, bless-ed Je - sus.
He will meet us with outstretched hand, This Je - sus, bless-ed Je - sus.
We will praise Him for - ev - er-more, Our Je - sus, bless-ed Je - sus.

430 Jesus is the Friend You Need

I. E. R.

I. E. REYNOLDS

1. When the sun shines bright and your heart is light, Je-sus is the Friend you need;
2. If you're lost in sin, all is dark with-in, Je-sus is the Friend you need;
3. When in that sad hour, when in death's grim pow'r, Je-sus is the Friend you need;
4. When the cares of life all a-round are rife, Je-sus is the Friend you need;

When the clouds hang low in this world of woe, Je-sus is the Friend you need.
God a-lone can save thro' the Son He gave, Je-sus is the Friend you need.
If you would pre-pare 'gainst the tempter's snare, Je-sus is the Friend you need.
Glo-ry to His name, al-ways He's the same, Je-sus is the Friend you need.

CHORUS

Je-sus is the Friend you need, Such a Friend is He in-
Je - sus is the Friend you need, Such a

deed; He who no-teth ev-'ry tear, He will
Friend is He in-deed;

ban-ish ev-'ry fear, Je-sus is the Friend you need.

431　Just When I Need Him Most

Rev. WM. Poole

Chas. H. Gabriel

1. Just when I need Him, Je-sus is near, Just when I fal-ter,
just when I fear; Read-y to help me, read-y to cheer,
Just when I need Him most.

2. Just when I need Him, Je-sus is true, Nev-er for-sak-ing
all the way thro'; Giv-ing for bur-dens pleas-ures a-new,
Just when I need Him most.

3. Just when I need Him, Je-sus is strong, Bear-ing my bur-dens
all the day long; For all my sor-row giv-ing a song,
Just when I need Him most.

4. Just when I need Him, He is my all, An-swer-ing when up-
on Him I call; Ten-der-ly watch-ing lest I should fall,
Just when I need Him most.

CHORUS.

Just when I need Him most, Just when I need Him most; Je-sus is near to com-fort and cheer, Just when I need Him most. A-MEN.

Jesus Took My Burden

Rev. Johnson Oatman, Jr.   Bertha Mae Lillenas

1. When I, a poor, lost sin-ner, Be-fore the Lord did fall, And in the name of
2. Oft-times the way is drear-y, And rugged seems the road, Oft-times I'm weak and
3. When I was crushed with sorrow I bowed in deep de-spair, My load of grief and
4. I'll trust Him for the fu-ture, He know-eth all the way, For with His eye He'll

Je - sus For par-don loud did call; He heard my sup-pli-ca-tion, And
wea - ry, When bent beneath some load; But when I cry in weak-ness, "How
heart-ache Seemed more than I could bear; 'Twas then I heard a whis-per, "You
guide me A - long life's pil-grim way; And I will tell in heav-en, While

soon the weak was strong, For Je-sus took my bur-den, And left me with a song.
long, O Lord, how long?" Then Je-sus takes the bur-den, And leaves me with a song.
to the Lord be-long," Then Je-sus took my bur-den, And left me with a song.
a - ges roll a-long, How Je-sus took my bur-den, And left me with a song.

CHORUS

Yes, Je - sus took my bur-den I could no lon-ger bear, Yes, Je-sus took my

bur-den In an - swer to my prayer; My anx-ious fears sub-sid-ed, My

Jesus Took My Burden

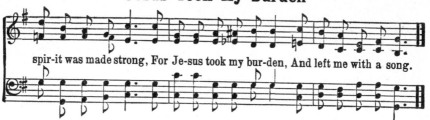

spir-it was made strong, For Je-sus took my bur-den, And left me with a song.

433 ## Hallelujah, 'Tis Done

P. P. B.

P. P. BLISS

1. 'Tis the prom - ise of God, full sal - va - tion to give
2. Tho' the path - way be lone - ly, and dan - ger - ous too,
3. Man - y loved ones have I in yon heav - en - ly throng,
4. There's a part in that cho - rus for you and for me,

Un - to him who on Je - sus, His Son, will be - lieve.
Sure - ly Je - sus is a - ble to car - ry me through.
They are safe now in glo - ry, and this is their song:
And the theme of our prais - es for - ev - er will be:

REFRAIN

Hal - le - lu - jah, 'tis done! I be-lieve on the Son; I am

saved by the blood of the cru - ci - fied One; cru - ci - fied One.

434 No Longer Lonely

R. H.

ROBERT HARKNESS

1. On life's pathway I am nev-er lone-ly, My Lord is with me, my Lord di-
2. I shall not be lone-ly in my sor-row, He will sus-tain me un-til the
3. I shall not be lone-ly in the val-ley, Tho' shadows gath-er, I will not

vine; Ev-er pre-sent Guide, I trust Him on-ly, No lon-ger
end; Dark-est night He turns to brightest mor-row, No lon-ger
fear; He has prom-ised ev-er to up-hold me, No lon-ger

CHORUS

lone-ly, for He is mine.
lone-ly! He is my Friend. No longer lone-ly, No longer lone-ly, For
lone-ly! He will be near.

Je-sus is the Friend of friends to me; . . . No lon-ger lone-ly, No lon-ger
to me;

lone-ly, For Je-sus is the Friend of friends to me.
of friends to me.

435   No, Not One!

JOHNSON OATMAN

GEO. C. HUGG

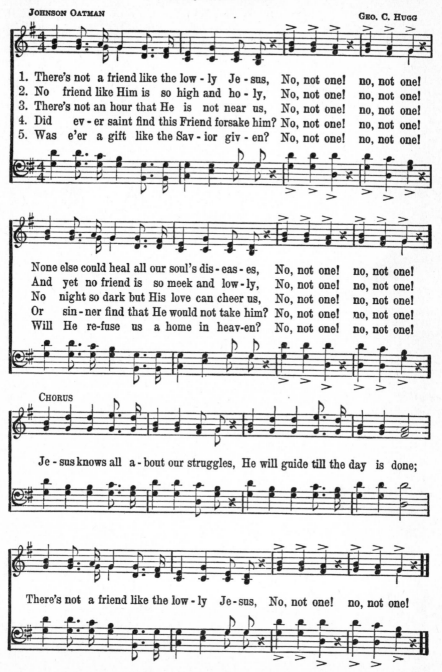

1. There's not a friend like the low - ly Je - sus, No, not one! no, not one!
2. No   friend like Him is   so high and ho - ly, No, not one! no, not one!
3. There's not an hour that He is   not near us, No, not one! no, not one!
4. Did   ev - er saint find this Friend forsake him? No, not one! no, not one!
5. Was   e'er a gift like the Sav - ior giv - en? No, not one! no, not one!

None else could heal all our soul's dis - eas - es, No, not one! no, not one!
And   yet no friend is   so meek and low - ly, No, not one! no, not one!
No   night so dark but His love can cheer us, No, not one! no, not one!
Or   sin - ner find that He would not take him? No, not one! no, not one!
Will   He re-fuse us   a home in heav-en? No, not one! no, not one!

CHORUS

Je - sus knows all a - bout our struggles, He will guide till the day is done;

There's not a friend like the low - ly   Je-sus, No, not one! no, not one!

436 I Am Resolved

Palmer Hartsough

J. H. Fillmore

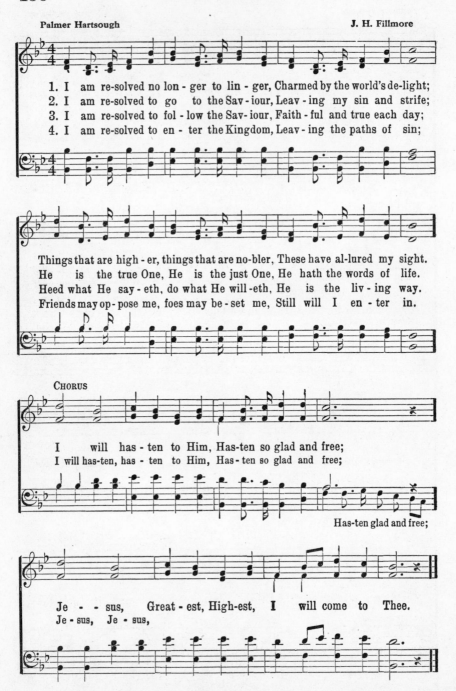

1. I am re-solved no lon - ger to lin - ger, Charmed by the world's de-light;
2. I am re-solved to go to the Sav-iour, Leav-ing my sin and strife;
3. I am re-solved to fol - low the Sav- iour, Faith-ful and true each day;
4. I am re-solved to en - ter the Kingdom, Leav-ing the paths of sin;

Things that are high - er, things that are no-bler, These have al-lured my sight.
He is the true One, He is the just One, He hath the words of life.
Heed what He say - eth, do what He will-eth, He is the liv - ing way.
Friends may op-pose me, foes may be - set me, Still will I en - ter in.

CHORUS

I will has - ten to Him, Has-ten so glad and free;
I will has-ten, has - ten to Him, Has-ten so glad and free;

Has-ten glad and free;

Je - - sus, Great - est, High-est, I will come to Thee.
Je - sus, Je - sus,

Safe in the Arms of Jesus

FANNY J. CROSBY

W. H. DOANE

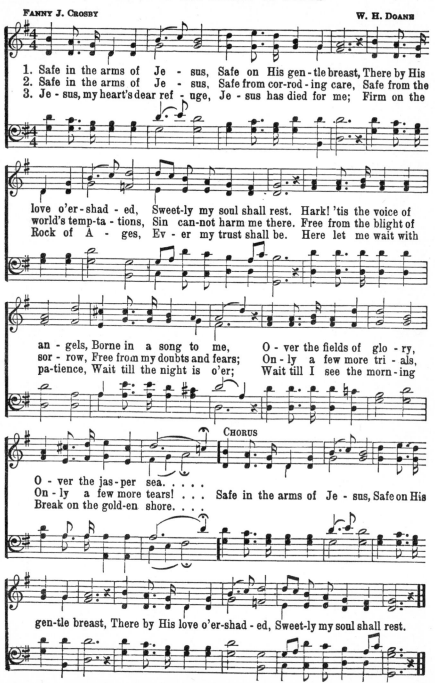

1. Safe in the arms of Je - sus, Safe on His gen - tle breast, There by His
2. Safe in the arms of Je - sus, Safe from cor-rod - ing care, Safe from the
3. Je - sus, my heart's dear ref - uge, Je - sus has died for me; Firm on the

love o'er-shad - ed, Sweet-ly my soul shall rest. Hark! 'tis the voice of
world's temp-ta - tions, Sin can-not harm me there. Free from the blight of
Rock of A - ges, Ev - er my trust shall be. Here let me wait with

an - gels, Borne in a song to me, O - ver the fields of glo - ry,
sor - row, Free from my doubts and fears; On - ly a few more tri - als,
pa - tience, Wait till the night is o'er; Wait till I see the morn - ing

CHORUS

O - ver the jas - per sea. . . . .
On - ly a few more tears! . . . Safe in the arms of Je - sus, Safe on His
Break on the gold-en shore. . . .

gen - tle breast, There by His love o'er-shad - ed, Sweet-ly my soul shall rest.

438 Have Thine Own Way, Lord

ADELAIDE A. POLLARD

GEO. C. STEBBINS

Slowly

1. Have Thine own way, Lord! Have Thine own way! Thou art the
2. Have Thine own way, Lord! Have Thine own way! Search me and
3. Have Thine own way, Lord! Have Thine own way! Wound-ed and
4. Have Thine own way, Lord! Have Thine own way! Hold o'er my

Pot - ter; I am the clay. Mould me and make me Aft - er Thy
try me, Mas-ter, to - day! Whit - er than snow, Lord, Wash me just
wea - ry, Help me, I pray! Pow - er—all pow - er—Sure - ly is
be - ing Ab - so - lute sway! Fill with Thy Spir - it Till all shall

will, While I am wait - ing, Yield - ed and still.
now, As in Thy pres - ence Hum - bly I bow.
Thine! Touch me and heal me, Sav - ior di - vine!
see Christ on - ly, al - ways, Liv - ing in me!

439 Peace in My Heart to Stay

W. P. L.

WENDELL P. LOVELESS

There's peace in my heart to - day, There's peace in my heart to stay; The
to-day, to stay;

Peace in My Heart to Stay

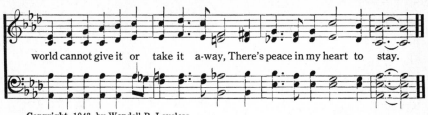

world cannot give it or take it a-way, There's peace in my heart to stay.

440 ## Hide Me

FANNY J. CROSBY

W. H. DOANE

1. Hide me, O my Sav-ior, hide me In Thy ho-ly place;
2. Hide me, when the storm is rag-ing O'er life's troub-led sea;
3. Hide me, when my heart is break-ing With its weight of woe;

Rest-ing there be-neath Thy glo-ry, O let me see Thy face.
Like a dove on o-cean's bil-lows, O let me fly to Thee.
When in tears I seek the com-fort Thou canst a-lone be-stow.

REFRAIN

Hide me, hide me, O bless-ed Sav-ior, hide me;
Hide me, hide me, safe-ly hide me,

O Sav-ior, keep me Safe-ly, O Lord, with Thee.
O my Sav-ior, keep Thou me,

441 Yesterday, Today, Forever

A. B. SIMPSON

J. H. BURKE

1. O how sweet the glo-rious mes-sage, Sim-ple faith may claim;
2. He who par-doned err-ing Pe-ter, Nev-er need'st thou fear;
3. He who 'mid the rag-ing bil-lows, Walked up-on the sea;
4. As of old He walked to Em-maus, With them to a-bide;

Yes-ter-day, to-day, for-ev-er, Je-sus is the same.
He that came to faith-less Tho-mas, All thy doubt will clear.
Still can hush our wild-est tem-pest, As on Gal-i-lee.
So thro' all life's way He walk-eth, Ev-er near our side.

Still He loves to save the sin-ful, Heal the sick and lame;
He who let the loved dis-ci-ple On His bos-om rest,
He who wept and prayed in an-guish, In Geth-sem-a-ne,
Soon a-gain shall we be-hold Him, Has-ten, Lord, the day!

Cheer the mourn-er, still the tem-pest, Glo-ry to His name!
Bids thee still, with love as ten-der, Lean up-on His breast.
Drinks with us each cup of trem-bling, In our ag-o-ny.
But 'twill still be "this same Je-sus," As He went a-way.

CHORUS

Yes-ter-day, to-day, for-ev-er, Je-sus is the same, All may change, but

Yesterday, Today, Forever

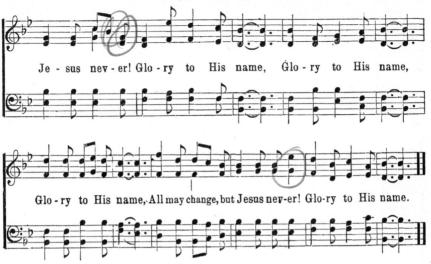

Je - sus nev - er! Glo - ry to His name, Glo - ry to His name,

Glo - ry to His name, All may change, but Jesus nev-er! Glo-ry to His name.

442   Jesus, Lover of My Soul

CHARLES WESLEY

S. B. MARSH
FINE

1. Je - sus, Lov - er of my soul, Let me to Thy bos - om fly,
While the near - er wa - ters roll, While the tem-pest still is high!
2. Oth - er ref - uge have I none; Hangs my help-less soul on Thee:
Leave, ah, leave me not a - lone, Still sup-port and com - fort me!
3. Thou, O Christ, art all I want; More than all in Thee I find;
Raise the fall - en, cheer the faint, Heal the sick, and lead the blind.
4. Plenteous grace with Thee is found, Grace to cov - er all my sin;
Let the heal-ing streams a-bound, Make and keep me pure with - in.

D. C.—Safe in - to the ha - ven guide, O re - ceive my soul at last!
D. C.—Cov - er my de-fense - less head With the shad-ow of Thy wing.
D. C.—False and full of sin I am, Thou art full of truth and grace.
D. C.—Spring Thou up with-in my heart, Rise to all e - ter - ni - ty.

D.C.

Hide me, O my Sav - ior, hide, Till the storm of life is past;
All my trust on Thee is stayed, All my help from Thee I bring;
Just and ho - ly is Thy name, I am all un-right-eous - ness;
Thou of life the foun - tain art; Free-ly let me take of Thee;

The Lord is My Shepherd

JAMES MONTGOMERY

THOMAS KOSCHAT, arr. by E. O. E.

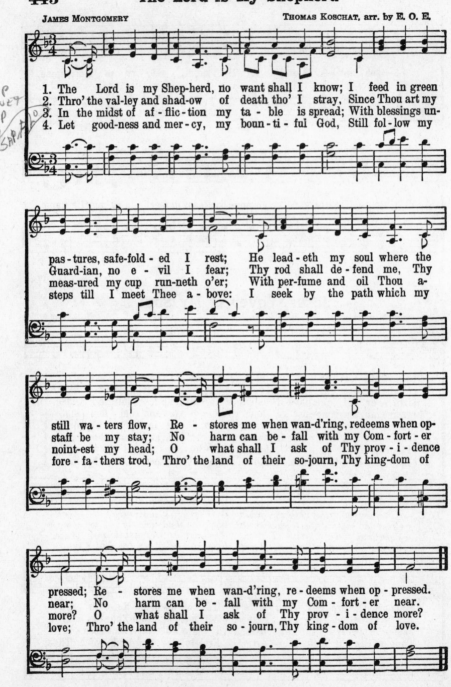

1. The Lord is my Shep-herd, no want shall I know; I feed in green
2. Thro' the val-ley and shad-ow of death tho' I stray, Since Thou art my
3. In the midst of af-flic-tion my ta-ble is spread; With blessings un-
4. Let good-ness and mer-cy, my boun-ti-ful God, Still fol-low my

pas-tures, safe-fold-ed I rest; He lead-eth my soul where the
Guard-ian, no e-vil I fear; Thy rod shall de-fend me, Thy
meas-ured my cup run-neth o'er; With per-fume and oil Thou a-
steps till I meet Thee a-bove: I seek by the path which my

still wa-ters flow, Re-stores me when wan-d'ring, redeems when op-
staff be my stay; No harm can be-fall with my Com-fort-er
noint-est my head; O what shall I ask of Thy prov-i-dence
fore-fa-thers trod, Thro' the land of their so-journ, Thy king-dom of

pressed; Re-stores me when wan-d'ring, re-deems when op-pressed.
near; No harm can be-fall with my Com-fort-er near.
more? O what shall I ask of Thy prov-i-dence more?
love; Thro' the land of their so-journ, Thy king-dom of love.

444

He Lifted Me

CHARLOTTE G. HOMER

CHAS. H. GABRIEL

1. In lov-ing-kind-ness Je-sus came My soul in mer-cy to re-claim,
2. He called me long be-fore I heard, Be-fore my sin-ful heart was stirred,
3. His brow was pierced with many a thorn, His hands by cru-el nails were torn,
4. Now on a high-er plane I dwell, And with my soul I know 'tis well;

And from the depths of sin and shame Thro' grace He lift-ed me......
But when I took Him at His word, For-giv'n He lift-ed me......
When from my guilt and grief, forlorn, In love He lift-ed me......
Yet how or why, I can-not tell, He should have lift-ed me......

He lift-ed me.

CHORUS.

From sink-ing sand He lift-ed me, With ten-der hand He lift-ed me,

From shades of night to plains of light, Oh, praise His name, He lift-ed me!

445 His Grace is Enough for Me

J. B. E.

J. BRUCE EVANS

1. Just when I am disheartened, Just when with cares oppressed, Just when my way is
2. Just when my hopes have vanished, Just when my friends forsake, Just when the fight is
3. Just when my tears are flowing, Just when with anguish bent, Just when temptation's

dark-est, Just when I am dis-tressed—Then is my Sav-ior near me, He knows my
thickest, Just when with fear I shake—Then comes a still small whisper: "Fear not, my
hard-est, Just when with sadness rent—Then comes a tho't of com-fort: "I know my

ev - 'ry care; Je-sus will nev-er leave me, He helps my bur-dens bear.
child, I'm near." Je-sus brings peace and comfort, I love His voice to hear.
Fa-ther knows," Je-sus has grace suf-fi-cient To con-quer all my foes.

CHORUS

His grace is e-nough for me, for me, His grace is e-nough for me;

Thro' sor-row and pain, Thro' loss or gain, His grace is e-nough for me.

446   In Tenderness He Sought Me

W. SPENCER WALTON

A. J. GORDON

1. In ten-der-ness He sought me, Wea-ry, and sick with sin,
2. He washed the bleed-ing sin-wounds, And poured in oil and wine;
3. He point-ed to the nail-prints, For me His blood was shed;
4. So while the hours are pass-ing, All now is per-fect rest;

And on His shoul-ders brought me Back to His fold a-gain; While
He whis-pered to as-sure me, "I've found thee, thou art Mine:" I
A mock-ing crown, so thorn-y, Was placed up-on His head: I
I'm wait-ing for the morn-ing, The bright-est and the best, When

an-gels in His pres-ence sang Un-til the courts of heav-en rang.
nev-er heard a sweet-er voice; It made my ach-ing heart re-joice!
won-dered what He saw in me To suf-fer such deep ag-o-ny.
He will call us to His side, To be with Him, His spot-less bride.

CHORUS.

Oh, the love that sought me! Oh, the blood that bought me! Oh, the grace that

brought me to the fold, Wondrous grace that brought me to the fold!

Saved By Grace

FANNY J. CROSBY   GEO. C. STEBBINS

1. Some day the sil - ver cord will break, And I no more as now shall sing;
2. Some day my earth-ly house will fall, I can-not tell how soon 'twill be,
3. Some day, when fades the gold-en sun Be-neath the ros - y - tint - ed west,
4. Some day: till then I'll watch and wait, My lamp all trimmed and burning bright,

But O, the joy when I shall wake With-in the pal-ace of the King!
But this I know—my All in All Has now a place in Heav'n for me.
My bless-ed Lord will say, "Well done!" And I shall en-ter in-to rest.
That when my Sav-ior opes the gate, My soul to Him may take its flight.

CHORUS

And I shall see Him face to face, And tell the sto-ry—Saved by grace;
shall see to face,

And I shall see Him face to face, And tell the sto-ry—Saved by grace.
shall see to face,

rit.

448   The Mercies of God

T. O. CHISHOLM   JESSE B. THOMAS

1. The mer-cies of God! what a theme for my song, Oh! I nev-er could
2. They greet me at morn when I wak-en from sleep, And they glad-den my
3. His an-gels of mer-cy en-compass me 'round, Whereso-ev-er my
4. His good-ness and mer-cy will fol-low me still, E-ven on to the

num-ber them o'er, They're more than the stars in the heav-en-ly dome,
heart at the noon; They fol-low me on in-to shades of the night
path-way may lead; Each turn of the road some new to-ken reveals—
end of the way, I have His sure prom-ise and that can-not fail,

Or the sands of the wave-beaten shore.
When the day with its la-bor is done.
Oh! for me life is bless-ed in-deed.
That His mer-cy en-dur-eth for aye.

CHORUS

For mer-cies so great, what re-turn can I make? For mer-cies so constant and sure? I'll love Him, I'll serve Him with all that I have As long as my life shall en-dure.

449 Wonderful Grace of Jesus

H. L.

HALDOR LILLENAS

1. Won-der-ful grace of Je-sus, Great-er than all my sin; ..
2. Won-der-ful grace of Je-sus, Reach-ing to all the lost, ..
3. Won-der-ful grace of Je-sus, Reach-ing the most de-filed, ...

How shall my tongue de-scribe it, Where shall its praise be-gin? ...
By it I have been pardoned, Saved to the ut-ter-most, ...
By its trans-form-ing pow-er, Mak-ing him God's dear child, ..

Tak-ing a-way my bur-den, Set-ting my spir-it free; ..
Chains have been torn a-sun-der, Giv-ing me lib-er-ty; ...
Pur-chas-ing peace and heav-en, For all e-ter-ni-ty; ...

For the won-der-ful grace of Je-sus reach-es me.
For the won-der-ful grace of Je-sus reach-es me.
And the won-der-ful grace of Je-sus reach-es me.

CHORUS

Won-der-ful the matchless grace of Je - - - sus,
the matchless grace of Je-sus,
Deep-er than the

Wonderful Grace of Jesus

450 My Hope Is in Thee

AVIS M. CHRISTIANSEN

GEORGE S. SCHULER

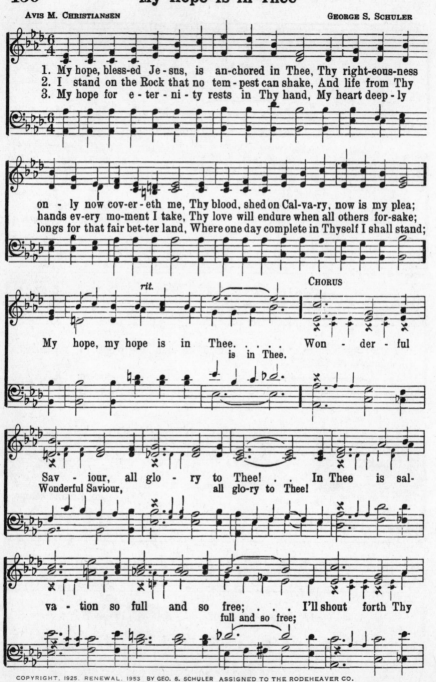

1. My hope, bless-ed Je-sus, is an-chored in Thee, Thy right-eous-ness
2. I stand on the Rock that no tem-pest can shake, And life from Thy
3. My hope for e-ter-ni-ty rests in Thy hand, My heart deep-ly

on-ly now cov-er-eth me, Thy blood, shed on Cal-va-ry, now is my plea;
hands ev-ery mo-ment I take, Thy love will endure when all others for-sake;
longs for that fair bet-ter land, Where one day complete in Thyself I shall stand;

rit.

CHORUS

My hope, my hope is in Thee. . . . Won - der - ful
is in Thee.

Sav - iour, all glo - ry to Thee! . . In Thee is sal-
Wonderful Saviour, all glo-ry to Thee!

va - tion so full and so free; . . . I'll shout forth Thy
full and so free;

My Hope Is in Thee

Women **Men**

prais - es thro' all e - ter - ni - ty; My Sav - iour, My Sav - iour,

Parts *ad lib.* My hope, my hope is in Thee.

My hope is in Thee, My hope is in Thee.

in Thee.

---

451 F. J. C.

Unsearchable Riches

Jno. R. Sweeney

1. O the un-search-a-ble rich- es of Christ!—Wealth that can nev-er be told;—
2. O the un-search-a-ble rich- es of Christ! Who shall their greatness de-clare!
3. O the un-search-a-ble rich- es of Christ! Free-ly, how free-ly they flow;
4. O the un-search-a-ble rich- es of Christ! Who would not glad-ly en - dure

Fine

Rich- es ex-haust-less of mer- cy and grace, Precious, more precious than gold!
Jew-els whose lus-ter our lives may a - dorn, Pearls that the poor-est may wear.
Mak-ing the souls of the faith-ful and true Hap - py wher-ev - er they go.
Tri - als, af-flic-tions, and cross-es on earth, Rich - es like these to se - cure!

D.S.—*O the un-search-a - ble rich - es of Christ! Precious, more precious than gold.*

Chorus

D. S.

Pre - cious, more pre - cious;—Wealth that can nev - er be told;

Cling to the Promises

ELIZABETH B. MILLER · GEORGE S. SCHULER

1. When doubts and fears as-sail thy soul And o'er thy heart like bil-lows roll,
2. When tempt-ed sore on ev - ery side To fol - low with the drift-ing tide,
3. When all is peace and joy and health, And fortune brings to you much wealth,
4. When ev - ery-thing is bright and gay, And when we hear the dear Lord say,

When wrath seems hovering like a cloud, O cling to the promise of God.
To leave the path thy Sav-iour trod, O cling to the promise of God.
For - get not in this cher-ished state To cling to the promise of God.
"Come, dwell up - on the moun-tain-top," Still cling to the promise of God.

CHORUS

O cling to the prom-is - es, They nev - er will fail; O cling
O cling   O cling

to the prom-is - es, to the prom-is - es of God; In Christ are the
                                                    In Christ

Unison   Parts

prom-is-es Yea and A - men! Then cling, O cling to the prom-is-es of God.

Tell It to Jesus

J. E. RANKIN

E. S. LORENZ

1. Are you wea - ry, are you heav - y-heart - ed? Tell it to Je - sus,
2. Do the tears flow down your cheeks un-bid - den? Tell it to Je - sus,
3. Do you fear the gath-'ring clouds of sor - row? Tell it to Je - sus,
4. Are you troub - led at the thought of dy - ing? Tell it to Je - sus,

Tell it to Je - sus; Are you griev - ing o - ver joys de - part - ed?
Tell it to Je - sus; Have you sins that to men's eyes are hid - den?
Tell it to Je - sus; Are you anx - ious what shall be to - mor-row?
Tell it to Je - sus; For Christ's com-ing King-dom are you sigh-ing?

CHORUS

Tell it to Je - sus a - lone. Tell it to Je - sus, tell it to Je - sus,

He is a friend that's well known; You've no oth - er

such a friend or broth - er, Tell it to Je - sus a - lone.

454

Jesus Loves Me

ANNA B. WARNER, alt.

WM. B. BRADBURY

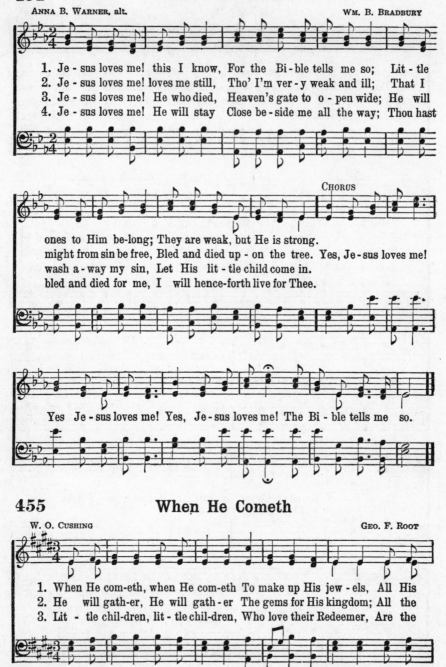

1. Je - sus loves me! this I know, For the Bi - ble tells me so; Lit - tle
2. Je - sus loves me! loves me still, Tho' I'm ver - y weak and ill; That I
3. Je - sus loves me! He who died, Heaven's gate to o - pen wide; He will
4. Je - sus loves me! He will stay Close be - side me all the way; Thou hast

CHORUS

ones to Him be-long; They are weak, but He is strong.
might from sin be free, Bled and died up - on the tree. Yes, Je - sus loves me!
wash a - way my sin, Let His lit - tle child come in.
bled and died for me, I will hence-forth live for Thee.

Yes Je - sus loves me! Yes, Je - sus loves me! The Bi - ble tells me so.

455

When He Cometh

W. O. CUSHING

GEO. F. ROOT

1. When He com-eth, when He com-eth To make up His jew - els, All His
2. He will gath-er, He will gath-er The gems for His kingdom; All the
3. Lit - tle chil-dren, lit - tle chil-dren, Who love their Redeemer, Are the

When He Cometh

jew - els, pre-cious jew - els, His loved and His own:
pure ones, all the bright ones, His loved and His own.
jew - els, pre-cious jew - els, His loved and His own.

Chorus

Like the stars of the
They shall shine in their

morn - ing, His bright crown a - dorn - ing,
beau - ty, (Omit....................)
Bright gems for His crown.

456   Dare to Be a Daniel

P. P. B.

P. P. Bliss

1. Stand-ing by a pur-pose true, Heed-ing God's command, Hon - or them, the
2. Man - y might-y men are lost, Dar - ing not to stand, Who for God had
3. Man - y gi-ants, great and tall, Stalk-ing thro' the land, Headlong to the
4. Hold the gos - pel ban-ner high! On to vic-t'ry grand! Sa - tan and His

faith - ful few! All hail to Dan-iel's Band!
been a host, By join-ing Dan-iel's Band!
earth would fall, If met by Dan-iel's Band!
host de - fy, And shout for Dan-iel's Band!

Chorus

Dare to be a Dan - iel,

Dare to stand a-lone! Dare to have a pur-pose firm! Dare to make it known!

Yield Not to Temptation

H. R. P.   Dr. H. R. PALMER

1. Yield not to temp-ta - tion, For yield-ing is sin; Each vic-tory will
2. Shun e - vil com-pan - ions, Bad lan-guage dis-dain; God's name hold in
3. To him that o'er-com - eth, God giv - eth a crown; Thro' faith we will

help you Some oth - er to win; Fight man - ful - ly on - ward,
rev-erence, Nor take it in vain; Be thought-ful and ear - nest,
con - quer, Though of-ten cast down; He who is our Sav - iour,

Dark pas-sions sub - due; Look ev - er to Je - sus, He'll car-ry you through.
Kind-heart-ed and true; Look ev - er to Je - sus, He'll car-ry you through.
Our strength will re-new; Look ev - er to Je - sus, He'll car-ry you through.

CHORUS

Ask the Sav - iour to help you, Com - fort, strength-en, and keep you;

He is will - ing to aid you, He will car - ry you through.

458   There Is a Green Hill Far Away

CECIL F. ALEXANDER

GEO. C. STEBBINS

1. There is a green hill far a-way, With-out a cit-y wall,
2. We may not know, we can-not tell What pains He had to bear;
3. He died that we might be for-giv'n, He died to make us good,
4. There was no oth-er good e-nough, To pay the price of sin;

Where the dear Lord was cru-ci-fied, Who died to save us all.
But we be-lieve it was for us He hung and suf-fered there.
That we might go at last to Heav'n, Saved by His pre-cious blood.
He on-ly could un-lock the gate Of Heav'n and let us in.

CHORUS

Oh, dear-ly, dear-ly has He loved, And we must love Him, too;

rit . . . .

And trust in His re-deem-ing blood, And try His works to do.

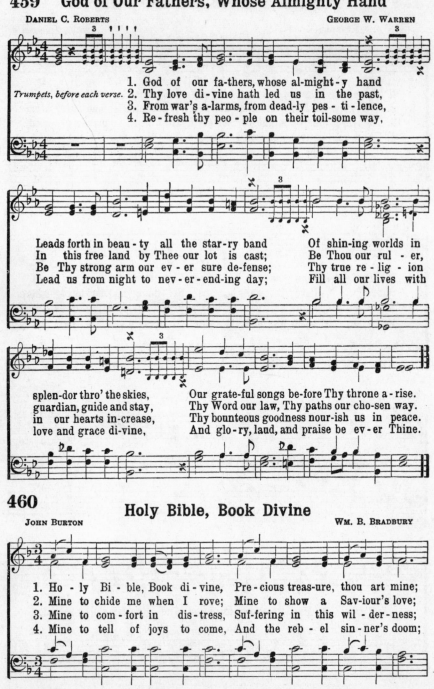

459 God of Our Fathers, Whose Almighty Hand

DANIEL C. ROBERTS

GEORGE W. WARREN

Trumpets, before each verse.

1. God of our fa-thers, whose al-might-y hand
2. Thy love di-vine hath led us in the past,
3. From war's a-larms, from dead-ly pes - ti-lence,
4. Re-fresh thy peo - ple on their toil-some way,

Leads forth in beau - ty all the star-ry band Of shin-ing worlds in
In this free land by Thee our lot is cast; Be Thou our rul - er,
Be Thy strong arm our ev - er sure de-fense; Thy true re - lig - ion
Lead us from night to nev - er-end-ing day; Fill all our lives with

splen-dor thro' the skies, Our grate-ful songs be-fore Thy throne a - rise.
guardian, guide and stay, Thy Word our law, Thy paths our cho-sen way.
in our hearts in-crease, Thy bounteous goodness nour-ish us in peace.
love and grace di-vine, And glo-ry, laud, and praise be ev - er Thine.

460 Holy Bible, Book Divine

JOHN BURTON

WM. B. BRADBURY

1. Ho - ly Bi - ble, Book di - vine, Pre - cious treas-ure, thou art mine;
2. Mine to chide me when I rove; Mine to show a Sav-iour's love;
3. Mine to com - fort in dis-tress, Suf-fering in this wil - der-ness;
4. Mine to tell of joys to come, And the reb - el sin-ner's doom;

Holy Bible, Book Divine

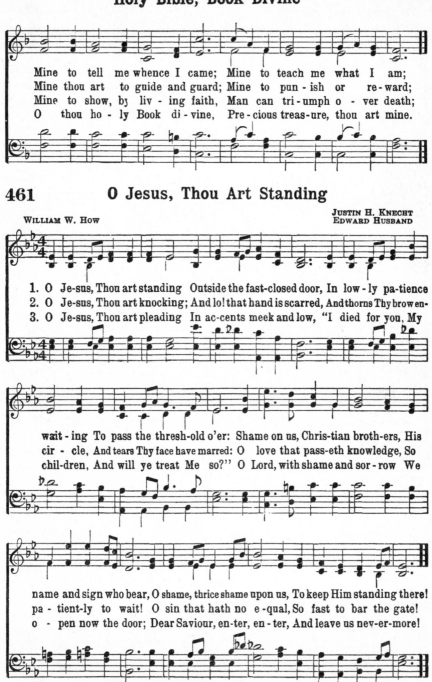

Mine to tell me whence I came; Mine to teach me what I am;
Mine thou art to guide and guard; Mine to pun-ish or re-ward;
Mine to show, by liv-ing faith, Man can tri-umph o-ver death;
O thou ho-ly Book di-vine, Pre-cious treas-ure, thou art mine.

461   O Jesus, Thou Art Standing

WILLIAM W. HOW

JUSTIN H. KNECHT
EDWARD HUSBAND

1. O Je-sus, Thou art standing Outside the fast-closed door, In low-ly pa-tience
2. O Je-sus, Thou art knocking; And lo! that hand is scarred, And thorns Thy brow en-
3. O Je-sus, Thou art pleading In ac-cents meek and low, "I died for you, My

wait-ing To pass the thresh-old o'er: Shame on us, Chris-tian broth-ers, His
cir-cle, And tears Thy face have marred: O love that pass-eth knowledge, So
chil-dren, And will ye treat Me so?" O Lord, with shame and sor-row We

name and sign who bear, O shame, thrice shame upon us, To keep Him standing there!
pa-tient-ly to wait! O sin that hath no e-qual, So fast to bar the gate!
o-pen now the door; Dear Saviour, en-ter, en-ter, And leave us nev-er-more!

462 America, the Beautiful

KATHERINE LEE BATES

SAMUEL A. WARD

1. O beau - ti - ful for spa-cious skies, For am - ber waves of grain,
2. O beau - ti - ful for pil - grim feet, Whose stern, im-pas-sioned stress
3. O beau - ti - ful for he - roes proved In lib - er - at - ing strife,
4. O beau - ti - ful for pa - triot dream That sees be - yond the years

For pur - ple moun-tain maj - es - ties, A - bove the fruit - ed plain!
A thor-ough-fare for free - dom beat A - cross the wil - der - ness!
Who more than self their coun - try loved, And mer - cy more than life!
Thine al - a - bas - ter cit - ies gleam, Undimmed by hu - man tears!

A - mer - i - ca! A - mer - i - ca! God shed His grace on thee,
A - mer - i - ca! A - mer - i - ca! God mend thine ev - 'ry flaw,
A - mer - i - ca! A - mer - i - ca! May God thy gold re - fine,
A - mer - i - ca! A - mer - i - ca! God shed His grace on thee,

And crown thy good with broth - er-hood From sea to shin - ing sea!
Con - firm thy soul in self - con-trol, Thy lib - er - ty in law!
Till all suc-cess be no - ble-ness, And ev - 'ry gain di - vine!
And crown thy good with broth - er-hood From sea to shin - ing sea!

463 **Mine Eyes Have Seen the Glory**

JULIA WARD HOWE

WILLIAM STEFFE

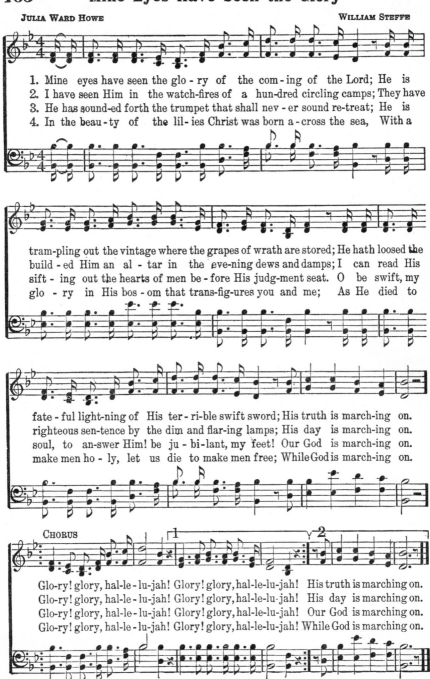

1. Mine eyes have seen the glo-ry of the com-ing of the Lord; He is
2. I have seen Him in the watch-fires of a hun-dred circling camps; They have
3. He has sound-ed forth the trumpet that shall nev-er sound re-treat; He is
4. In the beau-ty of the lil-ies Christ was born a-cross the sea, With a

tram-pling out the vintage where the grapes of wrath are stored; He hath loosed the
build-ed Him an al-tar in the eve-ning dews and damps; I can read His
sift-ing out the hearts of men be-fore His judg-ment seat. O be swift, my
glo-ry in His bos-om that trans-fig-ures you and me; As He died to

fate-ful light-ning of His ter-ri-ble swift sword; His truth is march-ing on.
righteous sen-tence by the dim and flar-ing lamps; His day is march-ing on.
soul, to an-swer Him! be ju-bi-lant, my feet! Our God is march-ing on.
make men ho-ly, let us die to make men free; While God is march-ing on.

CHORUS

Glo-ry! glory, hal-le-lu-jah! Glory! glory, hal-le-lu-jah! His truth is marching on.
Glo-ry! glory, hal-le-lu-jah! Glory! glory, hal-le-lu-jah! His day is marching on.
Glo-ry! glory, hal-le-lu-jah! Glory! glory, hal-le-lu-jah! Our God is marching on.
Glo-ry! glory, hal-le-lu-jah! Glory! glory, hal-le-lu-jah! While God is marching on.

The Star-Spangled Banner

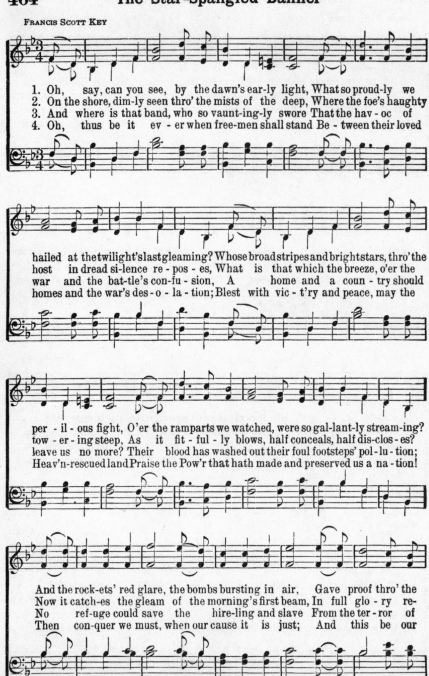

FRANCIS SCOTT KEY

1. Oh, say, can you see, by the dawn's ear-ly light, What so proud-ly we
2. On the shore, dim-ly seen thro' the mists of the deep, Where the foe's haughty
3. And where is that band, who so vaunt-ing-ly swore That the hav-oc of
4. Oh, thus be it ev-er when free-men shall stand Be-tween their loved

hailed at the twilight's last gleaming? Whose broad stripes and bright stars, thro' the
host in dread si-lence re-pos-es, What is that which the breeze, o'er the
war and the bat-tle's con-fu-sion, A home and a coun-try should
homes and the war's des-o-la-tion; Blest with vic-t'ry and peace, may the

per-il-ous fight, O'er the ramparts we watched, were so gal-lant-ly stream-ing?
tow-er-ing steep, As it fit-ful-ly blows, half conceals, half dis-clos-es?
leave us no more? Their blood has washed out their foul footsteps' pol-lu-tion;
Heav'n-rescued land Praise the Pow'r that hath made and preserved us a na-tion!

And the rock-ets' red glare, the bombs bursting in air, Gave proof thro' the
Now it catch-es the gleam of the morning's first beam, In full glo-ry re-
No ref-uge could save the hire-ling and slave From the ter-ror of
Then con-quer we must, when our cause it is just; And this be our

The Star-Spangled Banner

ff CHORUS

night that our flag was still there. Oh, say, does that star-span-gled
flect - ed, now shines on the stream: 'Tis the star-span-gled ban - ner; oh,
flight 'or the gloom of the grave. And the star-span-gled ban - ner in
mot - to: "In God is our trust!" And the star-span-gled ban - ner in

ban - ner yet wave O'er the land of the free, and the home of the brave?
long may it wave O'er the land of the free, and the home of the brave.
tri - umph doth wave O'er the land of the free, and the home of the brave.
tri - umph shall wave O'er the land of the free, and the home of the brave.

465 Our God, Our Help

From Psalm 90
ISAAC WATTS

WILLIAM CROFT

1. Our God, our help in a - ges past, Our hope for years to come,
2. Un - der the shad - ow of Thy throne Still may we dwell se - cure;
3. Be - fore the hills in or - der stood, Or earth re-ceived her frame,
4. Time, like an ev - er - roll - ing stream, Bears all its sons a - way;
5. Our God, our help in a - ges past, Our hope for years to come,

Our shel - ter from the storm - y blast, And our e - ter - nal home!
Suf - fi - cient is Thine arm a - lone, And our de-fense is sure.
From ev - er - last - ing Thou art God, To end-less years the same.
They fly, for - got - ten, as a dream Dies at the ope-ning day.
Be Thou our guide while life shall last, And our e - ter - nal home. A-MEN.

He Was Not Willing

L. R. M.

Lucy R. Meyer

1. "He was not will-ing that an - y should per - ish;" Je - sus en-throned in the
2. "He was not will-ing that an - y should per - ish:" Clothed in our flesh with its
3. Plen-ty for pleas-ure, but lit - tle for Je - sus; Time for the world with its
4. "He was not will-ing that an - y should per - ish;" Am I His fol - low - er,

glo - ry a - bove, Saw our poor fall-en world, pit - ied our sor - rows, Poured out His
sor - row and pain, Came He to seek the lost, com-fort the mourn-er, Heal the heart
trou-bles and toys, No time for Je-sus' work, feed-ing the hun - gry, Lift - ing lost
and can I live Lon-ger at ease with a soul go-ing down-ward, Lost for the

life for us, won-der-ful love! Per-ish-ing, per-ish-ing! Throng-ing our path-way,
bro-ken by sor-row and shame. Per-ish-ing, per-ish-ing! Har - vest is pass-ing;
souls to e - ter - ni-ty's joys. Per-ish-ing, per-ish-ing! Hark, how they call us;
lack of the help I might give? Per-ish-ing, per-ish-ing! Thou wast not will - ing;

Hearts break with bur-dens too heav - y to bear: Je - sus would save, but there's
Reap - ers are few and the night draw-eth near: Je - sus is call-ing thee,
Bring us your Sav-ior, oh, tell us of Him! We are so wea-ry, so
Mas - ter, for-give, and in-spire us a - new; Ban - ish our world-li - ness

no one to tell them, No one to lift them from sin and de - spair.
haste to the reap - ing, Thou shalt have souls, pre - cious souls for thy hire.
heav - i - ly la - den, And with long weep-ing our eyes have grown dim.
help us to ev - er Live with e - ter - ni-ty's val - ues in view.

467 Go Ye Into All the World

J. McG.

JAMES McGRANAHAN

1. Far, far a-way, in hea-then darkness dwell-ing, Mil-lions of souls for-
2. See o'er the world wide-o-pen doors in-vit-ing, Sol-diers of Christ, a-
3. "Why will ye die?" the voice of God is call-ing, "Why will ye die?" re-
4. God speed the day, when those of ev-'ry na-tion "Glo-ry to God!" tri-

ev-er may be lost; Who, who will go, sal-va-tion's sto-ry tell-ing,
rise and en-ter in! Chris-tians, a-wake! your forc-es all u-nit-ing,
ech-o in His name; Je-sus hath died to save from death ap-pall-ing,
um-phant-ly shall sing; Ran-somed, redeemed, re-joic-ing in sal-va-tion,

CHORUS

Look-ing to Je-sus, minding not the cost?
Send forth the gospel, break the chains of sin. "All pow'r is giv-en un-to Me,
Life and sal-va-tion therefore go pro-claim.
Shout Hal-le-lu-jah, for the Lord is King.

All pow'r is giv-en un-to Me, Go ye in-to all the world and

preach the gos-pel, And lo, I am with you al-way."

Launch Out

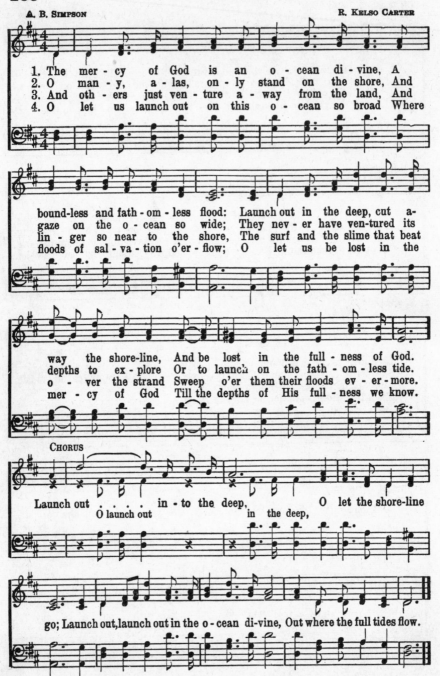

Jesus Saves

PRISCILLA J. OWENS

WM. J. KIRKPATRICK

1. We have heard the joy - ful sound: Je - sus saves! Je - sus saves!
2. Waft it on the roll - ing tide; Je - sus saves! Je - sus saves!
3. Sing a - bove the bat - tle strife, Je - sus saves! Je - sus saves!
4. Give the winds a might - y voice, Je - sus saves! Je - sus saves!

Spread the ti - dings all a - round: Je - sus saves! Je - sus saves!
Tell to sin - ners far and wide: Je - sus saves! Je - sus saves!
By His death and end - less life, Je - sus saves! Je - sus saves!
Let the na - tions now re - joice,— Je - sus saves! Je - sus saves!

Bear the news to ev - 'ry land, Climb the steeps and cross the waves;
Sing, ye is - lands of the sea; Ech - o back, ye o - cean caves;
Sing it soft - ly thro' the gloom, When the heart for mer - cy craves;
Shout sal - va - tion full and free; High - est hills and deep - est caves;

On - ward!—'tis our Lord's com-mand; Je - sus saves! Je - sus saves!
Earth shall keep her ju - bi - lee: Je - sus saves! Je - sus saves!
Sing in tri - umph o'er the tomb,— Je - sus saves! Je - sus saves!
This our song of vic - to - ry,— Je - sus saves! Je - sus saves!

470 Jesus Shall Reign

Isaac Watts

John Hatton

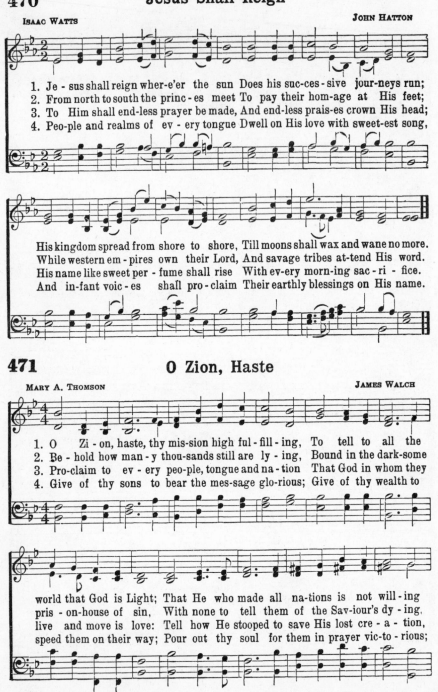

1. Je - sus shall reign wher-e'er the sun Does his suc-ces-sive jour-neys run;
2. From north to south the princ-es meet To pay their hom-age at His feet;
3. To Him shall end-less prayer be made, And end-less prais-es crown His head;
4. Peo-ple and realms of ev - ery tongue Dwell on His love with sweet-est song,

His kingdom spread from shore to shore, Till moons shall wax and wane no more.
While western em - pires own their Lord, And savage tribes at-tend His word.
His name like sweet per - fume shall rise With ev-ery morn-ing sac - ri - fice.
And in-fant voic - es shall pro - claim Their earthly blessings on His name.

471 O Zion, Haste

Mary A. Thomson

James Walch

1. O Zi - on, haste, thy mis-sion high ful - fill - ing, To tell to all the
2. Be - hold how man - y thou-sands still are ly - ing, Bound in the dark-some
3. Pro-claim to ev - ery peo-ple, tongue and na - tion That God in whom they
4. Give of thy sons to bear the mes-sage glo-rious; Give of thy wealth to

world that God is Light; That He who made all na-tions is not will - ing
pris - on-house of sin, With none to tell them of the Sav-iour's dy - ing,
live and move is love: Tell how He stooped to save His lost cre - a - tion,
speed them on their way; Pour out thy soul for them in prayer vic-to - rious;

O Zion, Haste

REFRAIN

One soul should per-ish, lost in shades of night.
Or of the life He died for them to win. Pub-lish glad ti-dings,
And died on earth that man might live a-bove.
And all thou spend-est Je-sus will re-pay.

Ti-dings of peace; Ti-dings of Je - sus, Re-demp-tion and re-lease.

472 Fling Out the Banner! Let It Float

GEORGE W. DOANE

J. BAPTISTE CALKIN

1. Fling out the ban-ner! let it float Sky-ward and sea-ward, high and wide;
2. Fling out the ban-ner! an-gels bend In anx-ious si-lence o'er the sign,
3. Fling out the ban-ner! hea-then lands Shall see from far the glo-rious sight;
4. Fling out the ban-ner! let it float Sky-ward and sea-ward, high and wide,
5. Fling out the ban-ner! wide and high, Sea-ward and sky-ward, let it shine;

The sun, that lights its shin-ing folds, The cross, on which the Sav-ior died.
And vain-ly seek to com-pre-hend The won-der of the love di-vine.
And na-tions crowd-ing to be born, Bap-tize their spir-its in its light.
Our glo-ry, on-ly in the cross; Our on-ly hope the Cru-ci-fied.
Nor skill, nor might, nor mer-it ours; We con-quer on-ly in that sign.

The Regions Beyond

A. B. Simpson

Margaret M. Simpson

1. To the re-gions be-yond I must go, I must go, Where the sto-ry has
2. To the hard-est of plac-es He calls me to go, Not think-ing of
3. Oh, ye that are spending your leisure and pow'rs In pleas-ures so
4. There are oth-er "lost sheep" that the Master must bring, And they must the

nev-er been told (been told); To the mil-lions that never have heard of His love,
com-fort or ease (or ease); The world may pronounce me a dreamer, a fool,
fool-ish and fond (and fond); A-wake from your self-ish-ness, fol-ly and sin,
mes-sage be told (be told); He sends me to gath-er them out of all lands,

CHORUS *With spirit*

I must tell the sweet sto-ry of old (of old).
E-nough if the Mas-ter I please (I please). To the re - - gions be-
And go to the re-gions be-yond (be-yond).
And wel come them back to His fold (His fold). I must go,

yond I must go, I must go, Till the
I must go, To the re-gions be-yond I must go,

rit.

world, all the world, His sal-va - - - tion shall know.
Till the world, all the world, His sal-va-tion shall know, shall know.

474   Till the Whole World Knows

Rev. A. H. Ackley   B. D. Ackley

1. I'll tell to all that God is love; For the world has nev-er known
2. I'll tell of mer-cy's boundless tide, Like the wa-ters of the sea,
3. I'll tell of grace that keeps the soul, Of a-bid-ing peace with-in,
4. E-ter-nal glo-ry is the goal That a-waits the sons of light;

The great com-pas-sion of His heart For the wayward and the lone.
That cov-ers ev-'ry sin of man; 'Tis sal-va-tion full and free.
Of faith that o-ver-comes the world, With its tu-mult and its din.
E-ter-nal dark-ness, black as death, For the children of the night.

CHORUS.

Till the whole world knows, Till the whole world
Till the world, till the whole world knows, Till the world, till the whole world,
Till the world, the whole world knows,

knows, I will shout and sing Of Christ my King, Till the whole world knows.
whole world knows,

475 Send the Light

C. H. G.

CHAS. H. GABRIEL

1. There's a call comes ring-ing o'er the rest-less wave, "Send the light! . . .
2. We have heard the Mac-e-do-nian call to-day, "Send the light! . . .
3. Let us pray that grace may ev-ery-where a-bound; Send the light! . . .
4. Let us not grow wea-ry in the work of love, Send the light! . . .

Send the light!

Send the light!" There are souls to res-cue, there are souls to save,
Send the light!" And a gold-en of-fering at the cross we lay,
Send the light! And a Christ-like spir-it ev-ery-where be found,
Send the light! Let us gath-er jew-els for a crown a-bove,

Send the light!

REFRAIN

Send the light! . . . Send the light! . . . Send the light! . . . the
Send the light! Send the light! Send the light!

bless-ed gos-pel light; Let it shine . . . . from shore to
the bless-ed gos-pel light; Let it shine

shore! . . . . shine . . . for-ev-er-more. . . .
from shore to shore! Let it shine for-ev-er-more.

Speed Away

FANNY J. CROSBY

I. B. WOODBURY

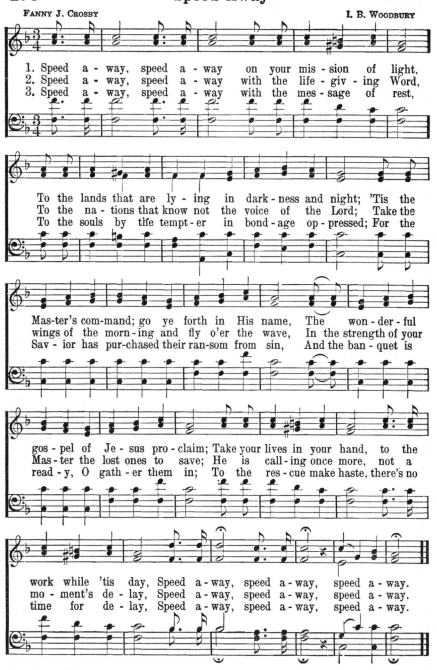

1. Speed a - way, speed a - way on your mis - sion of light,
2. Speed a - way, speed a - way with the life - giv - ing Word,
3. Speed a - way, speed a - way with the mes - sage of rest,

To the lands that are ly - ing in dark - ness and night; 'Tis the
To the na - tions that know not the voice of the Lord; Take the
To the souls by the tempt - er in bond - age op - pressed; For the

Mas-ter's com-mand; go ye forth in His name, The won - der - ful
wings of the morn-ing and fly o'er the wave, In the strength of your
Sav - ior has pur-chased their ran-som from sin, And the ban - quet is

gos - pel of Je - sus pro-claim; Take your lives in your hand, to the
Mas-ter the lost ones to save; He is call-ing once more, not a
read - y, O gath - er them in; To the res - cue make haste, there's no

work while 'tis day, Speed a - way, speed a - way, speed a - way.
mo - ment's de - lay, Speed a - way, speed a - way, speed a - way.
time for de - lay, Speed a - way, speed a - way, speed a - way.

477

To All The World

J. C. MaCaulay

Wendell P. Loveless

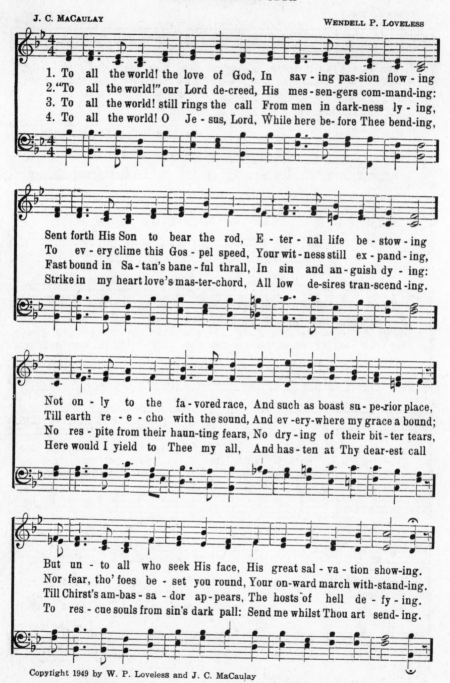

1. To all the world! the love of God, In sav-ing pas-sion flow-ing
2. "To all the world!" our Lord de-creed, His mes-sen-gers com-mand-ing:
3. To all the world! still rings the call From men in dark-ness ly-ing,
4. To all the world! O Je-sus, Lord, While here be-fore Thee bend-ing,

Sent forth His Son to bear the rod, E-ter-nal life be-stow-ing
To ev-ery clime this Gos-pel speed, Your wit-ness still ex-pand-ing,
Fast bound in Sa-tan's bane-ful thrall, In sin and an-guish dy-ing:
Strike in my heart love's mas-ter-chord, All low de-sires tran-scend-ing.

Not on-ly to the fa-vored race, And such as boast su-pe-rior place,
Till earth re-e-cho with the sound, And ev-ery-where my grace a-bound;
No res-pite from their haun-ting fears, No dry-ing of their bit-ter tears,
Here would I yield to Thee my all, And has-ten at Thy dear-est call

But un-to all who seek His face, His great sal-va-tion show-ing.
Nor fear, tho' foes be-set you round, Your on-ward march with-stand-ing.
Till Chirst's am-bas-sa-dor ap-pears, The hosts of hell de-fy-ing.
To res-cue souls from sin's dark pall: Send me whilst Thou art send-ing.

To All the World

CHORUS

To all the world! O word of love di-vine! To all the world! This is Thy blest design; To all the world! and lo, the task is mine. Send me! O Lord, send me.

478   Hallelujah to Thy Name!

GEORGE WALKER WHITCOMB   C. H. MARSH

Unison

1. O Thou God of end-less days, Who can ut-ter all Thy praise?
2. Thou hast giv-en us Thy word, From Thy heart our hearts have heard.
3. Thou hast full a-tone-ment made, And for all the ran-som paid.
4. Thou hast by Thy Spir-it's light Shined a-way our spir-it's night.
5. Thou hast pledged Thy presence here, Near-er than our sor-rows, near.
6. Thou hast prom-ised full re-ward, All in all art Thou, O Lord.

CHORUS

Hal-le-lu-jah to Thy name, Hal-le-lu-jah, we a-dore;

Hal-le-lu-jah to Thy name, O for grace to love Thee more.

We've a Story to Tell

COLIN STERNE

H. ERNEST NICHOL

1. We've a sto - ry to tell to the na - tions That shall turn their hearts
2. We've a song to be sung to the na - tions That shall lift their hearts
3. We've a mes-sage to give to the na - tions, That the Lord who reign-
4. We've a Sav - ior to show to the na - tions Who the path of sor-

1. That shall turn

to the right, A sto - ry of truth and mer - cy, A
to the Lord, A song that shall con - quer e - vil And
eth a - bove Hath sent us His Son to save us, And
row hath trod, That all of the world's great peo - ples Might

their hearts to the right,

sto - ry of peace and light, A sto - ry of peace and light.
shat - ter the spear and sword, And shat - ter the spear and sword.
show us that God is love, And show us that God is love.
come to the truth of God, Might come to the truth of God.

A sto ry of peace and light.

CHORUS

For the darkness shall turn to dawn-ing, And the dawning to noonday bright,

rall.

And Christ's great kingdom shall come to earth, The kingdom of love and light.

480 From Greenland's Icy Mountains

REGINALD HEBER

LOWELL MASON

1. From Green-land's i - cy moun-tains, From In - dia's cor - al strand;
2. What though the spi - cy breez - es Blow soft o'er Cey-lon's isle;
3. Shall we, whose souls are light - ed With wis-dom from on high,
4. Waft, waft, ye winds, His sto - ry, And you, ye wa - ters, roll,

Where Af - ric's sun - ny foun - tains Roll down their gold - en sand:
Though ev - ery pros-pect pleas - es, And on - ly man is vile?
Shall we to men be - night - ed The lamp of life de - ny?
Till, like a sea of glo - ry, It spreads from pole to pole:

From man-y an an - cient riv - er, From man-y a palm-y plain,
In vain with lav - ish kind - ness The gifts of God are strown;
Sal - va - tion! O sal - va - tion! The joy - ful sound pro - claim,
Till o'er our ran-somed na - ture The Lamb for sin - ners slain,

They call us to de - liv - er Their land from er - ror's chain.
The hea - then in his blind - ness Bows down to wood and stone.
Till earth's re - mot - est na - tion Has learned Mes-si - ah's name.
Re - deem - er, King, Cre - a - tor, In bliss re - turns to reign.

481 Where the Gates Swing Outward Never

C. H. G.

CHAS. H. GABRIEL

1. Just a few more days to be filled with praise, And to tell the
2. Just a few more years with their toil and tears, And the jour - ney
3. Tho' the hills be steep and the val - leys deep, With no flow'rs my
4. What a joy 'twill be when I wake to see Him for whom my

old, old sto - ry; Then, when twi - light falls, and my Sav - ior calls,
will be end - ed; Then I'll be with Him, where the tide of time
way a - dorn - ing; Tho' the night be lone and my rest a stone,
heart is burn - ing! Nev - er - more to sigh, nev - er - more to die—

CHORUS

I shall go to Him in glo - ry.
With e - ter - ni - ty is blend - ed. I'll ex-change my cross for a
Joy a - waits me in the morn - ing.
For that day my heart is yearn - ing.

star - ry crown, Where the gates swing out - ward nev - er; At His feet I'll

lay ev - 'ry bur - den down, And with Je - sus reign for - ev - er.

482 Face to Face

Mrs. Frank A. Breck

Grant Colfax Tullar

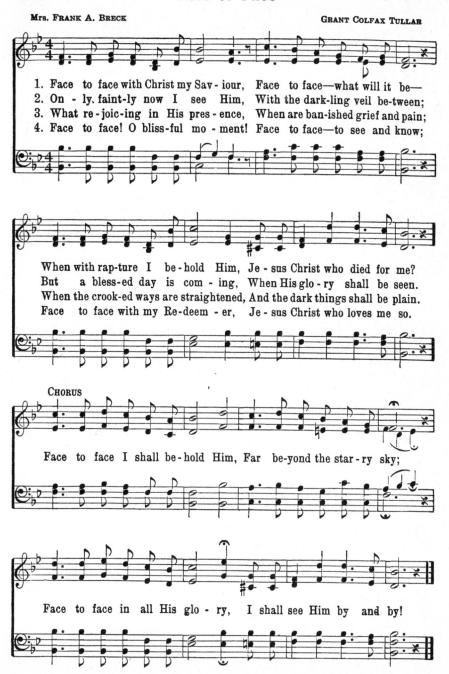

1. Face to face with Christ my Sav-iour, Face to face—what will it be—
2. On-ly, faint-ly now I see Him, With the dark-ling veil be-tween;
3. What re-joic-ing in His pres-ence, When are ban-ished grief and pain;
4. Face to face! O bliss-ful mo-ment! Face to face—to see and know;

When with rap-ture I be-hold Him, Je-sus Christ who died for me?
But a bless-ed day is com-ing, When His glo-ry shall be seen.
When the crook-ed ways are straightened, And the dark things shall be plain.
Face to face with my Re-deem-er, Je-sus Christ who loves me so.

CHORUS

Face to face I shall be-hold Him, Far be-yond the star-ry sky;

Face to face in all His glo-ry, I shall see Him by and by!

483
Take the Name of Jesus with You

Mrs. Lydia Baxter

W. H. Doane

1. Take the name of Je - sus with you, Child of sor-row and of woe;
2. Take the name of Je - sus ev - er, As a shield from ev-'ry snare;
3. O the pre-cious name of Je - sus! How it thrills our souls with joy,
4. At the name of Je - sus bow - ing, Fall - ing pros-trate at His feet,

It will joy and com-fort give you, Take it, then, wher-e'er you go.
If temp-ta-tions round you gath - er, Breathe that ho - ly name in prayer.
When His lov-ing arms re - ceive us, And His songs our tongues em-ploy!
King of kings in heav'n we'll crown Him, When our jour-ney is com-plete.

CHORUS

Pre-cious name, O how sweet! Hope of earth and joy of heav'n;
Pre-cious name, O how sweet!

Pre-cious name, O how sweet! Hope of earth and joy of heav'n.
Precious name, O how sweet, how sweet!

484
Hear Our Prayer, O Lord

GEORGE WHELPTON

pp

Hear our prayer, O Lord, Hear our prayer, O Lord,

Hear Our Prayer, O Lord

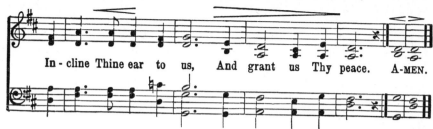

In-cline Thine ear to us, And grant us Thy peace. A-MEN.

485 Like a River Glorious

FRANCES R. HAVERGAL

J. MOUNTAIN

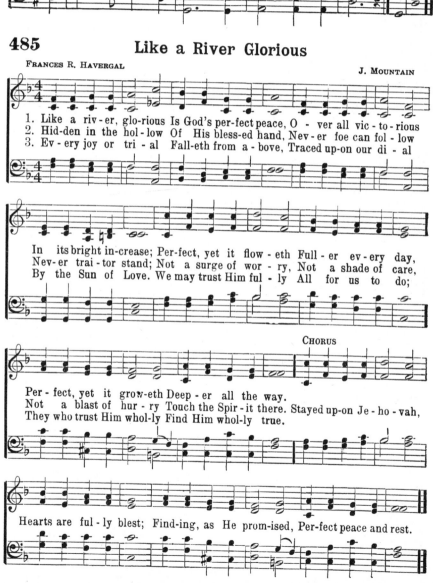

1. Like a riv-er, glo-rious Is God's per-fect peace, O - ver all vic-to-rious
2. Hid-den in the hol-low Of His bless-ed hand, Nev-er foe can fol-low
3. Ev-ery joy or tri-al Fall-eth from a-bove, Traced up-on our di-al

In its bright in-crease; Per-fect, yet it flow-eth Full-er ev-ery day,
Nev-er trai-tor stand; Not a surge of wor-ry, Not a shade of care,
By the Sun of Love. We may trust Him ful-ly All for us to do;

CHORUS

Per-fect, yet it grow-eth Deep-er all the way.
Not a blast of hur-ry Touch the Spir-it there. Stayed up-on Je-ho-vah,
They who trust Him whol-ly Find Him whol-ly true.

Hearts are ful-ly blest; Find-ing, as He prom-ised, Per-fect peace and rest.

486 Good Night and Good Morning

Lizzie DeArmond   Homer A. Rodeheaver

1. When comes to the wea-ry a bless-ed re-lease, When upward we
2. When fad-eth the day and dark shadows draw nigh, With Christ close at
3. When home-lights we see shin-ing bright-ly a-bove, Where we shall be

pass to His kingdom of peace, When free from the woes that on earth we must bear,
hand, it is not death to die; He'll wipe ev-'ry tear, roll a-way ev-'ry care;
soon, thro' His wonderful love, We'll praise Him who called us His heaven to share,

CHORUS.

We'll say "good-night," here, but "good-morning" up there.
We'll say "good-night," here, but "good-morning" up there. Good morning up there where
We'll say "good-night," here, but "good-morning" up there.

Christ is the Light, Good-morning up there where cometh no night; When we step from this

earth to God's heaven so fair, We'll say "good-night" here, but "good-morning" up there.

487 Hark, Hark, My Soul!

FREDERICK W. FABER

HENRY SMART

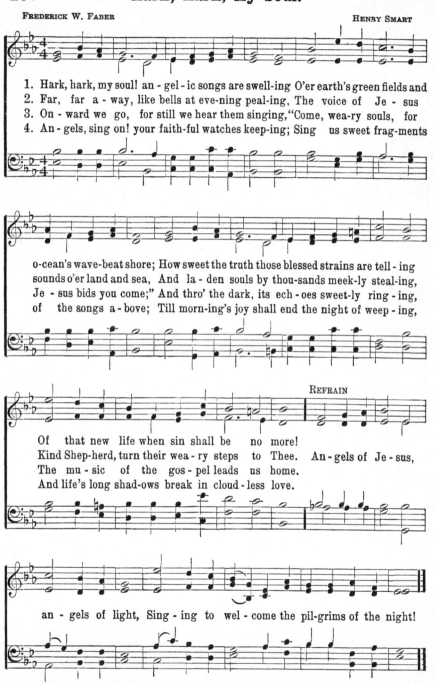

1. Hark, hark, my soul! an - gel - ic songs are swell-ing O'er earth's green fields and
2. Far, far a - way, like bells at eve-ning peal-ing, The voice of Je - sus
3. On - ward we go, for still we hear them singing, "Come, wea-ry souls, for
4. An - gels, sing on! your faith-ful watches keep-ing; Sing us sweet frag-ments

o-cean's wave-beat shore; How sweet the truth those blessed strains are tell - ing
sounds o'er land and sea, And la - den souls by thou-sands meek-ly steal-ing,
Je - sus bids you come;" And thro' the dark, its ech - oes sweet-ly ring - ing,
of the songs a - bove; Till morn-ing's joy shall end the night of weep - ing,

Of that new life when sin shall be no more! An - gels of Je - sus,
Kind Shep-herd, turn their wea - ry steps to Thee.
The mu - sic of the gos - pel leads us home.
And life's long shad-ows break in cloud - less love.

REFRAIN

an - gels of light, Sing - ing to wel - come the pil-grims of the night!

488 I Know I'll See Jesus Some Day

AVIS B. CHRISTIANSEN

SCOTT LAWRENCE

1. Sweet is the hope that is thrill-ing my soul— I know I'll see
2. Though I must trav-el by faith, not by sight, I know I'll see
3. Dark-ness is gath-'ring, but hope shines with-in, I know I'll see

Je-sus some day! Then what if the dark clouds of sin o'er me roll,
Je-sus some day! No e-vil can harm me, no foe can af-fright—
Je-sus some day! What joy when He comes to wipe out ev-'ry sin;

CHORUS

I know I'll see Je-sus some day! . . . I know I'll see Je-sus some

day! . . . I know I'll see Je-sus some day! . . . What a joy it will
some day! some day!

be When His face I shall see, I know I'll see Je-sus some day!

489   I Shall Dwell Forever There

Rev. A. H. Ackley

B. D. Ackley

1. When the night is o'er and the shad-ows past, And e-ter-nal dawn dis-
2. Tho' my sky be filled with the clouds of time, And my soul is burdened
3. How my heart will sing when I see the King, For there is no sov-reign

pels the gloom of earth-ly care, In the home of God I shall
with fore-bod-ings of de-spair, Yet, my heart is cheered, for the
that with Je-sus can com-pare; So the sac-ri-fice of a

rest at last, In the land of E-den I shall dwell for-ev-er there.
hope is mine, If I trust in Je-sus I shall dwell for-ev-er there.
life I'll bring, And with Him in glo-ry I shall dwell for-ev-er there.

CHORUS.

I shall walk the streets of the city of God With its Tree of Life so bright, so fair;

There will be no night—Je-sus is the Light.—I shall dwell for-ev-er there.

I Shall See the King

W. C. Poole

B. D. Ackley

1. I shall see the King Where the an-gels sing, I shall
2. In the land of song, In the glo-ry-throng, Where there
3. I shall see the King, All my trib-utes bring, And shall

see the King some day, In the bet-ter land, On the gold-en strand,
nev-er comes a night, With my Lord once slain I shall ev-er reign
look up-on His face; Then my song shall be How He ransomed me

And with Him shall ev-er stay.
In the glo-ry-land of light.
And has kept me by His grace.

REFRAIN.

In His glo-ry, I shall see the King, And for-ev-er end-less prais-es sing; 'Twas on

Cal-va-ry Je-sus died for me; I shall see the King some day.

491 My Savior First of All

FANNY J. CROSBY

JNO. R. SWENEY

1. When my life work is end-ed, and I cross the swell-ing tide, When the
2. Oh, the soul-thrill-ing rap-ture when I view His bless-ed face, And the
3. Oh, the dear ones in glo-ry, how they beck-on me to come, And our
4. Thro' the gates to the cit-y in a robe of spot-less white, He will

bright and glorious morning I shall see; I shall know my Re-deem-er when I
lus-ter of His kind-ly beaming eye; How my full heart will praise Him for the
part-ing at the riv-er I re-call; To the sweet vales of E-den they will
lead me where no tears shall ev-er fall; In the glad song of a-ges I shall

reach the oth-er side, And His smile will be the first to wel-come me.
mer-cy, love, and grace, That pre-pares for me a man-sion in the sky.
sing my wel-come home, But I long to meet my Sav-ior first of all.
min-gle with de-light; But I long to meet my Sav-ior first of all.

CHORUS

I shall know . . Him, I shall know Him, As redeemed by His side I shall stand;
I shall know

I shall know . . . Him, I shall know Him By the print of the nails in His hand.
I shall know

492 **Jerusalem the Golden**

BERNARD OF CLUNY
Tr. by J. M. NEALE

ALEXANDER EWING

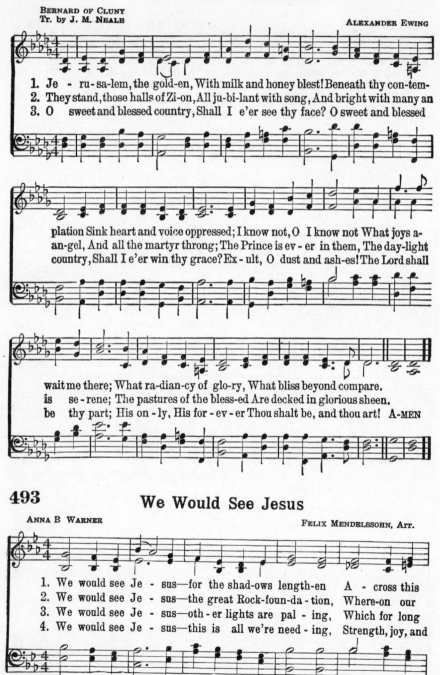

1. Je - ru - sa-lem, the gold-en, With milk and honey blest! Beneath thy con-tem-
2. They stand, those halls of Zi-on, All ju-bi-lant with song, And bright with many an
3. O sweet and blessed country, Shall I e'er see thy face? O sweet and blessed

plation Sink heart and voice oppressed; I know not, O I know not What joys a-
an-gel, And all the martyr throng; The Prince is ev - er in them, The day-light
country, Shall I e'er win thy grace? Ex - ult, O dust and ash-es! The Lord shall

wait me there; What ra-dian-cy of glo-ry, What bliss beyond compare.
is se - rene; The pastures of the bless-ed Are decked in glorious sheen.
be thy part; His on - ly, His for - ev - er Thou shalt be, and thou art! A-MEN

493 **We Would See Jesus**

ANNA B WARNER

FELIX MENDELSSOHN, Arr.

1. We would see Je - sus—for the shad-ows length-en   A - cross this
2. We would see Je - sus—the great Rock-foun-da - tion, Where-on our
3. We would see Je - sus—oth - er lights are pal - ing, Which for long
4. We would see Je - sus—this is all we're need - ing, Strength, joy, and

We Would See Jesus

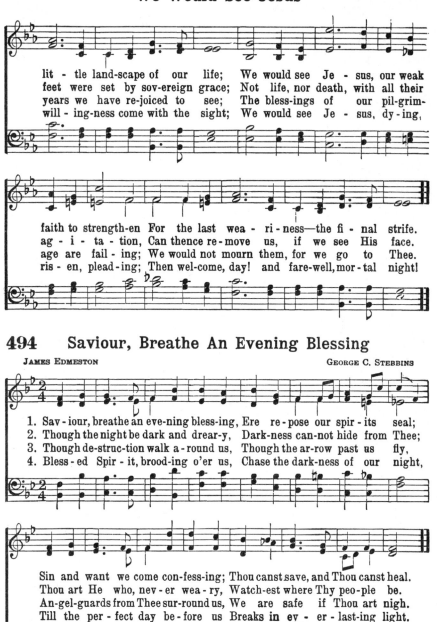

lit - tle land-scape of our life; We would see Je - sus, our weak
feet were set by sov-ereign grace; Not life, nor death, with all their
years we have re-joiced to see; The bless-ings of our pil-grim-
will - ing-ness come with the sight; We would see Je - sus, dy - ing,

faith to strength-en For the last wea - ri-ness—the fi - nal strife.
ag - i - ta - tion, Can thence re-move us, if we see His face.
age are fail - ing; We would not mourn them, for we go to Thee.
ris - en, plead-ing; Then wel-come, day! and fare-well, mor - tal night!

494   Saviour, Breathe An Evening Blessing

JAMES EDMESTON   GEORGE C. STEBBINS

1. Sav - iour, breathe an eve-ning bless-ing, Ere re-pose our spir - its seal;
2. Though the night be dark and drear-y, Dark-ness can-not hide from Thee;
3. Though de-struc-tion walk a - round us, Though the ar-row past us fly,
4. Bless - ed Spir - it, brood-ing o'er us, Chase the dark-ness of our night,

Sin and want we come con-fess-ing; Thou canst save, and Thou canst heal.
Thou art He who, nev - er wea - ry, Watch-est where Thy peo-ple be.
An-gel-guards from Thee sur-round us, We are safe if Thou art nigh.
Till the per - fect day be - fore us Breaks in ev - er - last-ing light.

495 Meet Me There

H. E. Blair.

Wm. J. Kirkpatrick.

1. On the hap-py, gold-en shore, Where the faithful part no more, When the
2. Here our fond-est hopes are vain, Dear-est links are rent in twain; But in
3. Where the harps of an-gels ring, And the blest for-ev-er sing, In the

storms of life are o'er, Meet me there; Where the night dis-solves a-way
Heav'n no throb of pain, Meet me there; By the riv-er spark-ling bright,
pal-ace of the King, Meet me there; Where in sweet com-mun-ion blend

In-to pure and per-fect day, I am go-ing home to stay, Meet me there.
In the cit-y of de-light, Where our faith is lost in sight, Meet me there.
Heart with heart and friend with friend, In a world that ne'er shall end, Meet me there.

CHORUS.

Meet me there,   Meet me there,   Where the tree of life is
Meet me there,   Meet me there,

bloom-ing, Meet me there;   When the storms of life are o'er, On the
Meet me there;

Meet Me There

happy, golden shore, Where the faithful part no more, Meet me there. A-MEN.

Meet me there.

496   Jesus Never Fails

A. A. L.

A. A. LUTHER

1. Earth-ly friends may prove un - true, Doubts and fears as - sail;
2. Tho' the sky be dark and drear, Fierce and strong the gale,
3. In life's dark and bit - ter hour Love will still pre - vail;

One still loves and cares for you: Je - sus nev - er fails.
                                                  nev - er fails.
Just re - mem - ber He is near, And He will not fail.
                                               will not fail.
Trust His ev - er - last-ing pow'r, Je - sus will not fail.
                                             will not fail.

CHORUS

Je - sus nev - er fails, Je - sus nev - er fails;

Heav'n and earth may pass a - way But Je - sus nev - er fails.

497 ## Bless the Lord, O My Soul

IPPOLITOF—IVANOFF

Bless the Lord, O my soul, Bless-ed art Thou, O Lord. A-MEN

498 ## Wounded for Me

GLADYS WATKIN ROBERTS   Music and first verse by   W. G. OVENS

1. Wound-ed for me, wound-ed for me, There on the cross
2. Dy - ing for me, dy - ing for me, There on the cross
3. Ris - en for me, ris - en for me, Up from the grave
4. Liv - ing for me, liv - ing for me, Up in the skies
5. Com - ing for me, com - ing for me, One day to earth

He was wound - ed for me; Gone my trans - gres - sions, and
He was dy - ing for me; Now in His death my re -
He has ris - en for me; Now ev - er - more from death's
He is liv - ing for me; Dai - ly He's plead - ing and
He is com - ing for me; Then with what joy His dear

dim.

now I am free, All be - cause Je - sus was wound-ed for me.
demp-tion I see, All be - cause Je - sus was dy - ing for me.
sting I am free, All be - cause Je - sus has ris - en for me.
pray-ing for me, All be - cause Je - sus is liv - ing for me.
face I shall see, Oh, how I praise Him! He's com - ing for me.

SAMUEL MEDLEY   WILLIAM CALDWELL

1. A-wake, my soul, to joy-ful lays, And sing thy great Redeemer's praise;
2. He saw me ru-ined by the fall, Yet loved me not-with-stand-ing all;
3. Tho' num'rous hosts of might-y foes, Tho' earth and hell my way op-pose,
4. When trouble, like a gloom-y cloud, Has gathered thick and thundered loud,

He just-ly claims a song from me, His lov-ing-kind-ness, oh, how free!
He saved me from my lost es-tate, His lov-ing-kind-ness, oh, how great!
He safe-ly leads my soul a-long, His lov-ing-kind-ness, oh, how strong!
He near my soul has al-ways stood, His lov-ing-kind-ness, oh, how good!

Lov-ing-kind-ness, lov-ing-kind-ness, His lov-ing-kind-ness, oh, how free!
Lov-ing-kind-ness, lov-ing-kind-ness, His lov-ing-kind-ness, oh, how great!
Lov-ing-kind-ness, lov-ing-kind-ness, His lov-ing-kind-ness, oh, how strong!
Lov-ing-kind-ness, lov-ing-kind-ness, His lov-ing-kind-ness, oh, how good!

500   **Almighty Father, Hear Our Prayer**

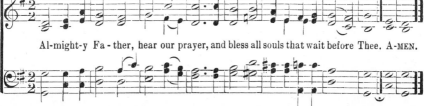

MENDELSSOHN

pp

Al-might-y Fa-ther, hear our prayer, and bless all souls that wait before Thee. A-MEN.

501 O That Will Be Glory

C. H. G.

CHAS. H. GABRIEL

1. When all my la-bors and tri-als are o'er, And I am safe on that beau-ti-ful shore, Just to be near the dear Lord I a-dore,
2. When, by the gift of His in-fi-nite grace, I am ac-cord-ed in Heav-en a place, Just to be there and to look on His face,
3. Friends will be there I have loved long a-go; Joy like a riv-er a-round me will flow; Yet, just a smile from my Sav-ior, I know,

Will thro' the a-ges be glo-ry for me. ....

CHORUS. Faster.

O that will be glo-ry for me, Glo-ry for me, glo-ry for me; When by His grace

O ...... that will be glo-ry for me, Glo-ry for me, glo-ry for me; ......

I shall look on His face, That will be glo-ry, be glo-ry for me. A-MEN.

502 Some Bright Morning

Charlotte G. Homer

Chas. H. Gabriel

1. Be not a-wea-ry, for la-bor will cease Some glad morn-ing;
2. Wea-ri-some bur-dens will all be laid down, Some glad morn-ing;
3. La-bor well done shall re-ceive its re-ward, Some glad morn-ing;
4. O what a time of re-joic-ing will come, Some glad morn-ing;
5. There with the loved ones who've gone on be-fore, Some glad morn-ing;

Tur-moil will change in-to in-fi-nite peace, Some bright morn-ing.
Then shall our cross be exchanged for a crown, Some bright morn-ing.
Thou who art faith-ful shall be with the Lord, Some bright morn-ing.
When all the ransomed are gathered at home, Some bright morn-ing.
We shall sing praise to the Lamb ev-er-more, Some bright morn-ing.

CHORUS

Some bright morn-ing, Some glad morn-ing, When the sun is shin-ing

in th'e-ter-nal sky; ... Some bright morn-ing, Some glad

cres.

morn-ing, We shall see the Lord of Har-vest, By and by.

503 Some Time We'll Understand

MAXWELL N. CORNELIUS

JAMES McGRANAHAN

1. Not now, but in the com-ing years, It may be in the bet-ter land,
2. We'll catch the broken thread a - gain, And fin - ish what we here be - gan;
3. We'll know why clouds instead of sun Were o - ver many a cherished plan;
4. God knows the way, He holds the key, He guides us with un - err - ing hand;

We'll read the meaning of our tears, And there, some time, we'll understand.
Heav'n will the mys-ter - ies ex - plain, And then, ah, then, we'll understand.
Why song has ceased when scarce begun; 'Tis there, some time, we'll understand.
Some time with tearless eyes we'll see; Yes, there, up there, we'll understand.

CHORUS. *A little faster*

Then trust in God thro' all the days; Fear not, for He doth hold thy hand;

doth hold thy hand;

A tempo   *cres.*   *ad lib.*

Though dark thy way, still sing and praise, Some time, some time, we'll understand.

504 Sunrise

W. C. Poole

B. D. Ackley

1. When I shall come to the end of my way, When I shall rest at the
2. When in His beau-ty I see the great King, Join with the ran-somed His
3. When life is o - ver and day-light is passed, In heav-en's har - bor my

close of life's day, When "Wel-come home" I shall hear Je - sus say, O
prais - es to sing, When I shall join them my trib-utes to bring, O
an - chor is cast, When I see Je - sus my Sav-iour at last, O

that will be sun-rise for me. . . . . Sun-rise to-mor-row, sun-rise to-

mor-row, Sun-rise in glo-ry is wait-ing for me; Sun-rise to-mor-row,

sun-rise to-mor-row, Sun-rise with Je-sus for e - ter-ni - ty.

Sweet By and By

S. F. BENNETT

J. P. WEBSTER

1. There's a land that is fair-er than day, And by faith we can
2. We shall sing on that beau-ti-ful shore The mel-o-di-ous
3. To our boun-ti-ful Fa-ther a-bove, We will of-fer our

see it a-far; For the Fa-ther waits o-ver the way, To pre-
songs of the blest, And our spir-its shall sor-row no more, Not a
trib-ute of praise, For the glo-ri-ous gift of His love, And the

CHORUS

pare us a dwell-ing-place there. In the sweet   by and
sigh for the bless-ing of rest.
bless-ings that hal-low our days.   In the sweet

by,   We shall meet on that beau-ti-ful shore;   In the
by and by,   by and by,

sweet   by and by,   We shall meet on that beau-ti-ful shore.
In the sweet   by and by,

506   The Last Mile of the Way

Rev. Johnson Oatman, Jr.

Wm. Edie Marks

1. If I walk in the path-way of du - ty, If I work till the
2. If for Christ I pro-claim the glad sto - ry, If I seek for His
3. Here the dear-est of ties we must sev - er, Tears of sor - row are
4. And if here I have ear - nest-ly striv - en, And have tried all His

close of the day; I shall see the great King in His beau - ty,
sheep gone a - stray, I am sure He will show me His glo - ry,
seen ev - 'ry day; But no sick-ness, no sigh-ing for - ev - er
will to o - bey, 'Twill en-hance all the rap-ture of heav - en,

CHORUS

When I've gone the last mile of the way. When I've gone the last mile of the
the last

way, ... I will rest at the close of the day, ... And I
mile of the way, at the close of the day,

know there are joys that a-wait me, When I've gone the last mile of the way.

The Sands of Time

ANNE ROSS COUSIN

CHRÉTIENE D'URHAN
Arr. by E. F. RIMBAULT

1. The sands of time are sink-ing, The dawn of heav-en breaks;
2. O Christ! He is the foun-tain, The deep, sweet well of love!
3. Oh, I am my Be-lov-ed's, And my Be-lov-ed's mine!
4. The Bride eyes not her gar-ment, But her dear Bridegroom's face;

The sum-mer morn I've sighed for, The fair, sweet morn a-wakes:
The streams on earth I've tast-ed, More deep I'll drink a-bove:
He brings a poor vile sin-ner In-to His "house of wine."
I will not gaze at glo-ry, But on my King of grace.

Dark, dark hath been the mid-night, But day-spring is at hand,
There, to an o-cean ful-ness, His mer-cy doth ex-pand,
I stand up-on His mer-it, I know no oth-er stand,
Not at the crown He giv-eth, But on His pierc-ed hand,

And glo-ry, glo-ry dwell-eth In Im-man-uel's land.
And glo-ry, glo-ry dwell-eth In Im-man-uel's land.
Not e'en where glo-ry dwell-eth In Im-man-uel's land.
The Lamb is all the glo-ry Of Im-man-uel's land. A-MEN.

508 The Unclouded Day

J. K. A.   Rev. J. K. Alwood

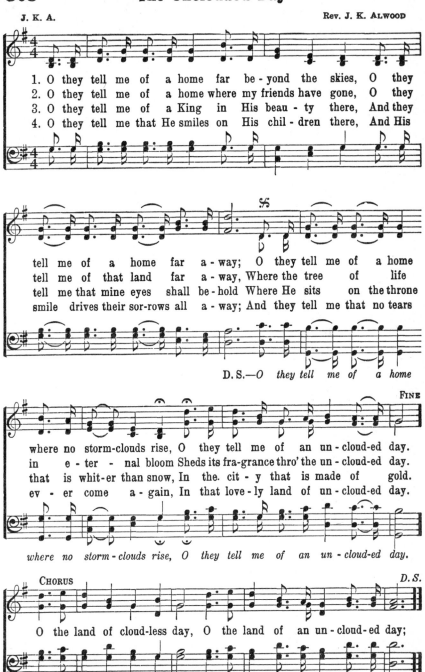

1. O they tell me of a home far be-yond the skies, O they
2. O they tell me of a home where my friends have gone, O they
3. O they tell me of a King in His beau-ty there, And they
4. O they tell me that He smiles on His chil-dren there, And His

tell me of a home far a-way; O they tell me of a home
tell me of that land far a-way, Where the tree of life
tell me that mine eyes shall be-hold Where He sits on the throne
smile drives their sor-rows all a-way; And they tell me that no tears

D. S.—*O they tell me of a home*

FINE

where no storm-clouds rise, O they tell me of an un-cloud-ed day.
in e-ter-nal bloom Sheds its fra-grance thro' the un-cloud-ed day.
that is whit-er than snow, In the cit-y that is made of gold.
ev-er come a-gain, In that love-ly land of un-cloud-ed day.

where no storm-clouds rise, O they tell me of an un-cloud-ed day.

CHORUS   D. S.

O the land of cloud-less day, O the land of an un-cloud-ed day;

To Eternity

PAUL RADER   ARTHUR W. McKEE

1. The riv-er of Thy grace is flow-ing free, We launch up-on its
2. The breez-es of Thy love are blow-ing free, They tell Thy love to
3. Thy Spir-it calls to all, "Come home to-day;" Come back and find the

depths to sail to Thee; In the o-cean of Thy love we soon shall
all hu-man-i-ty; They are sing-ing of the blood of Cal-va-
Sav-ior while you may; Find that Je-sus is the Life, the Truth, the

CHORUS

be, We are sail-ing to e-ter-ni-ty.
ry, Mak-ing white thro' all e-ter-ni-ty. Earth-ly joys can-not com-
Way, Lead-ing, guid-ing, to e-ter-'ni-ty.

pare with all the glo-ry, When our longing eyes shall see Thy face; We shall

have Thy fel-low-ship for-ev-er, In the splendor of the throne of grace.

510 When I Get to the End of the Way

Harriet Cole

Charlie D. Tillman

1. The sands have been washed in the foot-prints Of the Stran-ger on
2. There are so man-y hills to climb up-ward, I oft-en am
3. He loves me too well to for-sake me, Or give me a
4. When the last fee-ble steps have been tak-en, And the gates of that

D. S.— toils of the road will seem noth-ing, When I get to the

Gal-i-lee's shore— And the voice that sub-dued the rough bil-lows
long-ing for rest; But He who ap-points me my path-way,
tri-al too much; All His peo-ple have been dear-ly pur-chased,
cit-y ap-pear, And the beau-ti-ful songs of the an-gels

end of the way; And the toils of the road will seem noth-ing,
4. Then the

FINE

Will be heard in Ju-de-a no more. But the path of that lone Gal-i-
Knows just what is need-ful and best. I know in His Word He hath
And Sa-tan can nev-er claim such. By and by I shall see Him and
Float out on my lis-ten-ing ear; When all that now seems so mys-

When I get to the end of the way.

D. S.

le-an With joy I will fol-low to-day; And the
prom-ised That my strength "it shall be as my day;" And the
praise Him, In the cit-y of un-end-ing day; And the
te-rious Will be bright and as clear as the day; Then the

511 ## When the Roll is Called Up Yonder

J. M. B.

J. M. BLACK

1. When the trumpet of the Lord shall sound, and time shall be no more, And the
2. On that bright and cloudless morning when the dead in Christ shall rise, And the
3. Let us la - bor for the Mas - ter from the dawn till set - ting sun, Let us

morning breaks, e-ter-nal, bright and fair; When the saved of earth shall gather
glo - ry of His res - ur-rec-tion share; When His cho-sen ones shall gather
talk of all His wondrous love and care; Then when all of life is o - ver,

o - ver on the oth-er shore, And the roll is called up yon-der, I'll be there.
to their home beyond the skies, And the roll is called up yon-der, I'll be there.
and our work on earth is done, And the roll is called up yon-der, I'll be there.

CHORUS.

When the roll . . . . . . is called up yon - - - - der, When the
When the roll is called up yon - der, I'll be there,

roll . . . . is called up yon - - der, When the roll . . . . is called up
When the roll is called up yon-der, I'll be there, When the roll is called up

When the Roll is Called Up Yonder

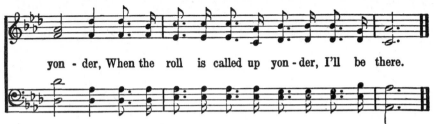

yon - der, When the roll is called up yon - der, I'll be there.

512   Christ Liveth in Me

Maj. D. W. WHITTLE (El Nathan)   JAMES McGRANAHAN

1. Once far from God and dead in sin, No light my heart could see;
2. As rays of light from yon - der sun, The flow'rs of earth set free,
3. As lives the flow'r with-in the seed, As in the cone the tree,
4. With long-ing all my heart is filled, That like Him I may be,

But in God's Word the light I found, Now Christ liv - eth in me.
So life and light and love came forth From Christ liv - ing in me.
So, praise the God of truth and grace, His Spir-it dwell-eth in me.
As on the won - drous tho't I dwell That Christ liv - eth in me.

CHORUS

Christ liv - eth in me,   Christ liv - eth in me,
Christ liv - eth in me,   Christ liv - eth in

Oh! what a sal - va - tion this, That Christ liv - eth in me.
me, Oh!

513   When the Mists Have Rolled Away

ANNIE HERBERT. ARR.

IRA D. SANKEY

1. When the mists have rolled in splen-dor From the beau-ty of the hills,
2. Oft we tread the path be-fore us With a wea-ry, bur-dened heart;
3. We shall come with joy and glad-ness, We shall gath-er round the throne;

And the sun-light falls in glad-ness On the riv-er and the rills,
Oft we toil a-mid the shad-ows, And our fields are far a-part:
Face to face with those that love us, We shall know as we are known:

We re-call our Fa-ther's prom-ise In the rain-bow of the spray:
But the Sav-ior's "Come, ye bless-ed," All our la-bor will re-pay,
And the song of our re-demp-tion Shall re-sound thro' end-less day,

rit.

We shall know each oth-er bet-ter When the mists have rolled a-way.
When we gath-er in the morning Where the mists have rolled a-way.
When the shad-ows have de-part-ed, And the mists have rolled a-way.

CHORUS

known, as we are known,

We shall know . . . as we are known, . . . Nev-er-more . . . to walk a-
We shall know   as we are known,   Nev-er-more to walk a-

When the Mists Have Rolled Away

lone, ... In the dawning of the morning Of that bright and happy day.
lone, to walk a-lone,

We shall know each oth - er bet - ter, When the mists have rolled a - way.

514   The Call for Reapers

J. O. THOMPSON   J. B. O. CLEMM

1. Far and near the fields are teem-ing With the waves of ri - pened grain;
2. Send them forth with morn's first beaming; Send them in the noontide's glare;
3. O thou, whom thy Lord is send-ing, Gath-er now the sheaves of gold;

Far and near their gold is gleam-ing O'er the sun - ny slope and plain.
When the sun's last rays are gleam-ing, Bid them gath-er ev - 'ry-where.
Heav'nward then at eve-ning wend-ing, Thou shalt come with joy un - told.

D. S.—*Send them now the sheaves to gath - er, Ere the har-vest-time pass by.*

CHORUS

Lord of har - vest, send forth reapers! Hear us Lord, to Thee we cry;

515   When the Shadows Flee Away

R. H.

ROBERT HARKNESS

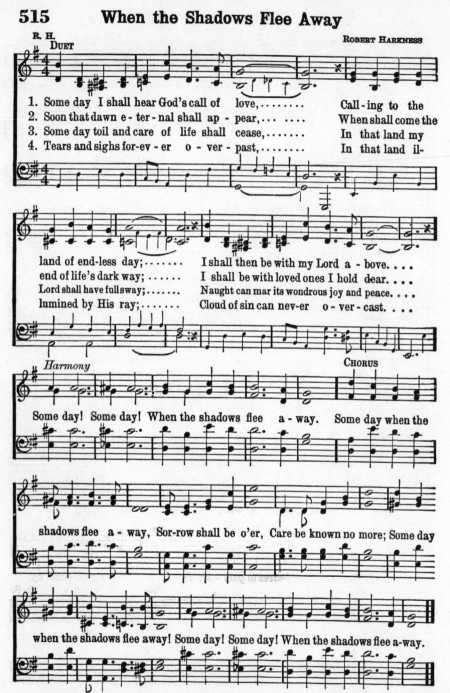

1. Some day I shall hear God's call of love,........ Call-ing to the
2. Soon that dawn e - ter - nal shall ap - pear,........ When shall come the
3. Some day toil and care of life shall cease,........ In that land my
4. Tears and sighs for-ev - er o - ver - past,........ In that land il-

land of end-less day;........ I shall then be with my Lord a - bove....
end of life's dark way;........ I shall be with loved ones I hold dear....
Lord shall have full sway;........ Naught can mar its wondrous joy and peace....
lumined by His ray;........ Cloud of sin can nev-er o - ver - cast....

Harmony   CHORUS

Some day! Some day! When the shadows flee a - way. Some day when the

shadows flee a - way, Sor-row shall be o'er, Care be known no more; Some day

when the shadows flee away! Some day! Some day! When the shadows flee a-way.

516 Blessed Redeemer

AVIS BURGESON CHRISTIANSEN

HARRY DIXON LOES

1. Up Cal-vary's mountain one dreadful morn, Walked Christ my Saviour, weary and worn;
2. "Fa-ther, forgive them!" thus did He pray, E'en while His life-blood flowed fast a-way;
3. O how I love Him, Sav-iour and Friend, How can my prais-es ev - er find end!

Fac-ing for sin-ners death on the cross, That He might save them from endless loss.
Pray-ing for sin-ners while in such woe— No one but Je - sus ev - er loved so.
Thro' years un-num-bered on heaven's shore, My tongue shall praise Him for-ev-er-more.

CHORUS

Bless-ed Re-deem - er! pre-cious Re-deem - er! Seems now I
Bless-ed Re-deem-er! bless - ed Re-deem - er!

see Him on Cal-va-ry's tree; Wound-ed and bleed - ing, for sin-ners
Wound-ed and bleed-ing,

plead - ing— Blind and un-heed - - ing— dy-ing for me!
for sin-ners plead-ing— Blind and un-heed-ing--

517 The Fight is On

C. H. M.

Mrs. C. H. MORRIS

1. The fight is on, the trump-et sound is ring-ing out, The cry "To
2. The fight is on, a-rouse, ye sol-diers brave and true! Je-ho-vah
3. The Lord is lead-ing on to cer-tain vic-to-ry; The bow of

arms!" is heard a-far and near; The Lord of hosts is march-ing
leads, and vic-t'ry will as-sure; Go, buck-le on the ar-mor
prom-ise spans the east-ern sky; His glo-rious name in ev-'ry

on to vic-to-ry, The tri-umph of the Christ will soon ap-pear.
God has giv-en you, And in His strength un-to the end en-dure.
land shall hon-ored be; The morn will break, the dawn of peace is nigh.

CHORUS. *Unison*

The fight is on, O Chris-tian sol-dier, And face to face in stern ar-ray,.... With

ar-mor gleaming, and col-ors streaming, The right and wrong engage to-day!

The Fight is On

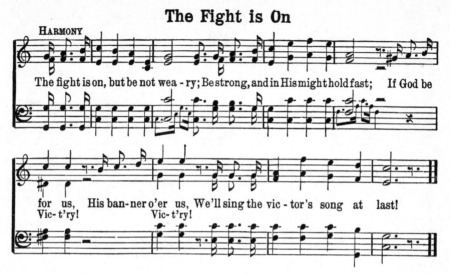

The fight is on, but be not wea - ry; Be strong, and in His might hold fast; If God be

for us, His ban - ner o'er us, We'll sing the vic - tor's song at last!
Vic - t'ry! Vic - t'ry!

518   The Lord Is In His Holy Temple

GEORGE F. ROOT

The Lord is in His ho - ly tem - ple, The Lord is in His ho - ly

tem - ple; Let all the earth keep si - lence, Let all the earth keep si - lence be-

fore Him, Keep si - lence, keep si - lence be - fore Him. A - MEN.

Amens

519 DRESDEN AMEN

A-men, A — men.

520 THREEFOLD AMEN

MARY L. YOUNG

A-men, A-men, A — men.

521 THREEFOLD AMEN

Traditional

A — — — men, A-men, A — — men.

522 FOURFOLD AMEN

JOHN STAINER

A — men, A — men, A — men, A — men.

523 SEVENFOLD AMEN

JOHN STAINER

A - men, A — — — men,

A - men, A-men, A — men, A — — men, A-

A — — men, A — — men,

A — — — men,

— — — men, A — — — men, A — men.

A — — men,

INDEX of RESPONSIVE READINGS

RESPONSIVE READINGS

1 CREATION
—Genesis 1:1-2, 26-31.

In the beginning God created the heavens and the earth.

And the earth was waste and void; and darkness was upon the face of the deep: and the Spirit of God moved upon the face of the waters.

And God said, Let us make man in our image, after our likeness: and let them have dominion over the fish of the sea, and over the birds of the heavens, and over the cattle, and over all the earth, and over every creeping thing that creepeth upon the earth.

And God created man in his own image, in the image of God created he him; male and female created he them.

And God blessed them: and God said unto them, Be fruitful, and multiply, and replenish the earth, and subdue it; and have dominion over the fish of the sea, and over the birds of the heavens, and over every living thing that moveth upon the earth.

And God said, Behold, I have given you every herb yielding seed, which is upon the face of all the earth, and every tree, in which is the fruit of a tree yielding seed; to you it shall be for food:

And to every beast of the earth, and to every bird of the heavens, and to everything that creepeth upon the earth, wherein there is life. I have given every green herb for food: and it was so.

And God saw everything that he had made, and, behold, it was very good. And there was evening and there was morning, the sixth day.

2 GOD REVEALED IN NATURE
—Psalm 19.

The heavens declare the glory of God;
And the firmament showeth his handiwork.

Day unto day uttereth speech,
And night unto night showeth knowledge.

There is no speech nor language,
Where their voice is not heard.

Their line is gone out through all the earth
And their words to the end of the world.
In them hath he set a tabernacle for the sun.

Which is as a bridegroom coming out of his chamber,
And rejoiceth as a strong man to run his course.

His going forth is from the end of the heavens,
And his circuit unto the ends of it;
And there is nothing hid from the heat thereof.

The law of the Lord is perfect, restoring the soul;
The testimony of the Lord is sure, making wise the simple.

The precepts of the Lord are right, rejoicing the heart:
The commandment of the Lord is pure, enlightening the eyes.

The fear of the Lord is clean, enduring for ever:
The ordinances of the Lord are true, and righteous altogether.

More to be desired are they than gold, yea, than much fine gold;
Sweeter also than honey and the droppings of the honey-comb.

Moreover by them is thy servant warned:
In keeping them there is great reward.

Who can discern his errors?
Clear thou me from hidden faults.

Keep back thy servant also from presumptuous sins;
Let them not have dominion over me:

Then shall I be upright,
And I shall be clear from great transgression.

Let the words of my mouth and the meditation of my heart
Be acceptable in thy sight,
O Lord, my rock, and my redeemer.

3   GOD'S GRACE AND CARE
—Psalm 34:1-19.

I will bless the Lord at all times:
His praise shall continually be in my mouth.

My soul shall make her boast in the Lord:
The meek shall hear thereof, and be glad.

Oh magnify the Lord with me,
And let us exalt his name together.

I sought the Lord, and he answered me,
And delivered me from all my fears.

They looked unto him, and were radiant;
And their faces shall never be confounded.

This poor man cried, and the Lord heard him,
And saved him out of all his troubles.

The angel of the Lord encampeth round about them that fear him,
And delivereth them.

Oh taste and see that the Lord is good:
Blessed is the man that taketh refuge in him.

Oh fear the Lord, ye his saints;
For there is no want to them that fear him.

The young lions do lack, and suffer hunger;
But they that seek the Lord shall not want any good thing.

Come, ye children, hearken unto me:
I will teach you the fear of the Lord.

What man is he that desireth life,
And loveth many days, that he may see good?

Keep thy tongue from evil.
And thy lips from speaking guile.

Depart from evil, and do good;
Seek peace, and pursue it.

The eyes of the Lord are toward the righteous,
And his ears are open unto their cry.

The face of the Lord is against them that do evil,
To cut off the remembrance of them from the earth.

The righteous cried, and the Lord heard,
And delivered them out of all their troubles.

The Lord is nigh unto them that are of a broken heart,
And saveth such as are of a contrite spirit.
Many are the afflictions of the righteous;
But the Lord delivereth him out of them all.

4 THE LORD OUR SHEPHERD
—Psalm 23.

The Lord is my shepherd; I shall not want.

He maketh me to lie down in green pastures;
He leadeth me beside still waters.

He restoreth my soul:
He guideth me in the paths of righteousness for his name's sake.

Yea, though I walk through the valley of the Shadow of death,
I will fear no evil; for thou art with me;
Thy rod and thy staff, they comfort me.

Thou preparest a table before me in the presence of mine enemies:
Thou hast anointed my head with oil;
My cup runneth over.

Surely goodness and loving-kindness shall follow me all the days of my life;
And I shall dwell in the house of the Lord for ever.

5 THE PRINCE OF PEACE
—Isaiah 9:2-7.

The people that walked in darkness have seen a great light: they that dwelt in the land of the shadow of death, upon them hath the light shined.

Thou hast multiplied the nation, thou hast increased their joy: they joy before thee according to the joy in harvest, as men rejoice when they divide the spoil.

For the yoke of his burden, and the staff of his shoulder, the rod of his oppressor, thou hast broken as in the day of Midian.

For all the armor of the armed man in the tumult, and the garments rolled in blood, shall be for burning, for fuel of fire.

For unto us a child is born, unto us a son is given; and the government shall be upon his shoulder: and his name shall be called Wonderful, Counsellor, Mighty God, Everlasting Father, Prince of Peace.

Of the increase of his government and of peace there shall be no end, upon the throne of David, and upon his kingdom, to establish it, and to uphold it with justice and with righteousness from henceforth even for ever. The zeal of the Lord of hosts will perform this.

6 THE BIRTH OF JESUS
—Luke 2:1-20.

Now it came to pass in those days, there went out a decree from Caesar Augustus, that all the world should be enrolled.

This was the first enrollment made when Quirinius was governor of Syria.

And all went to enroll themselves, every one to his own city.

And Joseph also went up from Galilee, out of the city of Nazareth, into Judaea, to the city of David, which is called Bethlehem, because he was of the house and family of David;

To enroll himself with Mary, who was betrothed to him, being great with child.

And it came to pass, while they were there, the days were fulfilled that she should be delivered.

And she brought forth her firstborn son; and she wrapped him in swaddling clothes, and laid him in a manger, because there was no room for them in the inn.

And there were shepherds in the same country abiding in the field, and keeping watch by night over their flock.

And an angel of the Lord stood by them, and the glory of the Lord shone round about them: and they were sore afraid.

And the angel said unto them, Be not afraid; for behold I bring you good tidings of great joy which shall be to all the people:

For there is born to you this day in the city of David a Saviour, who is Christ the Lord.

And this is the sign unto you: Ye shall find a babe wrapped in swaddling clothes, and lying in a manger.

And suddenly there was with the angel a multitude of the heavenly host praising God, and saying,

Glory to God in the highest, And on earth peace among men in whom he is well pleased.

And it came to pass, when the angels went away from them into heaven, the shepherds said one to another, Let us now go even unto Bethlehem, and see this thing that is come to pass, which the Lord hath made known unto us.

And they came with haste, and found both Mary and Joseph, and the babe lying in the manger.

And when they saw it, they made known concerning the saying which was spoken to them about this child.

And all that heard it wondered at the things which were spoken unto them by the shepherds.

But Mary kept all these sayings, pondering them in her heart.

And the shepherds returned, glorifying and praising God for all the things that they had heard and seen, even as it was spoken unto them.

7   THE BAPTISM AND TEMPTATION

—Matthew 3:13-17; 4:1-11.

Then cometh Jesus from Galilee to the Jordan unto John, to be baptized of him.

But John would have hindered him, saying, I have need to be baptized of thee, and comest thou to me?

But Jesus answering said unto him, Suffer it now: for thus it becometh us to fulfil all righteousness. Then he suffereth him.

And Jesus, when he was baptized, went up straightway from the water: and lo, the heavens were opened unto him, and he saw the Spirit of God descending as a dove, and coming upon him;

471

And lo, a voice out of the heavens, saying, This is my beloved Son, in whom I am well pleased.

Then was Jesus led up of the Spirit into the wilderness to be tempted of the devil.

And when he had fasted forty days and forty nights, he afterward hungered.

And the tempter came and said unto him, If thou art the Son of God, command that these stones become bread.

But he answered and said, It is written, Man shall not live by bread alone, but by every word that proceedeth out of the mouth of God.

Then the devil taketh him into the holy city; and he set him on the pinnacle of the temple,

And saith unto him, If thou art the Son of God, cast thyself down: for it is written,

He shall give his angels charge
    concerning thee:
and,

On their hands they shall bear
    thee up,

Lest haply thou dash thy foot
    against a stone.

Jesus said unto him, Again it is written, Thou shalt not make trial of the Lord thy God.

Again, the devil taketh him unto an exceeding high mountain, and showeth him all the kingdoms of the world, and the glory of them;

And he said unto him, All these things will I give thee, if thou wilt fall down and worship me.

Then saith Jesus unto him, Get thee hence, Satan: for it is written, Thou shalt worship the Lord thy God, and him only shalt thou serve.

Then the devil leaveth him; and behold, angels came and ministered unto him.

8 THE BEATITUDES
—Matthew 5:1-12.

And seeing the multitudes, he went up into the mountain: and when he had sat down, his disciples came unto him:

And he opened his mouth and taught them saying,

Blessed are the poor in spirit: for theirs is the kingdom of heaven.

Blessed are they that mourn: for they shall be comforted.

Blessed are the meek: for they shall inherit the earth.

Blessed are they that hunger and thirst after righteousness: for they shall be filled.

Blessed are the merciful: for they shall obtain mercy.

Blessed are the pure in heart: for they shall see God.

Blessed are the peacemakers: for they shall be called sons of God.

Blessed are they that have been persecuted for righteousness' sake: for theirs is the kingdom of heaven.

Blessed are ye when men shall reproach you, and persecute you, and say all manner of evil against you falsely, for my sake.

Rejoice, and be exceeding glad: for great is your reward in heaven: for so persecuted they the prophets that were before you.

9 CHRIST THE GOOD SHEPHERD
—John 10:1-16, 27-29.

Verily, verily, I say unto you, He that entereth not by the door into the fold of the sheep, but climbeth up some other way, the same is a thief and a robber.

But he that entereth in by the door is the shepherd of the sheep. To him the porter openeth; and the sheep hear his voice: and he calleth his own sheep by name, and leadeth them out.

When he hath put forth all his own, he goeth before them, and the sheep follow him: for they know his voice.

And a stranger they will not follow, but will flee from him: for they know not the voice of strangers.

This parable spake Jesus unto them: but they understood not what things they were which he spake unto them.

Jesus therefore said unto them again, Verily, verily, I say unto you, I am the door of the sheep.

All that came before me are thieves and robbers: but the sheep did not hear them.

I am the door; by me if any man enter in, he shall be saved, and shall go in and go out, and shall find pasture.

The thief cometh not, but that he may steal, and kill, and destroy: I came that they may have life, and may have it abundantly.

I am the good shepherd: the good shepherd layeth down his life for the sheep.

He that is a hireling, and not a shepherd, whose own the sheep are not, beholdeth the wolf coming, and leaveth the sheep, and fleeth, and the wolf snatcheth them, and scattereth them:

He fleeth because he is a hireling, and careth not for the sheep.

I am the good shepherd; and I know mine own, and mine own know me,

Even as the Father knoweth me, and I know the Father; and I lay down my life for the sheep.

And other sheep I have, which are not of this fold: them also I must bring, and they shall hear my voice; and they shall become one flock, one shepherd.

My sheep hear my voice, and I know them, and they follow me:

And I give unto them eternal life; and they shall never perish, and no one shall snatch them out of my hand.

My Father, who hath given them unto me, is greater than all; and no one is able to snatch them out of the Father's hand.

10 THE TRUE VINE AND THE BRANCHES
—John 15:1-12.

I am the true vine, and my Father is the husbandman.

Every branch in me that beareth not fruit, he taketh it away: and every branch that beareth fruit, he cleanseth it, that it may bear more fruit.

Already ye are clean because of the word which I have spoken unto you.

Abide in me, and I in you. As the branch cannot bear fruit of itself, except it abide in the vine; so neither can ye, except ye abide in me.

I am the vine, ye are the branches: He that abideth in me, and I in him, the same beareth much fruit: for apart from me ye can do nothing.

If a man abide not in me, he is cast forth as a branch, and is withered; and they gather them, and cast them into the fire, and they are burned.

If ye abide in me, and my words abide in you, ask whatsoever ye will, and it shall be done unto you.

Herein is my Father glorified that ye bear much fruit: and so shall ye be my disciples.

Even as the Father hath loved me, I also have loved you: abide ye in my love.

If ye keep my commandments, ye shall abide in my love; even as I have kept my Father's commandments, and abide in his love.

These things have I spoken unto you, that my joy may be in you, and that your joy may be made full.

This is my commandment, that ye love one another, even as I have loved you.

11 THE TRIUMPHAL ENTRY
—Mark 11:1-11.

And when they draw nigh unto Jerusalem, unto Bethphage and Bethany, at the mount of Olives, he sendeth two of his disciples,

And saith unto them, Go your way into the village that is over against you: and straightway as ye enter into it, ye shall find a colt tied, whereon no man ever yet sat; loose him, and bring him.

And if any one say unto you, Why do ye this? say ye, The Lord hath need of him; and straightway he will send him back hither.

And they went away, and found a colt tied at the door without in the open street; and they loose him.

And certain of them that stood there said unto them, What do ye, loosing the colt?

And they said unto them even as Jesus had said: and they let them go. And they bring the colt unto Jesus, and cast on him their garments; and he sat upon him.

And many spread their garments upon the way; and others branches which they had cut from the fields.

And they that went before, and they that followed, cried, Hosanna; Blessed is he that cometh in the name of the Lord:

Blessed is the kingdom that cometh, the kingdom of our father David: Hosanna in the highest.

And he entered into Jerusalem, into the temple; and when he had looked round about upon all things, it being now eventide, he went out unto Bethany with the twelve.

12 THE SUFFERING SERVANT
—Isaiah 52:13-15; 53:1-12.

Behold, my servant shall deal wisely, he shall be exalted and lifted up, and shall be very high. Like as many were astonished at thee (his visage was so marred more than any man, and his form more than the sons of men),

So shall he sprinkle many nations; kings shall shut their mouths at him: for that which had not been told them shall they see; and that which they had not heard shall they understand.

Who hath believed our message? and to whom hath the arm of the Lord been revealed?

For he grew up before him as a tender plant, and as a root out of a dry ground: he hath no form nor comeliness; and when we see him, there is no beauty that we should desire him.

He was despised, and rejected of men; a man of sorrows, and acquainted with grief: and as one from whom men hide their face he was despised; and we esteemed him not.

Surely he hath borne our griefs, and carried our sorrows; yet we did esteem him stricken, smitten of God, and afflicted.

But he was wounded for our transgressions, he was bruised for our iniquities; the chastisement of our peace was upon him; and with his stripes we are healed.

All we like sheep have gone astray; we have turned every one to his own way; and the Lord hath laid on him the iniquity of us all.

He was oppressed, yet when he was afflicted he opened not his mouth; as a lamb that is led to the slaughter, and as a sheep that before its shearers is dumb, so he opened not his mouth.

By oppression and judgment he was taken away; and as for his generation, who among them considered that he was cut off out of the land of the living for the transgression of my people to whom the stroke was due?

And they made his grave with the wicked, and with a rich man in his death; although he had done no violence, neither was any deceit in his mouth.

Yet it pleased the Lord to bruise him; he hath put him to grief: when thou shalt make his soul an offering for sin, he shall see his seed, he shall prolong his days, and the pleasure of the Lord shall prosper in his hand.

He shall see of the travail of his soul, and shall be satisfied: by the knowledge of himself shall my righteous servant justify many; and he shall bear their iniquities.

Therefore will I divide him a portion with the great, and he shall divide the spoil with the strong: because he poured out his soul unto death, and was numbered with the transgressors: yet he bare the sin of many, and made intercession for the transgressors.

13 THE AGONY IN THE GARDEN
—Matthew 26:36-46.

Then cometh Jesus with them unto a place called Gethsemane, and saith unto his disciples, Sit ye here, while I go yonder and pray.

And he took with him Peter and the two sons of Zebedee, and began to be sorrowful and sore troubled.

Then saith he unto them, My soul is exceeding sorrowful, even unto death: abide ye here, and watch with me.

And he went forward a little, and fell on his face, and prayed, saying, My Father, if it be possible, let this cup pass away from me: nevertheless, not as I will but as thou wilt.

And he cometh unto the disciples, and findeth them sleeping, and saith unto Peter, What, could ye not watch with me one hour?

Watch and pray, that ye enter not into temptation: the spirit indeed is willing, but the flesh is weak.

Again a second time he went away, and prayed, saying, My Father, if this cannot pass away, except I drink it, thy will be done.

And he came again and found them sleeping, for their eyes were heavy.

And he left them again, and went away, and prayed a third time, saying again the same words.

Then cometh he to the disciples, and saith unto them, Sleep on now, and take your rest: behold, the hour is at hand, and the Son of man is betrayed into the hands of sinners. Arise, let us be going: behold, he is at hand that betrayeth me.

14 THE LORD CRUCIFIED
—Matthew 27:24-38.

So when Pilate saw that he prevailed nothing, but rather that a tumult was arising, he took water, and washed his hands before the multitude, saying, I am innocent of the blood of this righteous man; see ye to it.

And all the people answered and said, His blood be on us, and on our children.

Then released he unto them Barabbas; but Jesus he scourged and delivered to be crucified.

Then the soldiers of the governor took Jesus into the Praetorium, and gathered unto him the whole band.

And they stripped him, and put on him a scarlet robe.

And they platted a crown of thorns and put it upon his head, and a reed in his right hand; and they kneeled down before him, and mocked him saying, Hail, King of the Jews!

And they spat upon him, and took the reed and smote him on the head.

And when they had mocked him, they took off from him the robe, and put on him his garments, and led him away to crucify him.

And as they came out, they found a man of Cyrene, Simon by name: him they compelled to go with them, that he might bear his cross.

And when they were come unto a place called Golgotha, that is to say, The place of a skull,

They gave him wine to drink mingled with gall: and when he had tasted it, he would not drink.

And when they had crucified him, they parted his garments among them, casting lots; and they sat and watched him there.

And they set up over his head his accusation written, This is Jesus the King of the Jews.

Then are there crucified with him two robbers, one on the right hand and one on the left.

15 THE DEATH OF CHRIST
—Matthew 27:39-54.

And they that passed by railed on him, wagging their heads,

And saying, Thou that destroyest the temple, and buildest it in three days, save thyself: if thou art the Son of God, come down from the cross.

In like manner also the chief priests mocking him, with the scribes and elders, said,

He saved others; himself he cannot save. He is the King of Israel; let him now come down from the cross, and we will believe on him.

He trusteth on God; let him deliver him now, if he desireth him: for he said, I am the Son of God.

And the robbers also that were crucified with him cast upon him the same reproach.

Now from the sixth hour there was darkness over all the land until the ninth hour.

And about the ninth hour Jesus cried with a loud voice, saying, Eli, Eli, lama sabachthani? that is, My God, my God, why hast thou forsaken me?

And some of them that stood there, when they heard it, said, This man calleth Elijah.

And straightway one of them ran, and took a sponge, and filled it with vinegar, and put it on a reed, and gave him to drink.

And the rest said, Let be; let us see whether Elijah cometh to save him.

And Jesus cried again with a loud voice, and yielded up his spirit.

And behold, the veil of the temple was rent in two from the top to the bottom; and the earth did quake; and the rocks were rent;

And the tombs were opened; and many bodies of the saints that had fallen asleep were raised;

And coming forth out of the tombs after his resurrection they entered into the holy city and appeared unto many.

Now the centurion, and they that were with him watching Jesus, when they saw the earthquake, and the things that were done, feared exceedingly, saying, Truly this was the Son of God.

16 THE RESURRECTION OF CHRIST
—John 20:1-18.

Now on the first day of the week cometh Mary Magdalene early, while it was yet dark, unto the tomb, and seeth the stone taken away from the tomb.

She runneth therefore, and cometh to Simon Peter, and to the other disciple whom Jesus loved, and saith unto them, They have taken away the Lord out of the tomb, and we know not where they have laid him.

Peter therefore went forth, and the other disciple, and they went toward the tomb.

And they ran both together; and the other disciple outran Peter, and came first to the tomb;

And stooping and looking in, he seeth the linen cloths lying; yet entered he not in.

Simon Peter therefore also cometh, following him, and entered into the tomb; and he beholdeth the linen cloths lying.

And the napkin, that was upon his head, not lying with the linen cloths, but rolled up in a place by itself.

Then entered in therefore the other disciple also, who came first to the tomb, and he saw, and believed.

For as yet they knew not the scripture, that he must rise again from the dead.

So the disciples went away again unto their own home.

But Mary was standing without at the tomb weeping; so, as she wept, she stooped and looked into the tomb;

And she beholdeth two angels in white sitting, one at the head, and one at the feet, where the body of Jesus had lain.

And they say unto her, Woman, why weepest thou? She saith unto them, Because they have taken away my Lord, and I know not where they have laid him.

When she had thus said, she turned herself back, and beholdeth Jesus standing, and knew not that it was Jesus.

Jesus saith unto her, Woman, why weepest thou? whom seekest thou? She, supposing him to be the gardener, saith unto him, Sir, if thou has borne him hence, tell me where thou has laid him, and I will take him away.

Jesus saith unto her, Mary. She turneth herself, and saith unto him in Hebrew, Rabboni; which is to say, Teacher.

Jesus saith to her, Touch me not; for I am not yet ascended unto the Father: but go unto my brethren, and say to them, I ascend unto my Father and your Father, and my God and your God.

Mary Magdalene cometh and telleth the disciples, I have seen the Lord; and that he had said these things unto her.

17 THE MEANING OF THE RESURRECTION
—1 Corinthians 15:12-23.

Now if Christ is preached that he hath been raised from the dead, how say some among you that there is no resurrection of the dead?

But if there is no resurrection of the dead, neither hath Christ been raised:

And if Christ hath not been raised, then is our preaching vain, your faith also is vain.

Yea, and we are found false witnesses of God; because we witnessed of God that he raised up Christ: whom he raised not up, if so be that the dead are not raised.

For if the dead are not raised, neither had Christ been raised:

And if Christ hath not been raised, your faith is vain; ye are yet in your sins.

Then they also that are fallen asleep in Christ have perished.

If we have only hoped in Christ in this life, we are of all men most pitiable.

But now hath Christ been raised from the dead, the firstfruits of them that are asleep.

For since by man came death, by man came also the resurrection of the dead.

For as in Adam all die, so also in Christ shall all be made alive.

But each in his own order: Christ the firstfruits; then they that are Christ's at his coming.

18 THE ASCENSION
—Acts 1:1-11.

The former treatise I made, O Theophilus, concerning all that Jesus began both to do and to teach, until the day in which he was received up, after that he had given commandment through the Holy Spirit unto the apostles whom he had chosen:

To whom he also showed himself alive after his passion by many proofs, appearing unto them by the space of forty days, and speaking the things concerning the kingdom of God:

And, being assembled together with them, he charged them not to depart from Jerusalem, but to wait for the promise of the Father, which, said he, ye heard from me:

For John indeed baptized with water; but ye shall be baptized in the Holy Spirit not many days hence.

They therefore, when they were come together, asked him, saying, Lord, dost thou at this time restore the kingdom to Israel?

And he said unto them, It is not for you to know times or seasons, which the Father hath set within his own authority.

But ye shall receive power, when the Holy Spirit is come upon you: and ye shall be my witnesses both in Jerusalem, and in all Judaea and Samaria, and unto the uttermost part of the earth.

And when he had said these things, as they were looking, he was taken up; and a cloud received him out of their sight.

And while they were looking steadfastly into heaven as he went, behold two men stood by them in white apparel;

Who also said, Ye men of Galilee, why stand ye looking into heaven? this Jesus, who was received up from you into heaven, shall so come in like manner as ye beheld him going into heaven.

19 THE PROMISE OF THE HOLY SPIRIT
—John 16:7-15.

Nevertheless I tell you the truth: It is expedient for you that I go away; for if I go not away, the Comforter will not come unto you; but if I go, I will send him unto you.

And he, when he is come, will convict the world in respect of sin, and of righteousness, and of judgment: of sin, because they believe not on me;

Of righteousness, because I go to the Father, and ye behold me no more;

Of judgment, because the prince of this world hath been judged.

I have yet many things to say unto you, but ye cannot bear them now.

Howbeit when he, the Spirit of truth, is come, he shall guide you into all the truth: for he shall not speak from himself; but what things soever he shall hear, these shall he speak: and he shall declare unto you the things that are to come.

He shall glorify me: for he shall take of mine, and shall declare it unto you.

All things whatsoever the Father hath are mine: therefore said I, that he taketh of mine, and shall declare it unto you.

20 THE DESCENT OF THE HOLY SPIRIT
—Acts 2:1-13.

And when the day of Pentecost was now come, they were all together in one place.

And suddenly there came from heaven a sound as of the rushing of a mighty wind, and it filled all the house where they were sitting.

And there appeared unto them tongues parting asunder, like as of fire; and it sat upon each one of them.

And they were all filled with the Holy Spirit, and began to speak with other tongues, as the Spirit gave them utterance.

Now there were dwelling at Jerusalem Jews, devout men, from every nation under heaven.

And when this sound was heard, the multitude came together, and were confounded, because that every man heard them speaking in his own language.

And they were all amazed and marvelled, saying, Behold, are not all these that speak Galilaeans?

And how hear we, every man in our own language wherein we were born?

Parthians and Medes and Elamites, and the dwellers in Mesopotamia, in Judaea and Cappadocia, in Pontus and Asia,

In Phrygia and Pamphylia, in Egypt and the parts of Libya about Cyrene, and sojourners from Rome, both Jews and proselytes,

Cretans and Arabians, we hear them speaking in our tongues the mighty works of God.

And they were all amazed, and were perplexed saying one to another, What meaneth this? But others mocking said, They are filled with new wine.

21 THE WORD OF GOD
—Psalm 119:9-16, 41-48.

Wherewith shall a young man cleanse his way?
By taking heed thereto according to thy word.

With my whole heart have I sought thee:
Oh let me not wander from thy commandments.

Thy word have I laid up in my heart,
That I might not sin against thee.

Blessed art thou, O Lord:
Teach me thy statutes.

With my lips have I declared
All the ordinances of thy mouth.

I have rejoiced in the way of thy testimonies,
As much as in all riches.

I will meditate on thy precepts,
And have respect unto thy ways.

I will delight myself in thy statutes:
I will not forget thy word.

Let thy loving kindnesses also come unto me, O Lord,
Even thy salvation, according to thy word.

So shall I have an answer for him that reproacheth me;
For I trust in thy word.

And take not the word of truth utterly out of my mouth;
For I have hoped in thine ordinances.

So shall I observe thy law continually
For ever and ever.

And I shall walk at liberty;
For I have sought thy precepts.

I will also speak of thy testimonies before kings.
And shall not be put to shame.

And I will delight myself in thy commandments,
Which I have loved.

I will lift up my hands also unto thy commandments, which I have loved;

And I will meditate on thy statutes.

22 THE POWER OF THE WORD
—Luke 8:4-15.

And when a great multitude came together, and they of every city resorted unto him, he spake by a parable:

The sower went forth to sow his seed: and as he sowed, some fell by the way side; and it was trodden under foot, and the birds of the heaven devoured it.

And other fell on the rock; and as soon as it grew, it withered away, because it had no moisture.

And the other fell amidst the thorns; and the thorns grew with it, and choked it.

And other fell into the good ground, and grew, and brought forth fruit a hundredfold. As he said these things, he cried, He that hath ears to hear, let him hear.

And his disciples asked him what this parable might be.

And he said, Unto you it is given to know the mysteries of the kingdom of God: but to the rest in parables; that seeing they may not see, and hearing they may not understand.

Now the parable is this: The seed is the word of God.

And those by the way side are they that have heard; then cometh the devil, and taketh away the word from their heart, that they may not believe and be saved.

And those on the rock are they who, when they have heard, receive the word with joy; and these have no root, who for a while believe, and in time of temptation fall away.

And that which fell among the thorns, these are they that have heard, and as they go on their way they are choked with cares and riches and pleasures of this life, and bring no fruit to perfection.

And that in the good ground, these are such as in an honest and good heart, having heard the word, hold it fast, and bring forth fruit with patience.

23 THE HOUSE OF GOD
—Psalm 84.

How amiable are thy tabernacles, O Lord of hosts!

My soul longeth, yea, even fainteth for the courts of the Lord;
My heart and my flesh cry out unto the living God.

Yea, the sparrow hath found her a house,
And the swallow a nest for herself where she may lay her young,
Even thine altars, O Lord of hosts,
My King, and my God.

Blessed are they that dwell in thy house:
They will be still praising thee.
[Selah

Blessed is the man whose strength is in thee;
In whose heart are the highways to Zion.

Passing through the valley of Weeping they make it a place of springs;
Yea, the early rain covereth it with blessings.

They go from strength to strength;
Every one of them appeareth before God in Zion.

O Lord God of hosts, hear my prayer;
Give ear, O God of Jacob.
[Selah

Behold, O God our shield,
And look upon the face of thine anointed.

For a day in thy courts is better than a thousand.
I had rather be a doorkeeper in the house of my God,
Than to dwell in the tents of wickedness.

For the Lord God is a sun and a shield:
The Lord will give grace and glory;
No good thing will he withhold from them that walk uprightly.

O Lord of hosts,
Blessed is the man that trusteth in thee.

24 THE DAY OF THE LORD
—Genesis 2:1-3; Exodus 20:8-11; Isaiah 58:13-14.

And the heavens and the earth were finished, and all the host of them. And on the seventh day God finished his work which he had made; and he rested on the seventh day from all his work which he had made.

And God blessed the seventh day and hallowed it; because that in it he rested from all his work which God had created and made.

Remember the sabbath day, to keep it holy.

Six days shalt thou labor, and do all thy work;

But the seventh day is a sabbath unto the Lord thy God: in it thou shalt not do any work, thou, nor thy son, nor thy daughter, thy man-servant, nor thy maid-servant, nor thy cattle, nor thy stranger that is within thy gates:

For in six days the Lord made heaven and earth, the sea, and all that in them is, and rested the seventh day: wherefore the Lord blessed the sabbath day, and hallowed it.

If thou turn away thy foot from the sabbath, from doing thy pleasure on my holy day; and call the sabbath a delight, and the holy of the Lord honorable; and shalt honor it, not doing thine own ways, nor finding thine own pleasure, nor speaking thine own words:

Then shalt thou delight thyself in the Lord; and I will make thee to ride upon the high places of the earth; and I will feed thee with the heritage of Jacob thy father: for the mouth of the Lord hath spoken it.

25 PENITENCE
—Psalm 51:1-17.

Have mercy upon me, O God, according to thy loving kindness:
According to the multitude of thy tender mercies blot out my transgressions.

Wash me thoroughly from mine iniquity,
And cleanse me from my sin.
For I know my transgressions;
And my sin is ever before me.

Against thee, thee only, have I sinned,
And done that which is evil in thy sight;
That thou mayest be justified when thou speakest,
And be clear when thou judgest.

Behold, I was brought forth in iniquity;
And in sin did my mother conceive me.

Behold, thou desirest truth in the inward parts;
And in the hidden part thou wilt make me to know wisdom.

Purify me with hyssop, and I shall be clean:
Wash me, and I shall be whiter than snow.

Make me to hear joy and gladness,
That the bones which thou hast broken may rejoice.

Hide thy face from my sins,
And blot out all mine iniquities.

Create in me a clean heart, O God;
And renew a right spirit within me.

Cast me not away from thy presence;
And take not thy holy Spirit from me.

Restore unto me the joy of thy salvation;
And uphold me with a willing spirit.

Then will I teach transgressors thy ways;
And sinners shall be converted unto thee.

Deliver me from bloodguiltiness, O God, thou God of my salvation;
And my tongue shall sing aloud of thy righteousness.

O Lord, open thou my lips;
And my mouth shall show forth thy praise.

For thou delightest not in sacrifice; else would I give it:
Thou hast no pleasure in burnt-offering.

The sacrifices of God are a broken spirit:
A broken and a contrite heart, O God, thou wilt not despise.

26 THE DIVINE KING
—Psalm 24.

The earth is the Lord's, and the fulness thereof;
The world and they that dwell therein.

For he hath founded it upon the seas,
And established it upon the floods.

Who shall ascend into the hill of the Lord?
And who shall stand in his holy place?

He that hath clean hands, and a pure heart;
Who hath not lifted up his soul unto falsehood,
And hath not sworn deceitfully.

He shall receive a blessing from the Lord,
And righteousness from the God of his salvation.

This is the generation of them that seek after him,
That seek thy face, even Jacob. [Selah

Lift up your heads, O ye gates;
And be ye lifted up, ye everlasting doors:
And the King of glory will come in.

Who is the King of glory?
The Lord strong and mighty,
The Lord mighty in battle.

Lift up your heads, O ye gates;
Yea, lift them up, ye everlasting doors:
And the King of glory will come in.

Who is the King of glory?
The Lord of hosts,
He is the King of glory. [Selah

27 FAITH IN GOD
—Psalm 25:1-15.

Unto thee, O Lord, do I lift up my soul.
Oh my God, in thee have I trusted,
Let me not be put to shame;
Let not mine enemies triumph over me.

Yea, none that wait for thee shall be put to shame:
They shall be put to shame that deal treacherously without cause.

Show me thy ways, O Lord;
Teach me thy paths.

Guide me in thy truth, and teach me;
For thou are the God of my salvation;
For thee do I wait all the day.

Remember, O Lord, thy tender mercies and thy lovingkindnesses;
For they have been ever of old.

Remember not the sins of my youth, nor my transgressions:
According to thy lovingkindness remember thou me,
For thy goodness' sake, O Lord.

Good and upright is the Lord:
Therefore will he instruct sinners in the way.

The meek will he guide in justice;
And the meek will he teach his way.

All the paths of the Lord are lovingkindness and truth
Unto such as keep his covenant and his testimonies.

For thy name's sake, O Lord,
Pardon mine iniquity, for it is great.

What man is he that feareth the Lord?
Him shall he instruct in the way that he shall choose.

His soul shall dwell at ease;
And his seed shall inherit the land.

The friendship of the Lord is with them that fear him;
And he will show them his covenant.

Mine eyes are ever toward the Lord;
For he will pluck my feet out of the net.

28 THE PRAYER OF FAITH
—Psalm 27:1-12.

The Lord is my light and my salvation;
Whom shall I fear?
The Lord is the strength of my life;
Of whom shall I be afraid?

When evil-doers came upon me to eat up my flesh,
Even mine adversaries and my foes, they stumbled and fell.

Though a host should encamp against me,
My heart shall not fear:
Though war should rise against me,
Even then will I be confident.

One thing have I asked of the Lord, that will I seek after:
That I may dwell in the house of the Lord all the days of my life,
To behold the beauty of the Lord, And to inquire in his temple.

For in the day of trouble he will keep me secretly in his pavilion:
In the covert of his tabernacle will he hide me;
He will lift me upon a rock.

And now shall my head be lifted up above mine enemies round about me;
And I will offer in his tabernacle sacrifices of joy;
I will sing, yea, I will sing praises unto the Lord.

Hear, O Lord, when I cry with my voice:
Have mercy also upon me, and answer me.

When thou saidst, Seek ye my face; my heart said unto thee,
Thy face, Lord, will I seek.

Hide not thy face from me;
Put not thy servant away in anger:
Thou hast been my help;
Cast me not off, neither forsake me, O God of my salvation.

When my father and my mother forsake me,
Then the Lord will take me up.

Teach me thy way, O Lord;
And lead me in a plain path,
Because of mine enemies.

Deliver me not over unto the will of mine adversaries:
For false witnesses are risen up against me,
And such as breathe out cruelty.

29 GOD'S KINDNESS
—Psalm 36:1-10.

The transgression of the wicked saith within my heart,
There is no fear of God before his eyes.

For he flattereth himself in his own eyes,
That his iniquity will not be found out and be hated.

The words of his mouth are
iniquity and deceit:
He hath ceased to be wise and to
do good.

He deviseth iniquity upon his bed;
He setteth himself in a way that
is not good;
He abhorreth not evil.

Thy lovingkindness, O Lord,
is in the heavens;
Thy faithfulness reacheth unto the
skies.

Thy righteousness is like the
mountains of God;
Thy judgments are a great deep:
O Lord, thou preserveth man and
beast.

How precious is thy lovingkindness, O God!
And the children of men take
refuge under the shadow of thy
wings.

They shall be abundantly satisfied
with the fatness of thy house;
And thou wilt make them drink
of the river of thy pleasures.

For with thee is the fountain of
life:
In thy light shall we see light.

Oh continue thy lovingkindness
unto them that know thee,
And thy righteousness to the up-
right in heart.

30 GOD OUR REFUGE
—Psalm 46.

God is our refuge and strength,
A very present help in trouble.

Therefore will we not fear, though
the earth do change,
And though the mountains be
shaken into the heart of the
seas;

Though the waters thereof roar
and be troubled,
Though the mountains tremble
with the swelling thereof.
[Selah

There is a river, the streams
whereof make glad the city of
God,
The holy place of the tabernacles
of the Most High.

God is in the midst of her; she
shall not be moved:
God will help her, and that right
early.

The nations raged, the kingdoms
were moved:
He uttered his voice, the earth
melted.

The Lord of hosts is with us;
The God of Jacob is our refuge.
[Selah

Come, behold the works of the
Lord,
What desolations he hath made
in the earth.

He maketh wars to cease unto the
end of the earth;
He breaketh the bow, and cutteth
the spear in sunder;
He burneth the chariots in the
fire.

Be still, and know that I am God:
I will be exalted among the na-
tions, I will be exalted in the
earth.
The Lord of hosts is with us:
The God of Jacob is our refuge.
[Selah

31 THANKSGIVING
—Psalm 65.

Praise waiteth for thee, O God,
in Zion;
And unto thee shall the vow be
performed.

O thou that heareth prayer,
Unto thee shall all flesh come.
Iniquities prevail against me:
As for our transgressions, thou wilt forgive them.

Blessed is the man whom thou chooseth, and causeth to approach unto thee,
That he may dwell in thy courts:
We shall be satisfied with the goodness of thy house,
Thy holy temple.

By terrible things thou wilt answer us in righteousness,
O God of our salvation,
Thou that art the confidence of all the ends of the earth,
And of them that are afar off upon the sea:

Who by his strength setteth fast the mountains,
Being girded about with might;
Who stilleth the roaring of the seas,
The roaring of their waves,
And the tumult of the peoples.

They also that dwell in the uttermost parts are afraid at thy tokens:
Thou makest the outgoings of the morning and evening to rejoice.
Thou visitest the earth, and waterest it,
Thou greatly enrichest it;
The river of God is full of water:
Thou providest them grain, when thou hast so prepared the earth.

Thou waterest its furrows abundantly;
Thou settlest the ridges thereof:
Thou makest it soft with showers;
Thou blessest the springing thereof.

Thou crownest the year with thy goodness;
And thy paths drop fatness.

They drop upon the pastures of the wilderness;
And the hills are girded with joy.
The pastures are clothed with flocks;
The valleys also are covered over with grain;
They shout for joy, they also sing.

32 SING UNTO THE LORD
—Psalm 96.

Oh sing unto the Lord a new song:
Sing unto the Lord, all the earth.
Sing unto the Lord, bless his name;
Show forth his salvation from day to day.

Declare his glory among the nations,
His marvellous works among all the peoples.
For great is the Lord, and greatly to be praised:
He is to be feared above all gods.
For all the gods of the peoples are idols;
But the Lord made the heavens.

Honor and majesty are before him:
Strength and beauty are in his sanctuary.
Ascribe unto the Lord, ye kindreds of the peoples,
Ascribe unto the Lord glory and strength.

Ascribe unto the Lord the glory due unto his name:
Bring an offering, and come into his courts.

Oh worship the Lord in holy
array:
Tremble before him, all the earth.

Say among the nations, the Lord
reigneth:
The world also is established that
it cannot be moved:
He will judge the peoples with
equity.

**Let the heavens be glad, and let
the earth rejoice;**
**Let the sea roar, and the fulness
thereof;**

Let the field exult, all that is
therein;
Then shall all the trees of the
wood sing for joy

Before the Lord; for he cometh,
For he cometh to judge the earth:
**He will judge the world with
righteousness,**
And the peoples with his truth.

33 THE CALL TO PRAISE

—Psalm 103.

Bless the Lord, O my soul;
And all that is within me, bless
his holy name.

Bless the Lord, O my soul,
And forget not all his benefits:

Who forgiveth all thine iniquities;
Who healeth all thy diseases;

**Who redeemeth thy life from de-
struction;**
**Who crowneth thee with loving-
kindness and tender mercies;**

Who satisfieth thy desire with
good things,
So that thy youth is renewed like
the eagle.

**The Lord executeth righteous
acts,**
**And judgments for all that are
oppressed.**

He made known his ways unto
Moses,
His doings unto the children of
Israel.

The Lord is mericiful and gracious,
**Slow to anger, and abundant in
lovingkindness.**

He will not always chide;
Neither will he keep his anger
for ever.

**He hath not dealt with us after
our sins,**
**Nor rewarded us after our iniq-
uities.**

For as the heavens are high above
the earth,
So great is his lovingkindness
toward them that fear him.

**As far as the east is from the
west,**
**So far hath he removed our trans-
gressions from us.**

Like as a father pitieth his
children,
So the Lord pitieth them that fear
him.

For he knoweth our frame;
He remembereth that we are dust.

As for man, his days are as grass;
As a flower of the field, so he
flourisheth.

**For the wind passeth over it, and
it is gone;**
**And the place thereof shall know
it no more.**

But the lovingkindness of the
Lord is from everlasting to
everlasting upon them that fear
him,
And his righteousness unto chil-
dren's children;

To such as keep his covenant,
**And to those that remember his
precepts to do them.**

The Lord hath established his throne in the heavens;
And his kingdom ruleth over all.

Bless the Lord, ye his angels,
That are mighty in strength, that fulfil his word,
Hearkening unto the voice of his word.

Bless the Lord, all ye his hosts,
Ye ministers of his, that do his pleasure.

Bless the Lord, all ye his works,
In all places of his dominion:
Bless the Lord, O my soul.

34 PRAISE THE LORD
—Psalm 148:1-13.

Praise ye the Lord.
Praise ye the Lord from the heavens:
Praise him in the heights.

Praise ye him, all his angels:
Praise ye him, all his host.

Praise ye him, sun and moon:
Praise him, all ye stars of light.

Praise him, ye heavens of heavens,
And ye waters that are above the heavens.

Let them praise the name of the Lord;
For he commanded, and they were created.

He hath also established them for ever and ever:
He hath made a decree which shall not pass away.

Praise the Lord from the earth,
Ye sea-monsters, and all deeps;
Fire and hail, snow and vapor;
Stormy wind, fulfilling his word;

Mountains and all hills;
Fruitful trees and all cedars;

Beasts and all cattle;
Creeping things and flying birds;

Kings of the earth and all peoples;
Princes and all judges of the earth;

Both young men and virgins;
Old men and children:

Let them praise the name of the Lord;
For his name alone is exalted:
His glory is above the earth and the heavens.

35 THE RANSOMED PEOPLE
—Isaiah 35.

The wilderness and the dry land shall be glad; and the desert shall rejoice, and blossom as the rose.

It shall blossom abundantly, and rejoice even with joy and singing; the glory of Lebanon shall be given unto it, the excellency of Carmel and Sharon: they shall see the glory of the Lord, the excellency of our God.

Strengthen ye the weak hands, and confirm the feeble knees.

Say to them that are of a fearful heart, Be strong, fear not: behold, your God will come with vengeance, with the recompense of God; he will come and save you.

Then the eyes of the blind shall be opened, and the ears of the deaf shall be unstopped.

Then shall the lame man leap as a hart, and the tongue of the dumb shall sing; for in the wilderness shall waters break out, and streams in the desert.

And the glowing sand shall become a pool, and the thirsty ground springs of water: in the habitation of jackals, where they lay, shall be grass with reeds and rushes.

And a highway shall be there, and a way, and it shall be called The way of holiness; the unclean shall not pass over it; but it shall be for the redeemed: the wayfaring men, yea fools, shall not err therein.

No lion shall be there, nor shall any ravenous beast go up thereon; they shall not be found there; but the redeemed shall walk there:

And the ransomed of the Lord shall return, and come with singing unto Zion; and everlasting joy shall be upon their heads; they shall obtain gladness and joy, and sorrow and sighing shall flee away.

36 THE DIVINE INVITATION
—Isaiah 55.

Ho, every one that thirsteth, come ye to the waters, and he that hath no money; come ye, buy, and eat; yea, come, buy wine and milk without money and without price.

Wherefore do ye spend money for that which is not bread? and your labor for that which satisfieth not? hearken diligently unto me, and eat ye that which is good, and let your soul delight itself in fatness.

Incline your ear, and come unto me; hear, and your soul shall live: and I will make an everlasting covenant with you, even the sure mercies of David.

Behold, I have given him for a witness to the peoples, a leader and commander to the peoples.

Behold, thou shalt call a nation that thou knowest not; and a nation that knew not thee shall run unto thee, because of the Lord thy God, and for the Holy One of Israel; for he hath glorified thee,

Seek ye the Lord while he may be found; call ye upon him while he is near: let the wicked forsake his way, and the unrighteous man his thoughts; and let him return unto the Lord, and he will have mercy upon him; and to our God, for he will abundantly pardon.

For my thoughts are not your thoughts, neither are your ways my ways, saith the Lord.

For as the heavens are higher than the earth, so are my ways higher than your ways, and my thoughts than your thoughts.

For as the rain cometh down and the snow from heaven, and returneth not thither, but watereth the earth, and maketh it bring forth and bud, and giveth seed to the sower and bread to the eater;

So shall my word be that goeth forth out of my mouth: it shall not return unto me void, but it shall accomplish that which I please, and it shall prosper in the thing whereto I sent it.

For ye shall go out with joy, and be led forth with peace: the mountains and the hills shall break forth before you into singing; and all the trees of the field shall clap their hands.

Instead of the thorn shall come up the fir-tree; and instead of the brier shall come up the myrtle-tree: and it shall be to the Lord for a name, for an everlasting sign that shall not be cut off.

37 THE FATHER'S CARE
—Matthew 6:19-34.

Lay not up for yourselves treasures upon the earth, where moth and rust consume, and where thieves break through and steal:

But lay up for yourselves treasures in heaven, where neither moth nor rust doth consume, and where thieves do not break through nor steal:

For where thy treasure is, there will thy heart be also.

The lamp of the body is the eye: if therefore thine eye be single, thy whole body shall be full of light.

But if thine eye be evil, thy whole body shall be full of darkness. If therefore the light that is in thee be darkness, how great is the darkness!

No man can serve two masters: for either he will hate the one, and love the other; or else he will hold to one, and despise the other. Ye cannot serve God and mammon.

Therefore I say unto you, Be not anxious for your life, what ye shall eat, or what ye shall drink; nor yet for your body, what ye shall put on. Is not the life more than the food, and the body than the raiment?

Behold the birds of the heaven, that they sow not, neither do they reap, nor gather into barns; and your heavenly Father feedeth them. Are not ye of much more value than they?

And which of you by being anxious can add one cubit unto the measure of his life?

And why are ye anxious concerning raiment? Consider the lilies of the field, how they grow; they toil not, neither do they spin:

Yet I say unto you, that even Solomon in all his glory was not arrayed like one of these.

But if God doth so clothe the grass of the field, which today is, and tomorrow is cast into the oven, shall he not much more clothe you, O ye of little faith?

Be not therefore anxious, saying, What shall we eat? or, What shall we drink? or, Wherewithal shall we be clothed?

For after all these things do the Gentiles seek; for your heavenly Father knoweth that ye have need of all these things.

But seek ye first his kingdom, and his righteousness; and all these things shall be added unto you.

Be not therefore anxious for the morrow: for the morrow will be anxious for itself. Sufficient unto the day is the evil thereof.

38 THE CHRISTIAN ARMOR
—Ephesians 6:10-18.

Finally, be strong in the Lord, and in the strength of his might. Put on the whole armor of God, that ye may be able to stand against the wiles of the devil.

For our wrestling is not against flesh and blood, but against the principalities, against the powers, against the world-rulers of this darkness, against the spiritual hosts of wickedness in the heavenly places.

Wherefore take up the whole armor of God, that ye may be able to withstand in the evil day, and, having done all, to stand.

Stand therefore, having girded your loins with truth, and having put on the breastplate of righteousness,

And having shod your feet with the preparation of the gospel of peace;

Withal taking up the shield of faith, wherewith ye shall be able to quench all the fiery darts of the evil one.

And take the helmet of salvation, and the sword of the Spirit, which is the word of God:

With all prayer and supplication praying at all seasons in the Spirit, and watching thereunto in all perseverance and supplication for all the saints.

39 THE SUPREMACY OF LOVE

—1 Corinthians 13.

If I speak with the tongues of men and of angels, but have not love, I am become sounding brass, or a clanging cymbal.

And if I have the gift of prophecy, and know all mysteries and all knowledge; and if I have all faith, so as to remove mountains, but have not love, I am nothing.

And if I bestow all my goods to feed the poor, and if I give my body to be burned, but have not love, it profiteth me nothing.

Love suffereth long, and is kind; love envieth not; love vaunteth not itself, is not puffed up,

Doth not behave itself unseemly, seeketh not its own, is not provoked, taketh not account of evil;

Rejoiceth not in unrighteousness, but rejoiceth with the truth;

Beareth all things, believeth all things, hopeth all things, endureth all things.

Love never faileth: but whether there be prophecies, they shall be done away; whether there be tongues, they shall cease; whether there be knowledge, it shall be done away.

For we know in part, and we prophesy in part; but when that which is perfect is come, that which is in part shall be done away.

When I was a child, I spake as a child, I felt as a child, I thought as a child: now that I am become a man, I have put away childish things.

For now we see in a mirror, darkly; but then face to face: now I know in part; but then shall I know fully even as also I was fully known.

But now abideth faith, hope, love, these three; and the greatest of these is love.

40 GOD'S LOVE
—John 3:14-21; John 4:7-10.

And as Moses lifted up the serpent in the wilderness, even so must the Son of man be lifted up;

That whosoever believeth may in him have eternal life.

For God so loved the world, that he gave his only begotten Son, that whosoever believeth on him should not perish, but have eternal life.

For God sent not the Son into the world to judge the world; but that the world should be saved through him.

He that believeth on him is not judged; he that believeth not hath been judged already, because he hath not believed on the name of the only begotten Son of God.

And this is the judgment, that the light is come into the world, and men loved the darkness rather than the light; for their works were evil.

For every one that doeth evil hateth the light, and cometh not to the light, lest his works should be reproved.

But he that doeth the truth cometh to the light, that his works may be made manifest, that they have been wrought in God.

Beloved, let us love one another: for love is of God; and every one that loveth is begotten of God, and knoweth God.

He that loveth not knoweth not God; for God is love.

Herein was the love of God manifested in us, that God hath sent his only begotten Son into the world that we might live through him.

Herein is love, not that we loved God, but that he loved us, and sent his Son to be the propitiation for our sins.

41 CHRISTIAN FORGIVENESS
—Colossians 3:12-17.

Put on therefore, as God's elect, holy and beloved, a heart of compassion, kindness, lowliness, meekness, longsuffering;

Forbearing one another, and forgiving each other, if any man have a complaint against any; even as the Lord forgave you, so also do ye:

And above all these things put on love, which is the bond of perfectness.

And let the peace of Christ rule in your hearts, to the which also ye were called in one body, and be ye thankful.

Let the word of Christ dwell in you richly; in all wisdom teaching and admonishing one another with psalms and hymns and spiritual songs, singing with grace in your hearts unto God.

And whatsoever ye do, in word or in deed, do all in the name of the Lord Jesus, giving thanks to God the Father through him.

42 NO CONDEMNATION
—Romans 8:1-11.

There is therefore now no condemnation to them that are in Christ Jesus. For the law of the Spirit of life in Christ Jesus made me free from the law of sin and of death.

493

For what the law could not do, in that it was weak through the flesh, God, sending his own Son in the likeness of sinful flesh and for sin, condemned sin in the flesh:

That the ordinance of the law might be fulfilled in us, who walk not after the flesh, but after the Spirit.

For they that are after the flesh mind the things of the flesh; but they that are after the Spirit the things of the Spirit.

For the mind of the flesh is death; but the mind of the Spirit is life and peace:

Because the mind of the flesh is enmity against God; for it is not subject to the law of God, neither indeed can it be:

And they that are in the flesh cannot please God.

But ye are not in the flesh but in the Spirit, if so be that the Spirit of God dwelleth in you. But if any man hath not the Spirit of Christ, he is none of his.

And if Christ is in you, the body is dead because of sin; but the spirit is life because of righteousness.

But if the Spirit of him that raised up Jesus from the dead dwelleth in you, he that raised up Christ Jesus from the dead shall give life also to your mortal bodies through his Spirit that dwelleth in you.

43 THE CHRISTIAN SECURITY
—Romans 8:31-39.

What then shall we say to these things? If God is for us, who is against us?

He that spared not his own Son, but delivered him up for us all, how shall he not also with him freely give us all things?

Who shall lay anything to the charge of God's elect? It is God that justifieth; who is he that condemneth? It is Christ Jesus that died, yea rather, that was raised from the dead, who is at the right hand of God, who also maketh intercession for us.

Who shall separate us from the love of Christ? shall tribulation, or anguish, or persecution, or famine, or nakedness, or peril, or sword?

Even as it is written,
For thy sake we are killed all the day long;
We were accounted as sheep for the slaughter.

Nay, in all these things we are more than conquerors through him that loved us.

For I am persuaded, that neither death, nor life, nor angels, nor principalities, nor things present, nor things to come, nor powers,

Nor height, nor depth, nor any other creature, shall be able to separate us from the love of God, which is in Christ Jesus our Lord.

44 EXHORTATION TO UNITY
—Philippians 2:1-11.

If there is therefore any exhortation in Christ, if any consolation of love, if any fellowship of the Spirit, if any tender mercies and compassions,

494

Make full my joy, that ye be of the same mind, having the same love, being of one accord, of one mind; doing nothing through faction or through vainglory, but in lowliness of mind each counting other better than himself;

Not looking each of you to his own things, but each of you also to the things of others.

Have this mind in you, which was also in Christ Jesus:

Who, existing in the form of God, counted not the being on an equality with God a thing to be grasped,

But emptied himself, taking the form of a servant, being made in the likeness of men;

And being found in fashion as a man, he humbled himself, becoming obedient even unto death, yea, the death of the cross.

Wherefore also God highly exalted him, and gave unto him the name which is above every name;

That in the name of Jesus every knee should bow, of things in heaven and things on earth and things under the earth,

And that every tongue should confess that Jesus Christ is Lord, to the glory of God the Father.

45 THE COMFORTING LORD
—John 14:1-14.

Let not your heart be troubled: believe in God, believe also in me.

In my Father's house are many mansions; if it were not so, I would have told you; for I go to prepare a place for you.

And if I go and prepare a place for you, I come again, and will receive you unto myself; that where I am, there ye may be also.

And whither I go, ye know the way.

Thomas saith unto him, Lord, we know not whither thou goest; how know we the way?

Jesus saith unto him, I am the way, and the truth, and the life: no one cometh unto the Father, but by me.

If ye had known me, ye would have known my Father also: from henceforth ye know him, and have seen him.

Philip saith unto him, Lord, show us the Father, and it sufficeth us.

Jesus saith unto him, Have I been so long time with you, and dost thou not know me, Philip? he that hath seen me hath seen the Father; how sayest thou, Show us the Father?

Believest thou not that I am in the Father, and the Father in me? the words that I say unto you I speak not from myself: but the Father abiding in me doeth his works.

Believe me that I am in the Father, and the Father in me; or else believe me for the very works' sake.

Verily, verily, I say unto you, He that believeth on me, the works that I do shall he do also; and greater works than these shall he do; because I go unto the Father.

And whatsoever ye shall ask in my name, that will I do, that the Father may be glorified in the Son.

If ye shall ask anything in my name, that will I do.

46 THE LORD'S SUPPER
—1 Corinthians 11:23-32.

For I received of the Lord that which also I delivered unto you, that the Lord Jesus in the night in which he was betrayed took bread;

And when he had given thanks, he brake it, and said, This is my body, which is for you: this do in remembrance of me.

In like manner also the cup, after supper, saying, This cup is the new covenant in my blood: this do, as often as ye drink it, in remembrance of me.

For as often as ye eat this bread, and drink the cup, ye proclaim the Lord's death till he come.

Wherefore whosoever shall eat the bread or drink the cup of the Lord in an unworthy manner, shall be guilty of the body and the blood of the Lord.

But let a man prove himself, and so let him eat of the bread, and drink of the cup.

For he that eateth and drinketh, eateth and drinketh judgment unto himself, if he discern not the body.

For this cause many among you are weak and sickly, and not a few sleep.

But if we discerned ourselves, we shall not be judged.

But when we are judged, we are chastened of the Lord, that we may not be condemned with the world.

47 THE CHILDHOOD OF JESUS
—Luke 2:41-52.

And his parents went every year to Jerusalem at the feast of the passover.

And when he was twelve years old, they went up after the custom of the feast;

And when they had fulfilled the days, as they were returning, the boy Jesus tarried behind in Jerusalem; and his parents knew it not;

But supposing him to be in the company, they went a day's journey; and they sought for him among their kinsfolk and acquaintance:

And when they found him not, they returned to Jerusalem, seeking for him.

And it came to pass, after three days they found him in the temple, sitting in the midst of the teachers, both hearing them, and asking them questions:

And all that heard him were amazed at his understanding and his answers.

And when they saw him, they were astonished; and his mother said unto him, Son, why hast thou thus dealt with us? behold, thy father and I sought thee sorrowing.

And he said unto them, How is it that ye sought me? know ye not that I must be in my Father's house?

And they understood not the saying which he spake unto them.

And he went down with them, and came to Nazareth; and he was subject unto them: and his mother kept all these sayings in her heart.

And Jesus advanced in wisdom and stature, and in favor with God and men.

48 CHRIST BLESSING THE CHILDREN
—Matthew 18:1-10; Luke 18:15-17.

In that hour came the disciples unto Jesus, saying, Who then is greatest in the kingdom of heaven?

And he called to him a little child, and set him in the midst of them, and said, Verily I say unto you, Ercept ye turn, and become as little children, ye shall in no wise enter into the kingdom of heaven.

Whosoever therefore shall humble himself as this little child, the same is the greatest in the kingdom of heaven.

And whoso shall receive one such little child in my name receiveth me:

But whoso shall cause one of these little ones that believe on me to stumble, it is profitable for him that a great millstone should be hanged about his neck, and that he should be sunk in the depth of the sea.

Woe unto the world because of occasions of stumbling! for it must needs be that the occasions come; but woe to that man through whom the occasion cometh!

And if thy hand or thy foot causeth thee to stumble, cut it off, and cast it from thee: it is good for thee to enter into life maimed or halt, rather than having two hands or two feet to be cast into the eternal fire.

And if thine eye causeth thee to stumble, pluck it out and cast it from thee: it is good for thee to enter into life with one eye, rather than having two eyes to be cast into the hell of fire.

See that ye despise not one of these little ones: for I say unto you, that in heaven their angels do always behold the face of my Father who is in heaven.

And they were bringing unto him also their babes, that he should touch them: but when the disciples saw it, they rebuked them.

But Jesus called them unto him, saying, Suffer the little children to come unto me, and forbid them not: for to such belongeth the kingdom of God.

Verily I say unto you, Whosoever shall not receive the kingdom of God as a little child, he shall in no wise enter therein.

49 THE RETURN OF THE LORD
—Matthew 24:37-44; 1 Thessalonians 4:13-18.

And as were the days of Noah, so shall be the coming of the Son of man.

For as in those days which were before the flood they were eating and drinking, marrying and giving in marriage, until the day that Noah entered into the ark,

And they knew not until the flood came, and took them all away; so shall be the coming of the Son of man.

Then shall two men be in the field; one is taken, and one is left:

Two women shall be grinding at the mill; one is taken, and one is left.

Watch therefore: for ye know not on what day your Lord cometh.

But know this, that if the master of the house had known in what watch the thief was coming, he would have watched, and would not have suffered his house to be broken through.

Therefore be ye also ready; for in an hour that ye think not the Son of man cometh.

But we would not have you ignorant, brethren, concerning them that fall asleep; that ye sorrow not, even as the rest, who have no hope.

For if we believe that Jesus died and rose again, even so them also that are fallen asleep in Jesus will God bring with him.

For this we say unto you by the word of the Lord, that we that are alive, that are left unto the coming of the Lord, shall in no wise precede them that are fallen asleep.

For the Lord himself shall descend from heaven, with a shout, with the voice of the archangel, and with the trump of God: and the dead in Christ shall rise first;

Then we that are alive, that are left, shall together with them be caught up in the clouds, to meet the Lord in the air: and so shall we ever be with the Lord.

Wherefore comfort one another with these words.

50   THE JUDGMENT
—2 Peter 3:1-14; Revelation 20:11-15.

This is now, beloved, the second epistle that I write unto you; and in both of them I stir up your sincere mind by putting you in remembrance;

That ye should remember the words which were spoken before by the holy prophets, and the commandment of the Lord and Savior through your apostles:

Knowing this first, that in the last days mockers shall come with mockery, walking after their own lusts,

And saying, Where is the promise of his coming? for, from the day that the fathers fell asleep, all things continue as they were from the beginning of creation.

For this they wilfully forget, that there were heavens from of old, and an earth compacted out of water and amidst water, by the word of God;

By which means the world that then was, being overflowed with water, perished:

But the heavens that now are, and the earth, by the same word have been stored up for fire, being reserved against the day of judgment and destruction of ungodly men.

But forget not this one thing, beloved, that one day is with the Lord as a thousand years, and a thousand years as one day.

The Lord is not slack concerning his promise, as some count slackness; but is longsuffering to you-ward, not wishing that any should perish, but that all should come to repentance.

But the day of the Lord will come as a thief; in the which the heavens shall pass away with a great noise, and the elements shall be dissolved with fervent heat, and the earth and the works that are therein shall be burned up.

Seeing that these things are thus all to be dissolved, what manner of persons ought ye to be in all holy living and godliness,

Looking for and earnestly desiring the coming of the day of God, by reason of which the heavens being on fire shall be dissolved, and the elements shall melt with fervent heat?

But according to his promise, we look for new heavens and a new earth, wherein dwelleth righteousness.

Wherefore, beloved, seeing that ye look for these things, give diligence that ye may be found in peace, without spot and blameless in his sight.

And I saw a great white throne, and him that sat upon it, from whose face the earth and the heaven fled away; and there was found no place for them.

And I saw the dead, the great and the small, standing before the throne; and books were opened: and another book was opened, which is the book of life: and the dead were judged out of the things which were written in the books, according to their works.

And the sea gave up the dead that were in it; and death and Hades gave up the dead that were in them: and they were judged every man according to their works.

And death and Hades were cast into the lake of fire. This is the second death, even the lake of fire. And if any was not found written in the book of life, he was cast into the lake of fire.

51 THE NEW HEAVEN AND THE NEW EARTH
—Revelation 21:1-7.

And I saw a new heaven and a new earth: for the first heaven and the first earth are passed away; and the sea is no more. And I saw the holy city, new Jerusalem, coming down out of heaven from God, made ready as a bride adorned for her husband.

And I heard a great voice out of the throne saying, Behold, the tabernacle of God is with men, and he shall dwell with them, and they shall be his peoples, and God himself shall be with them, and be their God:

And he shall wipe away every tear from their eyes; and death shall be no more; neither shall there be mourning, nor crying, nor pain, any more: the first things are passed away.

And he that sitteth on the throne said, Behold, I make all things new. And he saith, Write: for these words are faithful and true.

And he said unto me, They are come to pass. I am the Alpha and the Omega, the beginning and the end. I will give unto him that is athirst of the fountain of the water of life freely.

He that overcometh shall inherit these things; and I will be his God, and he shall be my son.

52 PARABLE OF THE PRODIGAL SON
—Luke 15:11-24.

And he said, A certain man had two sons:

And the younger of them said to his father, Father, give me the portion of thy substance that falleth to me. And he divided unto them his living.

And not many days after, the younger son gathered all together and took his journey into a far country; and there he wasted his substance with riotous living.

And when he had spent all, there arose a mighty famine in that country; and he began to be in want.

And he went and joined himself to one of the citizens of that country; and he sent him into his fields to feed swine.

And he would fain have filled his belly with the husks that the swine did eat: and no man gave unto him.

But when he came to himself he said, How many hired servants of my father's have bread enough and to spare, and I perish here with hunger!

I will arise and go to my father, and will say unto him, Father, I have sinned against heaven, and in thy sight:

I am no more worthy to be called thy son: make me as one of thy hired servants.

And he arose and came to his father. But while he was yet afar off, his father saw him, and was moved with compassion, and ran, and fell on his neck, and kissed him.

And the son said unto him, Father, I have sinned against heaven, and in thy sight: I am no more worthy to be called thy son.

But the father said to his servants, Bring forth quickly the best robe, and put it on him; and put a ring on his hand, and shoes on his feet:

And bring the fatted calf, and kill it, and let us eat, and make merry:

For this my son was dead, and is alive again; he was lost, and is found. And they began to be merry.

TOPICAL INDEX

TOPICAL INDEX

GENERAL INDEX

Titles are in SMALL CAPS; first lines in lower case type.

GENERAL INDEX

I

GENERAL INDEX

GENERAL INDEX

GENERAL INDEX

3/64   RAINBOW LITHOGRAPHING CO.
MUSIC PRINTERS-CHICAGO, ILL.

The Lord Bless You and Keep You

Peter C. Lutkin